SCHOLAR Study Guide

Higher Mathematics
Course Materials Part 2:
Topics 5 to 10

Authored by:

Margaret Ferguson

Reviewed by:

Jillian Hornby

Previously authored by:

Dorothy Watson

Jane Paterson

Heriot-Watt University

Edinburgh EH14 4AS, United Kingdom.

First published 2018 by Heriot-Watt University.

This edition published in 2018 by Heriot-Watt University SCHOLAR.

Copyright © 2018 SCHOLAR Forum.

Distributed by the SCHOLAR Forum.

SCHOLAR Study Guide Higher Mathematics: Course Materials

Higher Mathematics Course Code: C847 76

ISBN 978-1-911057-48-2

Print Production and Fulfilment in UK by Print Trail www.printtrail.com

Acknowledgements

Thanks are due to the members of Heriot-Watt University's SCHOLAR team who planned and created these materials, and to the many colleagues who reviewed the content.

We would like to acknowledge the assistance of the education authorities, colleges, teachers and students who contributed to the SCHOLAR programme and who evaluated these materials.

Grateful acknowledgement is made for permission to use the following material in the SCHOLAR programme:

The Scottish Qualifications Authority for permission to use Past Papers assessments.

The Scottish Government for financial support.

The content of this Study Guide is aligned to the Scottish Qualifications Authority (SQA) curriculum.

Contents

Topic 1

Differentiation

Contents

Learning objective

By the end of this topic, you should be able to:

- differentiate algebraic expressions;
- determine:
    - the equation of a tangent at a point on a curve;
    - stationary points;
    - the nature of stationary points;
- sketch functions by using differentiation to find the stationary points;
- determine:
    - where functions are increasing or decreasing;
    - the maximum or minimum value in a closed interval;
- sketch the graphs of derivatives;
- find the rate of change in context;
- calculate the maximum or minimum value in a context modelled on a given function;
- differentiate:
    - trigonometric expressions;
    - composite functions using the chain rule.

1.1   Looking back at National 5

Summary
Six laws of indices

1. $a^m \times a^n = a^{m+n}$

2. $\frac{a^m}{a^n} = a^{m-n}$

3. $(a^m)^n = a^{m \times n}$

4. $a^0 = 1$

5. $a^{-m} = \frac{1}{a^m}$

6. $a^{\frac{m}{n}} = \sqrt[n]{a^m}$

1.1.1   Multiplication and division of terms with positive indices

Using the laws of indices   Go online

Multiply an expression by a

$a^1 = a$

$a^2 = a \times a$

$a^3 = a \times a \times a$

$a^4 = a \times a \times a \times a$

$a^5 = a \times a \times a \times a \times a$

$a^6 = a \times a \times a \times a \times a \times a$

$a^7 = a \times a \times a \times a \times a \times a \times a$

$a^8 = a \times a \times a \times a \times a \times a \times a \times a$

$a^9 = a \times a \times a \times a \times a \times a \times a \times a \times a$

$a^{10} = a \times a \times a \times a \times a \times a \times a \times a \times a \times a$

Multiply the expression below by $a \times a$

$a^1 \times a^9 = a \times a \times a \times a \times a \times a \times a \times a \times a \times a$

$\qquad = a^{10}$

$\qquad = a^{1+9}$

> **General Rule**
>
> $a^n \times a^m = a^{n+m}$

$a^6 \times a^4 = a \times a \times a \times a \times a \times a \times a \times a \times a \times a$

$\qquad = a^{10}$

$\qquad = a^{6+4}$

Multiply the expression below by $\dfrac{a}{a}$

$$\frac{a^4}{a^1} = \frac{a \times a \times a \times a}{a}$$

$$= \frac{a \times a \times a}{1}$$

$$= a^3$$

$$= a^{4-1}$$

General Rule

$$\frac{a^n}{a^m} = a^{n-m}$$

$$\frac{a^7}{a^4} = \frac{a \times a \times a \times a \times a \times a \times a}{a \times a \times a \times a}$$

$$= a^3$$

$$= a^{7-4}$$

Examples

1. Problem:

Simplify $x^3 \times x^5 \div x^4$

Solution:

$$x^3 \times x^5 \div x^4 = x^{3+5-4} = x^4$$

. . . .

2. Problem:

Simplify $\frac{x^5 \times x^4}{x^2}$, $x \neq 0$

Solution:

$$\frac{x^5 \times x^4}{x^2} = x^{5+4-2} = x^7$$

. . . .

3. Problem:

Simplify $3x^{\frac{1}{3}} \times 4x^{\frac{2}{3}}$

Solution:

$$3x^{\frac{1}{3}} \times 4x^{\frac{2}{3}} = 3 \times 4 \times x^{\frac{1}{3}} \times x^{\frac{2}{3}}$$

$$= 3 \times 4 \times x^{\frac{1}{3} + \frac{2}{3}}$$

$$= 12 \times x^{\frac{3}{3}}$$

$$= 12x^1$$

$$= 12x$$

| Multiplication and division of indices exercise | Go online |

Q1: Simplify $x^6 \times x^4 \div x^5$

....

Q2: Simplify $\frac{x^6 \times x^2}{x^3}$, $x \neq 0$

....

Q3: Simplify $2x^{\frac{1}{4}} \times 5x^{\frac{1}{4}}$

1.1.2   Raising a power to a power

| How to raise a power to a power | Go online |

$$if \quad x = 1 \quad and \quad y = 1$$
$$(a^x)^y = (a^1)^1$$
$$= (a)^1$$
$$= a$$
$$if \quad x = 4 \quad and \quad y = 2$$
$$(a^x)^y = (a^4)^2$$
$$= (a \times a \times a \times a)^2$$
$$= (a \times a \times a \times a)(a \times a \times a \times a)$$
$$= a^8$$
$$= a^{4 \times 2}$$

Key point

We now have three laws of indices.

1. $a^m \times a^n = a^{m+n}$

2. $\frac{a^m}{a^n} = a^{m-n}$

3. $(a^m)^n = a^{m \times n}$

Examples

1. Problem:

Simplify $(a^3)^5$

Solution:

$$(a^3)^5 = a^{3 \times 5} = a^{15}$$

....

2. Problem:

Simplify $\left(2y^4\right)^2$

Solution:

$$\left(2y^4\right)^2 \ = \ 2^2 \ \times \ y^{4\,\times\,2} \ = \ 4y^8$$

. . . .

3. Problem:

Simplify $\left(2g^{\frac{1}{2}}\right)^6$

Solution:

$$\left(2g^{\frac{1}{2}}\right)^6 \ = \ 2^6 \ \times \ g^{\frac{1}{2}\,\times\,6} \ = \ 64g^{\frac{6}{2}} \ = \ 64g^3$$

Raising powers exercise   Go online

Q4: Simplify $\left(a^2\right)^7$

. . . .

Q5: Simplify $\left(3y^4\right)^3$

. . . .

Q6: Simplify $\left(5m^{\frac{3}{2}}\right)^2$

1.1.3 Negative and zero indices

Negative and zero indices   Go online

$$If \ x \ = \ 0, \ a^0 \ = \ 1$$
$$If \ x \ = \ -2, \ a^{-2} \ = \ \frac{1}{a \times a}$$
$$If \ x \ = \ -5, \ a^{-5} \ = \ \frac{1}{a \times a \times a \times a \times a}$$

Key point

We now have five laws of indices.

1. $a^m \ \times \ a^n \ = \ a^{m\,+\,n}$

2. $\frac{a^m}{a^n} \ = \ a^{m\,-\,n}$

3. $\left(a^m\right)^n \ = \ a^{m\,\times\,n}$

4. $a^0 \ = \ 1$

5. $a^{-m} \ = \ \frac{1}{a^m}$

Examples

1. Problem:

Simplify, giving your answer with a positive index $a^{-5} \times a^4 \times a^{-3}$

Solution:

$a^{(-5) + 4 + (-3)} \; = \; a^{-4} \; = \; \frac{1}{a^4}$

....

2. Problem:

Simplify, giving your answer with a positive index $\frac{y^7}{y^{10}}$

Solution:

$\frac{y^7}{y^{10}} \; = \; y^{7 - 10} \; = \; y^{-3} \; = \; \frac{1}{y^3}$

....

3. Problem:

Simplify $\left(2g^{-2}\right)^3$

Solution:

$\left(2g^{-2}\right)^3 \; = \; 2^3 \times g^{-2 \times 3} \; = \; 8g^{-6} \; = \; \frac{8}{g^6}$

Negative and zero indices exercise　　　　　　　　Go online　

Q7: Simplify, giving your answer with a positive index $\frac{a^{-3} \times a^5}{a^2}$

....

Q8: Simplify, giving your answer with a positive index $(3m^{-4})^2$

....

Q9: Simplify, giving your answer with a positive index $\frac{y^{-10} \times y^{\frac{3}{2}}}{y^{\frac{1}{2}}}$

1.1.4　Fractional indices

The purpose of a fractional index is to define a surd.

$a^{\frac{1}{2}} \; = \; \sqrt{a} \quad a^{\frac{1}{3}} \; = \; \sqrt[3]{a} \quad a^{\frac{1}{4}} \; = \; \sqrt[4]{a} \quad a^{\frac{3}{2}} \; = \; \sqrt{a^3} \quad a^{\frac{2}{3}} \; = \; \sqrt[3]{a^2}$

In essence the numerator of the index is the power and the denominator is the root.

Changing fractional indices　　　　　　　　　　Go online　

$a^{\frac{x}{y}} \; = \; \sqrt[y]{a^x}$

If $x \; = \; 1$ and $y \; = \; 2$ then $a^{\frac{1}{2}} \; = \; \sqrt{a}$

If $x = 3$ and $y = 2$ then $a^{\frac{3}{2}} = \sqrt{a^3}$

If $x = 4$ and $y = 3$ then $a^{\frac{4}{3}} = \sqrt[3]{a^4}$

If $x = 4$ and $y = 4$ then $a^{\frac{4}{4}} = \sqrt[4]{a^4} = a$

Key point

We now have six laws of indices.

1. $a^m \times a^n = a^{m+n}$

2. $\frac{a^m}{a^n} = a^{m-n}$

3. $(a^m)^n = a^{m \times n}$

4. $a^0 = 1$

5. $a^{-m} = \frac{1}{a^m}$

6. $a^{\frac{m}{n}} = \sqrt[n]{a^m}$

Examples

1. Evaluate $25^{\frac{1}{2}}$

$25^{\frac{1}{2}} = \sqrt{25} = 5$

....

2. Problem:

Evaluate $25^{\frac{3}{2}}$

Solution:

$25^{\frac{3}{2}} = \sqrt[2]{25^3} = 5^3 = 125$

It does not matter whether you square root or cube the term first and since you probably don't know 25^3 it is easier to find $\sqrt{25}$ then cube the answer.

....

3. Problem:

Evaluate $8^{-\frac{1}{3}}$

Solution:

$8^{-\frac{1}{3}} = \frac{1}{8^{\frac{1}{3}}} = \frac{1}{\sqrt[3]{8}} = \frac{1}{2}$

- Remember a negative index moves the term onto the denominator.
- The power a third means the cube root.
- The cube root of 8 is 2 because $2^3 = 8$.

Fractional indices exercise Go online

Q10: Evaluate $9^{\frac{1}{2}}$

....

Q11: Evaluate $49^{\frac{1}{2}}$

....

Q12: Evaluate $27^{\frac{1}{3}}$

....

Q13: Evaluate $16^{\frac{1}{4}}$

....

Q14: Evaluate $27^{\frac{2}{3}}$

....

Q15: Evaluate $4^{\frac{3}{2}}$

1.2 Differentiating algebraic expressions

Much of our understanding of the world we live in depends on our ability to describe how things change with time. This could range from the motion of a bouncing ball, the orbit of a planet, the flight path of a rocket, the spread of an epidemic, the growth of an economy or the decay of a radioactive substance.

Calculus was developed independently by two seventeenth century mathematicians Sir Isaac Newton (1642 - 1727) and Gottfried Leibniz (1646 - 1716) as a method for analysing the motion of moving objects. Indeed calculus can be used to study any situation involving a rate of change.

1.2.1 The derived function

The following diagram shows a distance-time graph for a car travelling along a road on the first 4 seconds of its journey.

Remember, it is possible to calculate average speed as, average speed $= \frac{\text{distance}}{\text{time}}$
Thus the average speed for the car in the first three seconds of its journey is,

$$\text{average speed} = \frac{\text{distance}}{\text{time}}$$
$$= \frac{9}{3}$$
$$= 3 \; ms^{-1}$$

Look again at the distance-time graph and answer the following questions.

Q16: When does it seem that the car is travelling faster, at $t = 1$ or at $t = 4$?

. . . .

Q17: How can you tell this from the graph?

. . . .

Q18: Why can the *average* speed only be calculated for the first few seconds of the journey and not the exact speed?

Consider this question.
What is the speed at exactly $t = 2$?

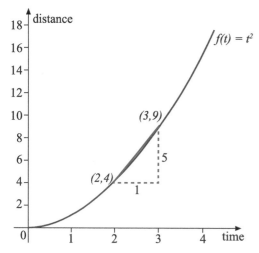

A first estimate can be found by calculating the average speed between $t = 2$ and $t = 3$ from the diagram above.

$$
\begin{aligned}
average\ speed &= \frac{\text{distance}}{time} \\
&= \frac{f(3) - f(2)}{3 - 2} \\
&= \frac{9 - 4}{3 - 2} \\
&= \frac{5}{1} \\
&= 5\ ms^{-1}
\end{aligned}
$$

To obtain a better estimate for the instantaneous speed at $t = 2$ we could choose shorter time intervals. See the following table of results,

Time Interval	Distance	Time	Average Speed
2 - 3	5	1	5
2 - 2·5	2·25	0·5	4·5
2 - 2·2	0·84	0·2	4·2
2 - 2·1	0·41	0·1	4·1
2 - 2·01	0·0401	0·01	4·01
2 - 2·001	0·004001	0·001	4·001

Notice that as the time tends to zero the speed tends to a limit of $4\ ms^{-1}$. It seems reasonable to conclude that the instantaneous speed of the car at $t = 2$ is $4\ ms^{-1}$.

In a similar way it is also possible to calculate the instantaneous speed at $t = 1, 2, 3, 4, 5...$ The results are shown here.

Time	1	2	3	4	5
Instantaneous Speed	2	4	6	8	10

Perhaps you have already noticed for the function $f(t) = t^2$ that the instantaneous speed at time t can be calculated as $2t\ ms^{-1}$.

The instantaneous speed, or rate of change of distance with respect to time, can be written as $f'(t)$, we say this as "f dashed t", and is known as the derived function of $f(t)$.

In a similar way it is also possible to consider other functions apart from $f(t) = t^2$ and the results that are obtained for the derived function are as listed here.

Distance $f(t)$	t	t^2	t^3	t^4	t^5	$\cdots$	t^n
Speed $f'(t)$	1	$2t$	$3t^2$	$4t^3$	$5t^4$	$\cdots$	nt^{n-1}

Notice that we have obtained a general rule for finding the **derived function**.

Key point

When $f(t) = t^n$ then $f'(t) = nt^{n-1}$.

We differentiate $f(t)$ to obtain $f'(t)$.

This process is called differentiation.

Differentiation from first principles

The instantaneous speed of a car at time $t = 2$ seconds can be obtained by calculating the average speed over smaller and smaller time intervals. It is important to relate this to the features of the graph for $f(t)$.

The first estimate was the average speed between $t = 2$ and $t = 3$. Notice that,

$$\text{average speed} = \frac{\text{distance}}{\text{time}}$$

$$= \text{gradient of chord AB}$$

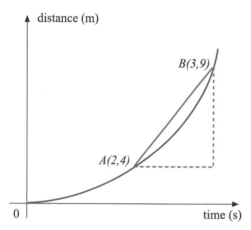

Better estimates for the instantaneous speed at $t = 2$ are obtained by taking progressively shorter time intervals. Notice that the gradients of the chords AB_1, AB_2 and AB_3 move closer to the gradient of the tangent to the curve at $t = 2$. Indeed the instantaneous speed at $t = 2$ is equal to the gradient of the tangent to the curve at that point.

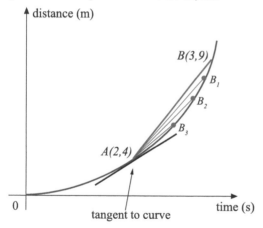

In general the instantaneous speed, $f'(t)$, is equal to the gradient of the tangent to the curve at that time.

The gradient of a tangent can now be used to calculate the instantaneous rate of change of any function.

$f'(x)$ is the derived function or the derivative of $f(x)$. It represents the gradient of the tangent to the graph of the function and the rate of change of the function.

The gradient of a curve at a point is defined to be the gradient of the tangent to the curve at that point.

When we use this method to obtain $f'(x)$ this is called differentiating from first principles. Differentiation is one area of Calculus.

Key point

The derived function represents:

1. The gradient of the tangent to the function.

2. The rate of change of the function.

1.2.2 Rules for differentiation

How to differentiate   Go online

Let's look at how to differentiate four different functions.

1. $f(x) = x^2$

2. $f(x) = x^{-5}$

3. $f(x) = x^{\frac{1}{2}}$

4. $f(x) = 4x^3 - 2x$

1. $f(x) = x^2$

$$f'(x) = 2 \times x^2 \qquad \text{Bring down the power}$$
$$f'(x) = 2x^{2-1} \qquad \text{Reduce the power by 1}$$
$$f'(x) = 2x^1 \qquad \text{Simplify}$$
$$f'(x) = 2x$$

2. $f(x) = x^{-5}$

$$f'(x) = -5 \times x^{-5} \qquad \text{Bring down the power}$$
$$f'(x) = -5x^{-5-1} \qquad \text{Reduce the power by 1}$$
$$f'(x) = -5x^{-6} \qquad \text{Simplify}$$
$$f'(x) = \frac{-5}{x^{-6}}$$

3. $f(x) = x^{\frac{1}{2}}$

$$f'(x) = \frac{1}{2} \times x^{\frac{1}{2}} \qquad \text{Bring down the power}$$
$$f'(x) = \frac{1}{2} x^{\frac{1}{2}-1} \qquad \text{Reduce the power by 1}$$
$$f'(x) = \frac{1}{2} x^{-\frac{1}{2}} \qquad \text{Simplify}$$
$$f'(x) = \frac{1}{2x^{\frac{1}{2}}} \qquad \text{Remember the power of a half is the square root}$$
$$f'(x) = \frac{1}{2\sqrt{x}}$$

4. $f(x) = 4x^3 - 2x$

$f'(x) =$
$3 \times 4x^{3-1} \times 2x^1$ Bring down the power

$f'(x) = 12x^{3-1} - 2x^{1-1}$ Reduce the power by 1

$f'(x) = 12x^2 - 2x^0$ Simplify

$f'(x) = 12x^2 - 2$ Remember $x^0 = 1$

Key point

$f(x) = x^n \Rightarrow f'(x) = nx^{n-1}$

$f(x) = c \Rightarrow f'(x) = 0$ where c is a constant.

Examples

1. Problem:

If $f(x) = 5x^2 - 4x + 7$ what is $f'(x)$?

Solution:

$f(x) = 5x^2 - 4x + 7$

$f'(x) = 2 \times 5x^1 - 4x^0 + 0$

$\quad\ = 10x - 4$

....

2. Problem:

Differentiate $g(x) = x^{\frac{4}{3}}$

Solution:

$g'(x) = \frac{4}{3}x^{\frac{4}{3} - 1}$

$\quad\ = \frac{4}{3}x^{\frac{4}{3} - \frac{3}{3}}$

$\quad\ = \frac{4}{3}x^{\frac{1}{3}}$

....

3. Problem:

Differentiate $f(x) = \sqrt{x}$

Solution:

First rewrite $f(x)$ in terms of x^n.

$f(x) = \sqrt{x} = x^{\frac{1}{2}}$

Therefore,

$$f'(x) \;=\; \frac{1}{2}x^{-\frac{1}{2}}$$
$$=\; \frac{1}{2x^{\frac{1}{2}}}$$
$$=\; \frac{1}{2\sqrt{x}}$$

....

4. Problem:

Differentiate $f(x) \;=\; \frac{1}{x}$

Solution:

Again rewrite $f(x)$ in terms of x^n

$f(x) \;=\; \frac{1}{x} \;=\; x^{-1}$

Therefore,

$$f'(x) \;=\; -x^{-2} \;=\; -\frac{1}{x^2}$$

....

5. Problem:

If $f(x) \;=\; 2x^4 \;-\; \frac{2}{\sqrt[3]{x}}$ what is $f'(x)$?

Solution:

We can't differentiate until we have simplified the second term.

So, $f(x) \;=\; 2x^4 \;-\; 2x^{-\frac{1}{3}}$

$$f'(x) \;=\; 4 \times 2x^3 \;-\; \left(-\frac{1}{3}\right) \times 2x^{-\frac{4}{3}} \qquad Note: \; -\frac{1}{3} - 1 \;=\; -\frac{1}{3} - \frac{3}{3} \;=\; -\frac{4}{3}$$
$$=\; 8x^3 \;+\; \frac{2}{3}x^{-\frac{4}{3}} \qquad\qquad Simplify$$
$$=\; 8x^3 \;+\; \frac{2}{3\sqrt[3]{x^4}} \qquad\qquad Note: \; x^{-\frac{4}{3}} \;=\; \frac{1}{\sqrt[3]{x^4}}$$

....

6. Problem:

$f(x) \;=\; \frac{3}{\sqrt{x}} \;+\; \frac{\sqrt{x}}{5}$

Solution:

We can't differentiate until we have simplified both terms.

$f(x) \;=\; \frac{3}{\sqrt{x}} \;+\; \frac{\sqrt{x}}{5} \;=\; 3x^{-\frac{1}{2}} \;+\; \frac{1}{5}x^{\frac{1}{2}}$

Now differentiate as follows,

$f'(x) \;=\; \left(-\frac{1}{2}\right) \times 3x^{-\frac{3}{2}} \;+\; \frac{1}{2} \times \frac{1}{5}x^{-\frac{1}{2}}$ *Note that:* $-\frac{1}{2} - 1 \;=\; -\frac{1}{2} - \frac{2}{2} \;=\; -\frac{3}{2}$ *and*
$\frac{1}{2} - 1 \;=\; \frac{1}{2} - \frac{2}{2} \;=\; -\frac{1}{2}.$

$f'(x) \;=\; -\frac{3}{2}x^{-\frac{3}{2}} \;+\; \frac{1}{10}x^{-\frac{1}{2}} \;=\; -\frac{3}{2\sqrt{x^3}} \;+\; \frac{1}{10\sqrt{x}}$

Key point

Make sure that each term in $f(x)$ takes the form ax^n before you start to differentiate.

If $f(x) = ax^n$ then $f'(x) = n \times ax^{n-1}$

Rules for differentiation exercise   Go online

Q19: Find the derivatives of the following:

  a) $f(x) = x^9$

  b) $f(x) = x^{-3}$

  c) $f(x) = x^{\frac{5}{4}}$

  d) f(x) = 1

  e) $f(x) = x^{\frac{4}{5}}$

  f) $f(x) = x^{-\frac{9}{2}}$

. . . .

Q20: Find the derivatives of the following:

  a) $f(x) = \frac{1}{x^7}$

  b) $f(x) = \frac{1}{x^{\frac{9}{8}}}$

  c) $f(x) = \frac{1}{x^{\frac{3}{5}}}$

  d) $f(x) = \sqrt{x^7}$

  e) $f(x) = \frac{1}{\sqrt{x^5}}$

. . . .

Q21: Find the derivatives of the following:

  a) $f(x) = -2x^4$

  b) $f(x) = \frac{3}{5}x^4$

  c) $f(x) = \frac{4}{x^3}$

  d) $f(x) = \frac{1}{9x^4}$

  e) $f(x) = \frac{9}{4x}$

  f) $f(x) = -\sqrt{x}$

. . . .

Q22: Find the derivatives of the following:

  a) $f(x) = \frac{2}{\sqrt{x}}$

  b) $f(x) = -8x^{\frac{5}{4}}$

  c) $f(x) = -x^2 + 4x - 1$

  d) $f(x) = 5x^5 + \frac{1}{3x^6}$

  e) $f(x) = \frac{1}{2x} + \frac{4}{\sqrt{x}}$

  f) $f(x) = -1 - 9\sqrt{x} + 4x^5$

1.2.3 Differentiating products and quotients

Differentiating products Go online

Differentiate the function: $f(x) = (x + 3)(2x - 5)$

This function is written as a product. First you should expand the expression for $f(x)$.

$f(x) = (x + 3)(2x - 5) = 2x^2 + x - 15$

Now you are ready to differentiate.

$f'(x) = 4x + 1$

Examples

1. Problem:

If $f(x) = (x + 7)(x - 3)$ what is $f'(x)$?

Solution:

We can't differentiate until we have expanded the brackets.

$f(x) = (x + 7)(x - 3) = x^2 + 4x - 21$

$f'(x) = 2x + 4$

. . . .

2. Problem:

Differentiate the function $f(x) = \left(\sqrt{x} + \frac{1}{\sqrt{x}}\right)^2$

Solution:

Multiply out the brackets in the function so that it can be expressed as a sum of individual terms.

$$
\begin{aligned}
f(x) &= \left(\sqrt{x} + \frac{1}{\sqrt{x}}\right)^2 \\
&= \left(\sqrt{x} + \frac{1}{\sqrt{x}}\right)\left(\sqrt{x} + \frac{1}{\sqrt{x}}\right) \\
&= \sqrt{x}^2 + 2\frac{\sqrt{x}}{\sqrt{x}} + \frac{1}{(\sqrt{x})^2} \\
&= x + 2 + \frac{1}{x} \\
&= x + 2 + x^{-1}
\end{aligned}
$$

Now differentiate term by term.

$$
\begin{aligned}
f'(x) &= 1 - x^{-2} \\
&= 1 - \frac{1}{x^2}
\end{aligned}
$$

Differentiating quotients   Go online

Differentiate the function $f(x) = \frac{x^5 + 3x^2 - x}{x^2}$

This function is written as a quotient. We need to simplify the expression for $f(x)$ before we are able to differentiate.

$$f(x) = \frac{x^5 + 3x^2 - x}{x^2}$$
$$= \frac{x^5}{x^2} + \frac{3x^2}{x^2} - \frac{x}{x^2}$$

Notice that we break the quotient apart into separate functions.

$$f(x) = \frac{x^5 + 3x^2 - x}{x^2}$$
$$= \frac{x^5}{x^2} + \frac{3x^2}{x^2} - \frac{x}{x^2}$$
$$= x^3 + 3 - x^{-1}$$

We are now able to differentiate.

$$f'(x) = 3x^2 + x^{-2}$$
$$= 3x^2 + \frac{1}{x^2}$$

Examples

1. Problem:

If $f(x) = \frac{(x + 2)(x - 3)}{x^2}$ what is $f'(x)$?

Solution:

We cannot differentiate until we have expanded the brackets and the quotient is broken up.

$$f(x) = \frac{(x + 2)(x - 3)}{x^2}$$
$$= \frac{x^2 - x - 6}{x^2}$$
$$= \frac{x^2}{x^2} - \frac{x}{x^2} - \frac{6}{x^2}$$
$$= 1 - x^{-1} - 6x^{-2}$$

We are now able to differentiate.

$$f'(x) = x^{-2} + 12x^{-3}$$
$$= \frac{1}{x^2} + \frac{12}{x^3}$$

. . . .

2. Problem:

If $f(x) = \frac{x-1}{\sqrt{x}}$ what is $f'(x)$?

Solution:

We cannot differentiate until we have rearranged the equation so that we can expand the brackets.

$$f(x) = \frac{x - 1}{\sqrt{x}}$$
$$= x^{-\frac{1}{2}}(x - 1) \quad \textit{Note that: } x^{-\frac{1}{2}} \times x = x^{-\frac{1}{2} + 1} = x^{\frac{1}{2}}$$
$$= x^{\frac{1}{2}} - x^{-\frac{1}{2}}$$

We are now able to differentiate.

$$f'(x) = \frac{1}{2}x^{-\frac{1}{2}} + \frac{1}{2}x^{-\frac{3}{2}} \quad \textit{Note that: } x^{-\frac{1}{2}} = \frac{1}{\sqrt{x}} \quad \textit{and} \quad x^{-\frac{3}{2}} = \frac{1}{\sqrt{x^3}}$$
$$= \frac{1}{2\sqrt{x}} + \frac{1}{2\sqrt{x^3}}$$

Differentiating products and quotients exercise	Go online

Q23: When $f(x) = (4x + 7)(x - 2)$ then $f'(x) = ?$

....

Q24: When $f(x) = \sqrt{x}(x - \sqrt{x})$ then $f'(x) = ?$

....

Q25: When $f(x) = \frac{(2x + 6)(4x - 4)}{x}$ then $f'(x) = ?$

....

Q26: When $f(x) = \left(x - \frac{3}{x}\right)^2$ then $f'(x) = ?$

....

Q27: When $\frac{8x + 2}{\sqrt{x}}$

....

Q28: When $f(x) = \frac{x^3 - 8x^4}{x\sqrt{x}}$ then $f'(x) = ?$

1.3 Calculating the value of the derivative

In calculus, Leibniz's notation, named in honour of the 17th Century German philosopher and mathematician Gottfried Wilhelm Leibniz, uses $\frac{dy}{dx}$ instead of $f'(x)$ for the derivative.

> **Key point**
>
> Given a function in the form $f(x) = x^n$ we would express the derivative in the form $f'(x) = nx^{n-1}$.
>
> Given a function in the form $y = x^n$ we would use Leibniz notation to express the derivative as $\frac{dy}{dx} = nx^{n-1}$.

For $\frac{dy}{dx}$ we say *"dy by dx"*.

Examples

1. Problem:

If $y = 2x^3 - 5x$, find the value of the derivative at $x = 1$.

Solution:

Find the derivative $\frac{dy}{dx} = 6x^2 - 5$.

Substitute $x = 1$ into the derivative:

$\frac{dy}{dx} = 6 \times 1^2 - 5 = 1$

....

2. Problem:

If $f(x) = \frac{(x-1)(x+3)}{x}$, find $f'(-2)$.

Solution:

Simplify the function,

$$f(x) = \frac{(x-1)(x+3)}{x}$$
$$= \frac{x^2}{x} + \frac{2x}{x} - \frac{3}{x}$$
$$= x + 2 - 3x^{-1}$$

Differentiate,

$$f'(x) = 1 + 3x^{-2}$$
$$= 1 + \frac{3}{x^2}$$

Substitute $x = -2$ into $f'(x)$,

$$f'(-2) = 1 + \frac{3}{(-2)^2}$$
$$= 1 + \frac{3}{4}$$
$$= 1\frac{3}{4}$$

....

3. Problem:

What is the gradient of the tangent to the function $y = x^3 - 3x^2 + x + 6$ at the point (2,1).

Solution:

$\frac{dy}{dx} = 3x^2 - 6x + 1$

To find the gradient of the tangent at (2,1), substitute $x = 2$ into $\frac{dy}{dx}$.

Giving,

$$m_{tangent} = 3 \times (2)^2 - 6 \times (2) + 1$$
$$= 12 - 12 + 1$$
$$= 1$$

Key point

Remember the derived function, $f'(x)$ or $\frac{dy}{dx}$, represents:

1. the gradient of the tangent to the function;

2. the rate of change of the function.

Examples

1. Problem:

Find the rate of change of $8\sqrt[4]{x^3}$ at $x = 16$.

Solution:

$8\sqrt[4]{x^3} = 8x^{\frac{3}{4}}$

Since the expression was not given as $y = 8\sqrt[4]{x^3}$ we express the derivative as $\frac{d}{dx} = 6x^{-\frac{1}{4}} = \frac{6}{\sqrt[4]{x}}$.

Substituting $x = 16$ into the derivative gives $\frac{6}{\sqrt[4]{16}} = \frac{6}{2} = 3$.

. . . .

2. Problem:

Water flowing in a stream travels $\sqrt{t^3}$ metres from its source in t seconds.

Calculate the speed of the water or rate of change after 16 seconds.

Solution:

The distance travelled by the water is $d(t) = \sqrt{t^3} = t^{\frac{3}{2}}$

Thus the speed of the water is given by,

$$d'(t) = \frac{3}{2}t^{\frac{1}{2}}$$
$$= \frac{3}{2}\sqrt{t}$$

After 16 seconds the speed of the water is,

$$d'(16) = \frac{3}{2}\sqrt{16}$$
$$= 6\,ms^{-1}$$

. . . .

3. Problem:

What is the gradient of the function $y = x^3 - 3x^2 + x + 6$ at the point (-2,1).

Solution:

$\frac{dy}{dx} = 3x^2 - 6x + 1$

To find the gradient of the tangent at (2,1), substitute $x = 2$ into $\frac{dy}{dx}$

Giving,

$$m_{tangent} = 3 \times (2)^2 - 6 \times (2) + 1$$
$$= 12 - 12 + 1$$
$$= 1$$

Calculating the value of the derivative exercise Go online

Q29: When $f(x) = x^{\frac{1}{2}}$ then $f'(4) = ?$

. . . .

Q30: Given $y = \sqrt[3]{x^4}$

  a) What is the value of the derivative at $x = 8$?

  b) What is the rate of change at $x = \frac{1}{125}$?

  c) What is the derivative at $x = -27$?

. . . .

Q31: An object is launched from the ground.

The equation for the objects height h at time t seconds after launch is $h(t) = -5t^2 + 20t$, where h is in metres.

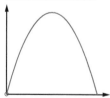

  a) What is the rate of change of the object at the moment of launch?

  b) What is the rate of change after 3 seconds?

. . . .

Q32: When $f(x) = x^{-\frac{2}{3}}$, what is the rate of change of f when $x = 8$?

....

Q33: When $s(t) = \frac{1}{t^3}$ what is the speed of the particle when $t = 2$?

....

Q34: What is the gradient of the function $y = 2x^3 - 5x^2 + x + 4$ at the point (3,2).

1.4 Determining the equation of a tangent to a curve

Key point

The gradient of a function $f(x)$ at the point P(*a,b*) is called the derivative of f at a and is written as $f'(a)$.

Examples

1. Problem:

If $f(x) = 3x^2 - 4x - 2$, what is the gradient of the tangent at the point (0,-2)?

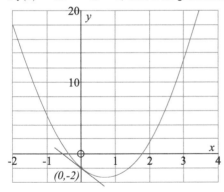

Solution:

To find the gradient of a tangent to a curve we need the derivative.

$f'(x) = 6x - 4$

We want the gradient at the point (0,-2) i.e. when $x = 0$

$f'(0) = 6 \times 0 - 4 = -4$

$m_{\text{tangent}} = -4$

....

2. Problem:

What are the coordinates of the points on the curve with equation $y = x^3 - 9x^2 + 14x$ where the gradient of the tangent is -1?

Solution:

The gradient of a tangent is the derivative $\frac{dy}{dx} = 3x^2 - 18x + 14$

but we know that the gradient is -1 so $3x^2 - 18x + 14 = -1$

Solve to find the x-coordinates of the points of contact of the tangents.

$$3x^2 - 18x + 15 = 0$$
$$3\left(x^2 - 6x + 5\right) = 0$$
$$3\left(x - 1\right)\left(x - 5\right) = 0$$
$$x - 1 = 0 \quad and \quad x - 5 = 0$$
$$x = 1 \quad and \quad x = 5$$

Now we need the y-coordinates so substitute back into the equation of the curve $y = x^3 - 9x^2 + 14x$

When $x = 1, y = 1^3 - 9 \times 1^2 + 14 \times 1 = 6$ giving (1,6)

and when $x = 5, y = 5^3 - 9 \times 5^2 + 14 \times 5 = -30$ giving (5,-30).

Key point

The tangent to a curve is a straight line so the equation for the tangent can be written in the form $y - b = m(x - a)$

The following strategy is useful when finding the equation of the tangent.

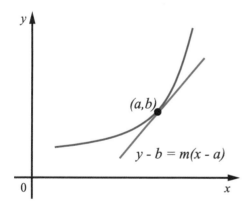

1. Find the coordinates of (*a, b*), the point of contact of the tangent with the curve.

2. Calculate the gradient, m, which is equal to the value of $\frac{dy}{dx}$ at $x = a$.

Examples

1. Problem:

Find the equation of the tangent to the curve $y = 3\sqrt{x}$ at $x = 4$

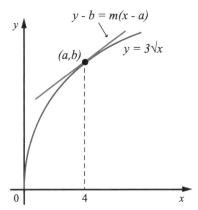

Solution:

Step 1: Find the coordinates of the point of contact.

Substitute $x = 4$ into $y = 3\sqrt{x}$: $y = 3\sqrt{x} = 3\sqrt{4} = 6$

So the point of contact is (4,6).

Step 2: Differentiate to find the gradient of the tangent.

$y = 3\sqrt{x} = 3x^{\frac{1}{2}}$

$\frac{dy}{dx} = \frac{1}{2} \times 3x^{-\frac{1}{2}} = \frac{3}{2\sqrt{x}}$

We want the gradient when $x = 4$ so $m = \frac{3}{2\sqrt{4}} = \frac{3}{4}$

Step 3: Find the equation of the tangent.

Using $y - b = m(x - a)$ with $m = \frac{3}{4}$ and the point (4,6) we get

$$y - b = m(x - a)$$
$$y - 6 = \frac{3}{4}(x - 4)$$
$$4(y - 6) = 3(x - 4)$$
$$4y - 24 = 3x - 12$$
$$4y - 3x - 12 = 0$$

....

2. Problem:

The parabola with equation $y = x^2 - 12x + 40$ has a tangent at the point (7,5).

(a) Find the equation of this tangent.

This tangent is also a tangent to the parabola with equation $y = -x^2 - 10$

(b) Find the coordinates of the point of contact.

Solution:

(a)

$y = x^2 - 12x + 40$ so $\frac{dy}{dx} = 2x - 12$

When $x = 7$, $m = 2 \times 7 - 12 = 2$

When we have $m = 2$ and the point (7,5) we get $y - 5 = 2(x - 7)$

So the equation of the tangent is $y = 2x - 9$

(b)

The tangent occurs when $-x^2 - 10 = 2x - 9$

$-x^2 - 2x - 1 = 0$

$-(x^2 + 2x + 1) = 0$

$-(x + 1)(x + 1) = 0$

Note that equal roots confirms tangency.

$x + 1 = 0$ so $x = -1$ and using the equation of the tangent $y = 2x - 9$

$y = 2 \times -1 - 9 = -11$

So the point of contact is (-1,-11).

Determining the equation of a tangent to a curve exercise   Go online

Q35: What is the equation of the tangent to the curve $y = 2x^2 - 9x - 8$ at the point (3,-17)?

....

Q36: What is the equation of the tangent to the curve $y = \frac{9}{x}$ at the point (-1,-9)?

A curve $y = (2x + 6)(x + 2)$ has a tangent at a point where the gradient is -2.

Q37: What are the coordinates of the point on the curve $y = (2x + 6)(x + 2)$ at which the gradient of the tangent is -2?

....

Q38: What is the equation of this tangent?

A curve $y = \sqrt{x^3}$ has a tangent at a point where the gradient is 3.

Q39: What are the coordinates of the point on the curve $y = \sqrt{x^3}$ at which the gradient of the tangent is 3?

....

Q40: What is the equation of this tangent?

1.5 Determining stationary points

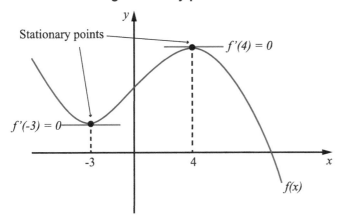

Note that there are two points on this graph where the tangent to the curve is horizontal. These are called **stationary points**.

> **Key point**
>
> At stationary points $f'(x) = 0$.

The nature of a stationary point is determined by the sign of $f'(x)$ on either side. Stationary points can be any of the following types.

Stationary points	Go online

The gradient of the tangent to the curve changes from positive to negative.

the gradient of the tangent,
f'(x) is positive

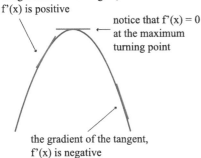

notice that f'(x) = 0
at the maximum
turning point

the gradient of the tangent,
f'(x) is negative

The gradient of the tangent to the curve changes from negative to positive.

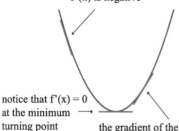

the gradient of the tangent,
f'(x) is negative

notice that f'(x) = 0
at the minimum ⟶
turning point

the gradient of the tangent,
f'(x) is positive

The gradient of the tangent to the curve is positive on either side of the point of inflection. This is a rising point of inflection.

notice that f'(x) = 0
at the point of inflection

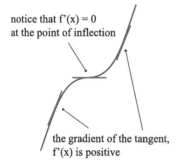

the gradient of the tangent,
f'(x) is positive

The gradient of the tangent to the curve is negative on either side of the point of inflection. This is a falling point of inflection.

the gradient of the tangent,
f'(x) is negative

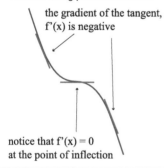

notice that f'(x) = 0
at the point of inflection

Example

Problem:

Find the stationary points on the curve $f(x) = 3x^4 + 8x^3 + 6$.

Solution:

$f(x) = 3x^4 + 8x^3 + 6$

$f'(x) = 12x^3 + 24x^2 = 12x^2(x + 2)$

Stationary points occur when $f'(x) = 0$

It is essential that you make this statement to gain full marks.

Hence to find the stationary points we must solve,

$$12x^2(x + 2) = 0$$
$$12x^2 = 0 \quad or \quad x + 2 = 0$$
$$x = 0 \quad or \quad x = -2$$

When $x = 0$ then $f(0) = 6$
When $x = -2$ then $f(-2) = -10$

Thus the coordinates of the stationary points are (0,6) and (-2,-10).

The nature of the stationary points in the previous example is determined by making a nature table using the derivative $f'(x) = 12x^2(x + 2)$. Work through the next activity to see how to make a nature table.

Making a nature table Go online

Make a table using the factors of the derivative and the stationary points.
The arrows are for determining what the gradient of the tangents to the curve are before -2, between -2 and 0 and after 0.

x	$\rightarrow$	-2	$\rightarrow$	0	$\rightarrow$
$12x^2$					
$(x + 2)$					
$f'(x)$					
shape					

It is often easier to think of a value just before -2 i.e.-3, between -2 and 0 i.e.-1 and just after 0 i.e.1 and to uses these values to determine whether the result is positive or negative.

x	-3 $\rightarrow$	-2	-1 $\rightarrow$	0	1 $\rightarrow$
$12x^2$					
$(x + 2)$					
$f'(x)$					
shape					

When $x = -3$, $12x^2 = 12 \times (-3)^2 = 108$ which is positive.
Do the same thing across the row.

x	-3 $\rightarrow$	-2	-1 $\rightarrow$	0	1 $\rightarrow$
$12x^2$	+	+	+	0	+
$(x + 2)$					
$f'(x)$					
shape					

Notice that when $x = 0$, $12x^2 = 12 \times 0^2 = 0$
Now substitute your values x into $(x + 2)$
When $x = -3$, $x + 2 = -3 + 2 = -1$ which is negative.

x	-3 $\rightarrow$	-2	-1 $\rightarrow$	0	1 $\rightarrow$
$12x^2$	+	+	+	0	+
$(x + 2)$	-	0	+	+	+
$f'(x)$					
shape					

$f'(x) = 12x^2(x + 2)$ which means $12x^2$ times $(x + 2)$ so to find the next row we multiply the values in the columns above.

a positive $\times$ a negative is negative
a positive $\times$ zero is zero
a positive $\times$ a positive is positive
a positive $\times$ zero is zero
a positive $\times$ a positive is positive

x	-3 $\rightarrow$	-2	-1 $\rightarrow$	0	1 $\rightarrow$
$12x^2$	+	+	+	0	+
$(x + 2)$	-	0	+	+	+
$f'(x)$	-	0	+	0	+
shape					

Now let's draw the shape of $f(x)$ depending on the value of $f'(x)$.

$f'(-3)$ is negative and a negative gradient slopes downwards from left to right giving,

x	-3 $\rightarrow$	-2	-1 $\rightarrow$	0	1 $\rightarrow$
$12x^2$	+	+	+	0	+
$(x + 2)$	-	0	+	+	+
$f'(x)$	-	0	+	0	+
shape	\	—	/	—	/

This gives us a minimum turning point at (-2, -10) and a rising point of inflection at (0, 6).

Example

Problem:

Find the stationary points on the curve $y = 2x^3 - 6x + 1$ and determine their nature.

Solution:

$y = 2x^3 - 6x + 1$ and $\frac{dy}{dx} = 6x^2 - 6$

Stationary points occur when $\frac{dy}{dx} = 0$

$$6x^2 - 6 = 0$$
$$6(x^2 - 1) = 0$$
$$6(x - 1)(x + 1) = 0$$
$$x - 1 = 0 \quad or \quad x + 1 = 0$$
$$x = 1 \quad or \quad x = -1$$

When $x = -1, y = 2(-1)^3 - 6(-1) + 1 = 5$
When $x = 1, y = 2(1)^3 - 6(1) + 1 = -3$

Thus the stationary points occur at (-1,5) and (1,-3).
To determine their nature we draw a nature table.

x	-2 $\rightarrow$	-1	0 $\rightarrow$	1	2 $\rightarrow$
$(x - 1)$	-	-	-	0	+
$(x + 1)$	-	0	+	+	+
$6(x - 1)(x + 1)$	+	0	-	0	+
shape	/	—	\	—	/

This gives us a maximum turning point at (-1, 5) and a minimum turning point at (1, -3).

Determining stationary points exercise   Go online

Q41: Find the stationary points on the curve $y = x^4 - 4x^3 + 1$ and determine their nature.

....

Q42: Find the coordinates of the stationary points on the curve $-2x^2 + 20x + 5$?
Determine the nature of these stationary points and justify your answer.

....

Q43: Find the coordinates of the stationary points on the curve $y = x^3 + 3x^2 + 9$
Determine the nature of these stationary points and justify your answer.

....

Q44: Find the coordinates of the stationary points on the curve $8x^3 + x^4$
Determine the nature of these stationary points and justify your answer.

....

Q45: Find the stationary points on the curve $f(x) = x^4 - 8x^2 - 1$ and determine their nature.

1.6   Sketching algebraic functions and graphs of derivatives

You should already know how to sketch the graphs of many functions and you now have an additional tool to help you do this.

By finding stationary points and making a nature table you get an instant picture of what the sketch should look like. This will also allow you to identify the intervals for which the function is increasing or decreasing.

It is important to be able to sketch and use both the graphs of functions and of derivatives.

We investigate these in the next three sections.

1.6.1   Curve sketching

Key point

In order to make a good sketch of a curve some information about the curve is required.

1. The coordinates of the y-intercept

2. The coordinates of the roots.

3. The coordinates of the stationary points and their nature.

4. The behaviour of the curve for large positive and negative values of x.

Examples

1. Problem:

Sketch the curve $y = 3x^2 - x^3$

Solution:

Step 1: Write down the y-intercept.

The y-intercept occurs when $x = 0$ so $y = 3 \times 0^2 - 0^3 = 0$

Hence the y-intercept is (0, 0).

Step 2: Find the roots.

The roots occur when $y = 0$

Factorise $3x^2 - x^3 = 0$ gives,

$$x^2 (3 - x) = 0$$
$$x^2 = 0 \quad or \quad (3 - x) = 0$$
$$x = 0 \quad or \quad x = 3$$

Hence the roots are (0,0) and (3,0).

Step 3: Find the stationary points and their nature.

$\frac{dy}{dx} = 6x - 3x^2$

Stationary points occur when $\frac{dy}{dx} = 0$

$$6x - 3x^2 = 0$$
$$3x (2 - x) = 0$$
$$3x = 0 \quad or \quad (2 - x) = 0$$
$$x = 0 \quad or \quad x = 2$$

When $x = 0$ then $y = 3 \times 0^2 - 0^3 = 0$
When $x = 2$ then $y = 3 \times 2^2 - 2^3 = 4$

Thus the stationary points are (0, 0) and (2, 4).

x	-1 $\rightarrow$	0	1 $\rightarrow$	2	3 $\rightarrow$
$3x$	-	0	+	+	+
$(2 - x)$	+	+	+	0	-
$3x(2 - x)$	-	0	+	0	-
shape	\	—	/	—	\

This gives us a minimum turning point at (0,0) and a maximum turning point at (2,4).

Step 4: Check the behaviour of the curve when x takes large positive and negative values.

For large positive and negative values of x, y behaves like $-x^3$, this is the term with the highest degree.

When x is very large and negative $-x^3$ is very large and positive and we write this as,
As $x \rightarrow -\infty$ then $y \rightarrow +\infty$

When x is very large and positive $-x^3$ is very large and negative. and we write this as,
As $x \to +\infty$ then $y \to -\infty$

This matches what is happening at the start and end of our nature table.

Step 5: Plot the points that you have found to make a good sketch of the curve.

Notice that the shape matches our nature table and the important points on the curve are clearly labelled.

. . . .

2. Problem:

Sketch the curve $f(x) = x^3 - 3x + 2$

Solution:

Step 1: Write down the y-intercept.

The y-intercept occurs when $x = 0$ so $y = 0^3 - 3 \times 0 + 2 = 2$

Hence the y-intercept is (0,2).

Step 2: Find the roots.

The roots occur when $f(x) = 0$

$x^3 - 3x + 2$ is a polynomial so to factorise we need synthetic division.

Firstly we could try dividing by $(x - 1)$. We place 1 into the synthetic division. If the remainder is equal to 0 then $(x - 1)$ is a factor.

$$
\begin{array}{c|cccc}
1 & 1 & 0 & -3 & 2 \\
  &   & 1 & 1 & -2 \\
\hline
  & 1 & 1 & -2 & 0 \\
\end{array}
$$

$$
\begin{aligned}
x^3 - 3x + 2 &= (x - 1)\left(x^2 + x - 2\right) \\
&= (x - 1)(x + 2)(x - 1)
\end{aligned}
$$

$$(x - 1)(x + 2)(x - 1) = 0$$
$$x - 1 = 0 \quad or \quad x + 2 = 0$$
$$x = 1 \quad or \quad x = -2$$

Hence the roots are (1,0) and (-2,0).

Step 3: Find the stationary points and their nature.

$\frac{dy}{dx} = 3x^2 - 3$

Stationary points occur when $\frac{dy}{dx} = 0$

$$3x^2 - 3 = 0$$
$$3\left(x^2 - 1\right) = 0$$
$$3(x - 1)(x + 1) = 0$$
$$x - 1 = 0 \quad or \quad x + 1 = 0$$
$$x = 1 \quad or \quad x = -1$$

When $x = 1$ then $y = 1^3 - 3 \times 1 + 2 = 0$
When $x = -1$ then $y = (-1)^3 - 3 \times (-1) + 2 = 4$

Thus the stationary points are (1, 0) and (-1, 4).

x	$\begin{array}{c}-2\\\rightarrow\end{array}$	-1	$\begin{array}{c}0\\\rightarrow\end{array}$	1	$\begin{array}{c}2\\\rightarrow\end{array}$
$(x - 1)$	-	-	-	0	+
$(x + 1)$	-	0	+	+	+
$3(x - 1)(x + 1)$	+	0	-	0	+
shape	/	—	\	—	/

This gives us a maximum turning point at (-1,4) and a minimum turning point at (1,0).

Step 4: Check the behaviour of the curve when x takes large positive and negative values.

For large positive and negative values of x, y behaves like x^3, this is the term with the highest degree.

As $x \rightarrow -\infty$ then $y \rightarrow -\infty$

As $x \rightarrow +\infty$ then $y \rightarrow +\infty$

This matches what is happening at the start and end of our nature table.

Step 5: Plot the points that you have found to make a good sketch of the curve.

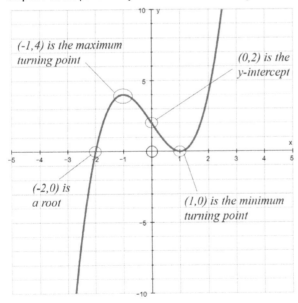

Notice that the shape matches our nature table and the important points on the curve are clearly labelled.

Curve sketching exercise   Go online

The equation of a curve is $y = x^2 - 5x + 6$.

Q46: Identify where the curve cuts the x-axis.

....

Q47: What are the coordinates of the y-intercept?

....

Q48: What are the coordinates of the stationary point?

....

Q49: What is the nature of the stationary point?

....

Q50: As $x \to \infty$ then:

a) $y \to -\infty$
b) $y \to +\infty$

....

Q51: As $x \to -\infty$ then:

a) $y \to -\infty$
b) $y \to +\infty$

....

Q52: Now using this information, sketch the curve $y = x^2 - 5x + 6$.

The equation of a curve is $y = 6x^2 - x^3$.

Q53: Identify where the curve cuts the x-axis.

....

Q54: What are the coordinates of the y-intercept?

....

Q55: What are the coordinates of the stationary point furthest to the left?

....

Q56: What is the nature of the stationary point furthest to the left?

....

Q57: What is the nature of the stationary point furthest to the right?

....

Q58: As $x \to \infty$ then:

a) $y \to -\infty$

b) $y \to +\infty$

....

Q59: As $x \to -\infty$ then:

a) $y \to -\infty$

b) $y \to +\infty$

....

Q60: Now using this information, sketch the curve $y = 6x^2 - x^3$.

The equation of a curve is $y = x^3 + x^2 - x - 1$.

Q61: What are the coordinates of the y-intercept?

....

Q62: What are the values of the roots?

....

Q63: What is the nature of the stationary point furthest to the left?

....

Q64: What are the coordinates of the stationary point furthest to the left?

....

Q65: What is the nature of the stationary point furthest to the right?

....

Q66: What are the coordinates of the stationary point furthest to the left?

....

Q67: As $x \to \infty$ then:

a) $y \to -\infty$

b) $y \to +\infty$

....

Q68: As $x \to -\infty$ then:

a) $y \to -\infty$

b) $y \to +\infty$

....

Q69: Now using this information, sketch the curve $y = x^3 + x^2 - x - 1$.

1.6.2   Increasing and decreasing functions

Increasing or decreasing functions   Go online

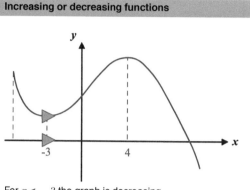

For $x < -3$ the graph is decreasing.

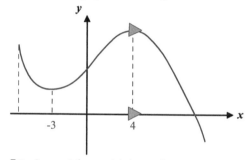

For $-3 < x < 4$ the graph is increasing.

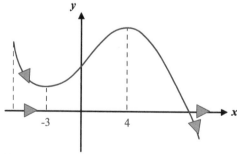

For $-3 < x < 4$ the graph is increasing.
For $x < -3$ and $x > 4$ the graph is decreasing.

Now study the same graph again as shown here. Remember that a straight line that slopes up from left to right has positive gradient whereas a line that slopes down from left to right has negative gradient.

Key point

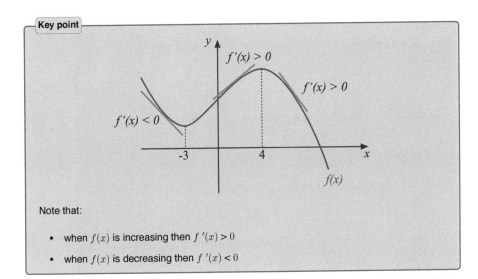

Note that:

- when $f(x)$ is increasing then $f'(x) > 0$
- when $f(x)$ is decreasing then $f'(x) < 0$

Examples

1. Problem:

State the interval for which $f(x) = x^3 - 6x^2 + 5$ is increasing.

Solution:

The function is increasing when $f'(x) > 0$

$f'(x) = 3x^2 - 12x$

Stationary points occur when $f'(x) = 0$

$3x^2 - 12x = 0$

$3x(x - 4) = 0$

$3x = 0 \ or \ x - 4 = 0$

$x = 0 \ or \ x = 4$

x	$\begin{matrix}-1\\\rightarrow\end{matrix}$	0	$\begin{matrix}2\\\rightarrow\end{matrix}$	4	$\begin{matrix}5\\\rightarrow\end{matrix}$
$3x$	-	0	+	+	+
$(x - 4)$	-	-	-	0	+
$3x(x - 4)$	+	0	-	0	+

Since the gradient is positive before $x = 0$ and after $x = 4$ the function is increasing for $x < 0$ and $x > 4$.

. . . .

2. Problem:

Show that the function $f(x) = \frac{1}{3}x^3 + 2x^2 + 4x$ is never decreasing.

Solution:

$$f(x) = \frac{1}{3}x^3 + 2x^2 + 4x \Rightarrow f'(x) = x^2 + 4x + 4$$
$$= (x + 2)^2$$

Since $(x + 2)^2 \geq 0$ for all values of x then $f(x)$ is never decreasing.

Increasing and decreasing functions exercise   Go online

Q70: In which of the following intervals is the function $y = x^2 + 6x + 6$ increasing?

a) $x > 0$

b) $x > -3$

c) $x < -3$

....

Q71: In which of the following intervals is the function $y = 2x^2 + 4x^3$ increasing?

a) $x < {}^{-1}/_3$

b) ${}^{-1}/_3 < x < 0$

c) $x > 0$

....

Q72: In which of the following intervals is the function $f(x) = x^4 + 4x^3$ is decreasing?

a) $x > -3$

b) $x < 0$

c) $x > 0$

d) $x < -3$

....

Q73: In which of the following intervals is the function $f(x) = 2x^3 + 3x^2 - 12x + 1$ increasing?

a) $x > -2$

b) $-2 < x < 1$

c) $x > 1$

....

Q74: In which of the following intervals is the function $f(x) = -x^3 + 3x^2$ decreasing?

a) $x < 0$

b) $x > 2$

c) $0 < x < 2$

1.6.3 The graph of the derivative

When we are given the graph of a function, $f(x)$ then it is usually possible to make a sketch of its derivative, $f'(x)$.

The following example shows how this is done.

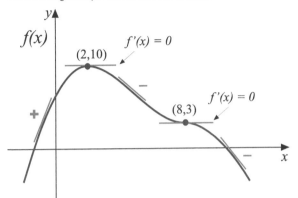

x	$\rightarrow$	2	$\rightarrow$	8	$\rightarrow$
shape	/	—	\	—	\
$f'(x)$	+	0	-	0	-
Derived function	above	on	below	on	below

The words *above*, *on* and *below* refer to the position of the graph of the derived function in relation to the x-axis.

To draw the graph of the derivative start by plotting the points where the graph crosses the x-axis.

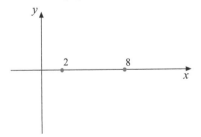

Before $x = 2$ the graph is above the x-axis so we get,

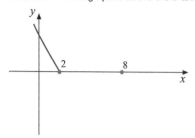

The graph is below the x-axis between $x = 2$ and $x = 8$ so we get,

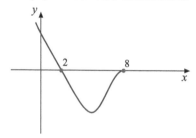

The graph is below the x-axis after $x = 8$ so we get,

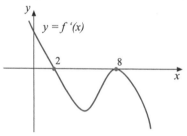

Key point

These results can be summarised as follows:

1. The stationary points on $f(x)$ become x-intercepts for $f'(x)$.

2. When $f(x)$ is increasing the graph for $f'(x)$ is above the x-axis.

3. When $f(x)$ is decreasing the graph for $f'(x)$ is below the x-axis.

Note that:

- if $f(x)$ is a quadratic function then the derived function $f'(x)$ will be a straight line;
- if $f(x)$ is a cubic function then the derived function $f'(x)$ will be a quadratic function.

Example

Problem:

For the graph of the function below, sketch the graph of the derived function.

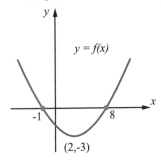

Solution:

Make a table.

x	$\rightarrow$	2	$\rightarrow$
shape	\	—	/
$f'(x)$	-	0	+
Derived function	below	on	above

Sketch the graph of the derivative.

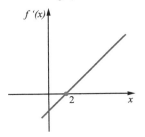

Notice that $f(x)$ is a quadratic and the graph of the derivative is a straight line.

Derivative puzzle   Go online

Q75: Put the graphs in order in each column so that the derivatives sit below the graphs of their function above.

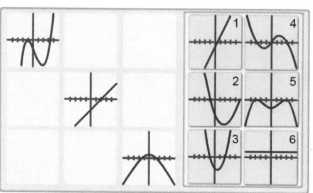

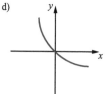

The graph of the derivative exercise   Go online

Q76: Which of the following represents the derived function of the graph below?

a)

b)

c)

d)

. . . .

Q77: Which of the following represents the derived function of the graph below?

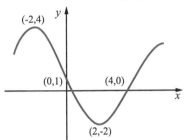

a)

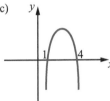

b)

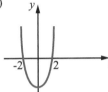

c)

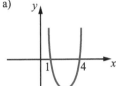

d)

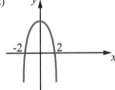

. . . .

Q78: Which of the following represents the derived function of the graph below?

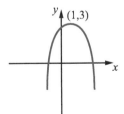

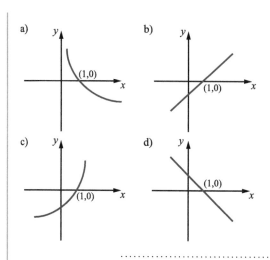

....

Q79: Which of the following represents the derived function of the graph below?

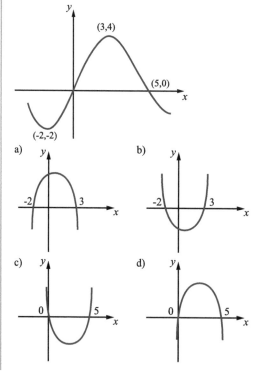

Q80: Which of the following represents the derived function of the graph below?

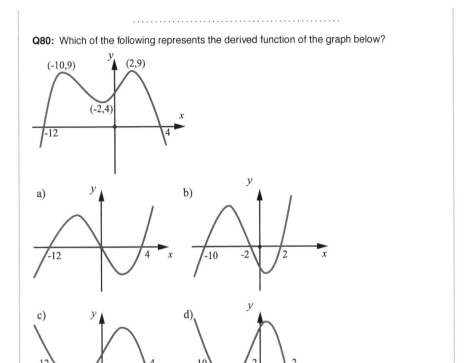

1.7 Closed intervals

Key point

The maximum or minimum value in a closed interval occurs at either the stationary point or an endpoint.

Maximums and minimums on a closed interval   Go online

The graph has been drawn with a closed interval of $-5 \leq x \leq 7$.

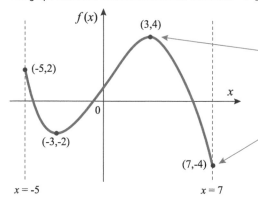

The maximum value of the function is 4 which occur at the stationary point (3,4).

The minimum value of the function is -4 which occur at the end point (7,-4).

Notice that the minimum turning point is at (-3, -2), but in this case the end point is at (7,-4) which gives a lower value for the function.

Whereas the maximum turning point is at (3, 4) which gives a higher value than the end point which is at (-5,2).

Example

Problem:

Find the maximum and minimum values of $f(x) = 3x - x^3$ in the closed interval $-1 \cdot 5 \geq x \geq 3$.

Solution:

It is much easier to spot the maximum and minimum values if we make a sketch.

Step 1: Find the stationary points and their nature,
$f'(x) = 3 - 3x^2$

Stationary points occur when $f'(x) = 0$

$$3 - 3x^2 = 0$$
$$3(1 - x^2) = 0$$
$$3(1 - x)(1 + x) = 0$$
$$1 - x = 0 \ or \ 1 + x = 0$$
$$x = 1 \ or \ x = -1$$

When $x = 1$ then $y = 3 \times 1 - 1^3 = 2$
When $x = -1$ then $y = 3 \times (-1) - (-1)^3 = -2$

Thus the stationary points are (1, 2) and (-1, -2).

x	-2 $\rightarrow$	-1	0 $\rightarrow$	1	2 $\rightarrow$
$(1 - x)$	+	+	+	0	-
$(1 + x)$	-	0	+	+	+
$3(1 - x)(1 + x)$	-	0	+	0	-
shape	\	—	/	—	\

This gives us a maximum turning point at (1, 2) and a minimum turning point at (-1, -2).

Step 2: Find the end points.

When $x = -1 \cdot 5$ then $f(-1 \cdot 5) = -1 \cdot 125$.
When $x = 3$ then $f(3) = -18$.

Step 3: Make a sketch.

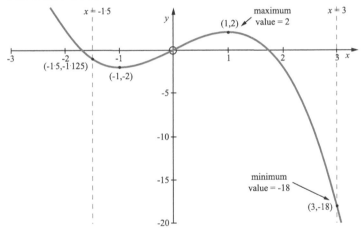

Hence the maximum value is 2 at the maximum turning point (1, 2) and the minimum value is -18 at the end point (3, -18).

Closed intervals exercise   Go online

This graph is drawn for the closed interval $-4 \geq x \geq 7$.

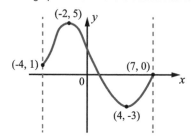

Q81: Identify the maximum and minimum values within the given closed interval.

This graph is drawn for the closed interval $0 \geq x \geq 9$.

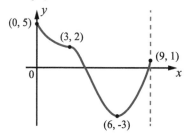

Q82: Identify the maximum and minimum values within the given closed interval.

A function $y = 4x^2 - 16x + 2$ is drawn in the closed interval $0 \geq x \geq 6$.

Q83: What is the stationary value of the function $y = 4x^2 - 16x + 2$?

....

Q84: When $x = 0$ then $y = ?$

....

Q85: When $x = 6$ then $y = ?$

....

Q86: Which of these statements is true?

a) The function $y = 4x^2 - 16x + 2$ has a minimum at (0, 2) and a maximum at (6, 50).
b) The function $y = 4x^2 - 16x + 2$ has a minimum at (2, -14) and a maximum at (0, 2).
c) The function $y = 4x^2 - 16x + 2$ has a minimum at (2, -14) and a maximum at (6, 50).

A function $y = 3x^3 - 9x^2 + 6$ is drawn in the closed interval $0 \geq x \geq 4$.

Q87: What is the maximum stationary value of the function $y = 3x^3 - 9x^2 + 6$?

....

Q88: What is the minimum stationary value of the function $y = 3x^3 - 9x^2 + 6$?

....

Q89: When $x = 0$ then $y = ?$

....

Q90: When $x = 6$ then $y = ?$

....

Q91: Which of these statements is true?

a) The function $y = 3x^3 - 9x^2 + 6$ has a maximum at (4, 54) and a minimum at (2, -6).

b) The function $y = 3x^3 - 9x^2 + 6$ has a maximum at (4, 54) and a minimum at (0, -6).

c) The function $y = 3x^3 - 9x^2 + 6$ has a maximum at (0, -6) and a minimum at (2, -6).

1.8 Applying differential calculus

Until now we have looked at differentiation in a mainly abstract way. Differential calculus can also be used to solve problems in context. We investigate this in the next two sections.

1.8.1 Rate of Change

Problems can often be solved by forming some kind of mathematical model such as a formula, an equation or a graph. The derivative of a function at a particular value describes the rate of change of the function at that value.

Example : Rate of change of volume

Problem:

A sphere with radius r and volume $V = \frac{4}{3}\pi r^3$ is inflated.

Find

a) the rate of change of the volume of the sphere with respect to the radius;

b) the rate of change of the volume when the radius is 2 cm.

Solution:

a) The rate of change of the volume of the sphere with respect to the radius is $\frac{dV}{dr}$.

$$V = \frac{4}{3}\pi r^3$$

$$\frac{dV}{dr} = 3 \times \frac{4}{3}\pi r^2$$

$$= 4\pi r^2$$

Note that $\frac{4}{3}\pi$ is a constant.

b) The rate of change of the volume when the radius is 2 cm is

$$4\pi \times 2^2 = 16\pi$$

Key point

Velocity or speed is a rate of change of distance (or displacement) s at time t so the velocity, $v = \frac{ds}{dt}$ or $s'(t)$.

Key point

Acceleration, a, is a rate of change for velocity (or speed), v at time t, so $a = \frac{dv}{dt}$ or $s''(t)$.

Example : Distance (s) - Velocity (v) - Acceleration (a)

Problem:

The displacement of a particle at time t, relative to its starting position, is given by the formula
$$s(t) = 2t^3 - 6t^2 + 10t + 5$$

$s(t)$ is the distance in centimetres and t is the time in seconds.

Calculate:

a) the velocity of the particle when $t = 4$

b) the acceleration of the particle when $t = 4$

Solution:

a) Velocity, $\frac{ds}{dt} = 6t^2 - 12t + 10$

When $t = 4$ then velocity $= 6 \times 4^2 - 12 \times 4 + 10 = 58 cm\ s^{-1}$

b) To find an expression for acceleration we find the second derivative of displacement. This is the same as differentiating our formula for velocity.

Acceleration, $a = \frac{dv}{dt} = 12t - 12$

When $t = 4$ then acceleration $= 12 \times 4 - 12 = 36\ cms^{-2}$

Rate of change exercise   Go online

The volume of air, $V \; cm^3$, in a balloon as it is inflated is given by the formula
$V(t) \; = \; 4t^3 \; + \; t^2 \; + \; t$.

Find the rate of change of the volume when $t \; = \; 1$ (seconds).

Q92: What is the rate of change of the volume when $t \; = \; 1$?

The displacement (in metres) of a particle at time t (seconds), relative to its starting position, is given by the formula $s(t) \; = \; 3t^3 \; - \; 2t^2 \; + \; 4t \; + \; 4$.

Find the velocity and acceleration of the particle when $t \; = \; 1$.

Q93: What is the velocity of the particle when $t \; = \; 1$?

. . . .

Q94: What is the acceleration of the particle when $t \; = \; 1$?

The radius (in cm) of an ink blot, t seconds after the start of an experiment, is given by the formula $R(t) \; = \; 4\sqrt{t}$

Calculate the rate of change of the radius when $t \; = \; 9$.

Q95: What is the rate of change of the radius when $t \; = \; 9$?

1.8.2 Optimisation

Many problems involve finding a maximum or minimum value where the context is modelled on a function. These values can be found by using differentiation to find stationary points.

Examples

1. Maximum height

Problem:

The height, h, of a ball thrown upwards is given by the formula $h(t) \; = \; 20t \; - \; 5t^2$, where t is the time in seconds from when the ball is thrown.

   a) When does the ball reach its maximum height?

   b) Calculate the maximum height that the ball reaches?

Solution:

a) The ball reaches its maximum height at a stationary point i.e. when $h'(t) = 0$.

$$h'(t) = 20 - 10t$$
$$20 - 10t = 0$$
$$20 = 10t$$
$$t = 2$$

It is important to check that the stationary point is a maximum by making a nature table.

t	$1 \rightarrow$	2	$3 \rightarrow$
$h'(t)$	+	0	-
shape	/	—	\

Thus there is a maximum at $t = 2$ and the ball reaches its maximum height after 2 seconds.

b) The ball reaches its maximum height when $t = 2$.
To find the height we must let $t = 2$ in $h(t)$.
h(2) = 20 × 2 - 5 × 2² = 20
Hence the ball reaches a maximum height of 20 metres.

. . . .

2. Maximum Area

Problem:

A farmer has 80 metres of fencing to make a rectangular sheep pen against an existing wall.

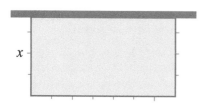

a) Show that the area of the sheep pen is given by $A = 80x - 2x^2$

b) Find the greatest area that the farmer can enclose.

Solution:

a) First assign variables for the length and breadth of the rectangle.
   If x is the breadth of the rectangle then, since there is 80 metres of fencing in total, the length of the rectangle must be $80 - 2x$ metres.
   Thus the area of the rectangle is,

$$A(x) = length \times breadth = (80 - 2x)x = 80x - 2x^2$$

b) The pen will have it's maximum area at a stationary point i.e. $A'(x) = 0$.

$$A'(x) = 80 - 4x$$
$$80 - 4x = 0$$
$$80 = 4x$$
$$x = 20$$

Check that the stationary point at $x = 20$ is a maximum by making a nature table.

x	19 $\rightarrow$	20	21 $\rightarrow$
$A'(x)$	+	0	-
shape	/	—	\

Thus there is a maximum area at $x = 20$.

The dimensions of the pen are:

$$breadth = x$$
$$= 20\ m$$

and

$$length = 80 - 2x$$
$$= 40\ m$$

$$\text{Maximum area} = length \times breadth$$
$$= 40 \times 20$$
$$= 800\ m^2$$

....

3. Problem:

A family hope to build a room in their attic.

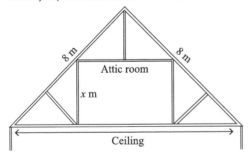

The roof space is in the shape of an isosceles right-angled triangle.

a) Find the length of the ceiling.

b) Given that the height of the attic room is x metres, show that the area of the room is given by $A = 8\sqrt{2}x - 2x^2$

c) Find the dimensions of the attic room which maximises the area of the space.

Solution:

a) The roof space is a right angled triangle.

The length of the ceiling $= \sqrt{8^2 + 8^2} = 8\sqrt{2}$

b)

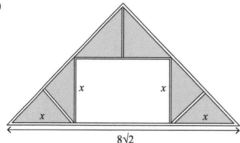

The shaded triangles are all isosceles right-angled triangles.

Length of attic room $= 8\sqrt{2} - 2x$

Area of the attic room

$$= \left(8\sqrt{2} - 2x\right) \times x$$
$$= \left(8\sqrt{2}\right)x - 2x^2 \quad \text{as required.}$$

c) The attic room will have its maximum area at a stationary point i.e. $\frac{dA}{dx} = 0$

$$\frac{dA}{dx} = 8\sqrt{2} - 4x$$
$$8\sqrt{2} - 4x = 0$$
$$8\sqrt{2} = 4x$$
$$x = 2\sqrt{2}$$

Check that the stationary point at $x = 2\sqrt{2}$ is a maximum by making a nature table.

x	$\underset{\rightarrow}{2}$	$2\sqrt{2}$	$\underset{\rightarrow}{3}$
$\frac{dA}{dx}$	+	0	-
shape	/	—	\

Thus there is a maximum area at $x = 2\sqrt{2}$.

The dimensions of the attic room are:

$breadth = x$ and $length = 8\sqrt{2} - 2x$
$\qquad = 2\sqrt{2}\ m$ $\qquad\qquad\qquad = 4\sqrt{2}\ m$

Maximum area = length × breadth

$$=4\sqrt{2} \times 2\sqrt{2}$$
$$=16 \ m^2$$

Optimisation exercise Go online

Q96: The sum of two numbers x and y is 20.
An expression for the product of the two numbers is $P = xy$.

a) Give the expression for P in terms of x.
b) Find the value of x which maximises P.

. . . .

Q97: The speed of a skier on part of a slope is given by the formula $v(t) = 6\sqrt{t} - 0 \cdot 6t$.

a) When does the skier reach their maximum speed (in seconds)?
b) What is the maximum speed in $km \ h^{-1}$ reached?

. . . .

Q98: A rectangle has breadth x cm and perimeter 20 cm.

a) Find, in terms of x, an expression for the area of the rectangle.
b) Find the value of x for maximum area.

. . . .

Q99: A cardboard square of side $S = 18 \ cm$ has squares of side x cm cut from each corner.
The cardboard is then folded to make an open box as shown in the diagram.

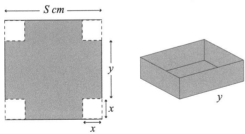

a) Find an expression for y in terms of x cm.
b) Write down an expression for the volume of the box in terms of x alone.
c) Calculate the value of x for maximum volume.

. . . .

Q100: A box is made in the shape of a cuboid with square base and no lid as shown in the diagram.
The volume of the box is $4 \ cm^3$.

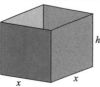

a) Find an expression for the height of the box in terms of x.
b) Find an expression for the total surface area, S, of the box.
   Give your answer in terms of x.
c) Find the value of x which minimises the surface area.
d) Find the corresponding value of h which minimises the surface area?

1.9 Differentiating trigonometric and composite functions

There are some other types of functions which we need to know how to differentiate. We investigate these in the next four sections.

1.9.1 Differentiating sin x and cos x

A ball, attached to the end of a stretched spring, is released at time $t = 0$. The displacement y (cm) of the ball from the x-axis at time t (seconds) is given by the formula $y = 10 \sin t$.

Differentiation of the sine function   Go online

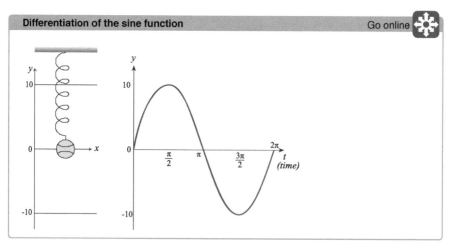

The following questions might be posed:

- What is the speed of the ball after 2 seconds?
- When is the ball first stationary?

Since speed is the rate of change of distance with respect to time, the speed of the ball is given by the differential equation

$$\frac{dy}{dt} = \frac{d}{dt} (10 \sin t)$$

The derivative of the sine function is required to answer these questions.

Derivative of sin x

Go online

The graph for $y = \sin x$ is shown here.

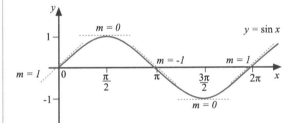

Notice that the tangent to the curve is drawn at various points. The value for the gradient of the tangent at these points is recorded in the following table.

x	0	$\frac{\pi}{2}$	π	$\frac{3\pi}{2}$	2π
m_T	1	0	-1	0	1

When these points are plotted and joined with a smooth curve the result is as follows.

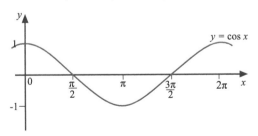

Since the gradient of the tangent at the point $(a, f(a))$ on the curve $y = f(x)$ is $f'(a)$ then the above graph represents the graph of the derivative of $\sin x$.
Then for $y = \sin x$ it appears that $\frac{dy}{dx} = \cos x$
(This can be checked by calculating gradients at intermediate points).

Key point

When $f(x) = \cos x$ then $f'(x) = -\sin x$

When $f(x) = \sin x$ then $f'(x) = \cos x$

Note: x must be measured in ***radians***

Examples

1. Problem:

Find $f'(x)$ when $f(x) = 3 \cos x$.

Solution:

When $f(x) = 3 \cos x$

then $f'(x) = -3 \sin x$

....

2. Problem:

Find $f'(x)$ when $f(x) = 2 \sin x - \cos x + 4x^2$.

Solution:

$$f'(x) = 2 \cos x - (-\sin x) + 8x$$
$$= 2 \cos x + \sin x + 8x$$

Differentiating sin x and cos x exercise   Go online

Q101: Study the graph for $y = \cos x$ as shown here.

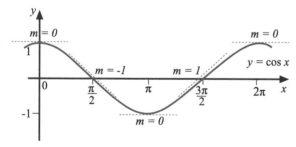

Complete the following table for the gradient of the tangents.

x	0	$\frac{\pi}{2}$	π	$\frac{3\pi}{2}$	2π
m_T	...	...	...	...	...

Plot the points and join with a smooth curve.

....

Q102: When $y = \cos x$ it appears that $^{dy}/_{dx} = $?

a) $\sin x$
b) $\cos x$
c) $-\sin x$
d) $-\cos x$

....

Q103: When $f(x) = 7 \sin x$ then what is $f'(x)$?

....

Q104: When $f(x) = -5 \cos x$ then what is $f'(x)$?

....

Q105: When $f(x) = -\sin x - 8 \cos x$ then what is $f'(x)$?

....

Q106: When $f(x) = 4x^2 - 2 \cos x$ then what is $f'(x)$?

....

Q107: When $f(x) = \frac{2 + 8x \sin x}{7x}$ then what is $f'(x)$?

1.9.2 Differentiating (x + a)ⁿ

Expressions such as $(x + 5)^2$ and $(x - 4)^3$ can be differentiated by expanding the brackets and differentiating term by term.

Examples

1. Problem:

Find $f'(x)$ when $f(x) = (x + 5)^2$.

Solution:

By expanding the brackets first we get:

$f(x) = (x + 5)^2 = (x + 5)(x + 5) = x^2 + 10x + 25$

Now differentiate term by term:

$f'(x) = 2x + 10$
$\qquad = 2(x + 5)$

....

2. Problem:

Find $f'(x)$ when $f(x) = (x - 4)^3$.

Solution:

Again by expanding the brackets first we get:

$$\begin{aligned}
f(x) &= (x - 4)^3 \\
&= (x - 4)(x - 4)(x - 4) \\
&= (x - 4)(x^2 - 8x + 16) \\
&= x^3 - 8x^2 + 16x - 4x^2 + 32x - 64 \\
&= x^3 - 12x^2 + 48x - 64
\end{aligned}$$

Now differentiate term by term:

$$\begin{aligned}
f'(x) &= 3x^2 - 24x + 48 \\
&= 3(x^2 - 8x + 16) \\
&= 3(x - 4)^2
\end{aligned}$$

Is there a pattern to these answers?

Differentiation of $(x + a)^n$ Go online

Make a prediction for the derivatives of the following functions **without** expanding the expressions.

Q108:

  a) $f(x) = (x + 3)^4$
  b) $f(x) = (x + 3)^5$
  c) $f(x) = (x + 3)^6$
  d) $y = (x - 2)^4$
  e) $y = (x - 2)^5$
  f) $y = (x - 2)^6$

Key point

When $f(x) = (x + a)^n$ then $f'(x) = n(x + a)^{n-1}$

Examples

1. Problem:

Differentiate $f(x) = \dfrac{1}{(x - 3)^5}$

Solution:

First rewrite the expression for $f(x)$.

$$f(x) = \frac{1}{(x-3)^5}$$
$$= (x-3)^{-5}$$

Now differentiate using the above rule.

$$f'(x) = -5(x-3)^{-6}$$
$$= \frac{-5}{(x-3)^6}$$

....

2. Problem:

Find

$$\frac{d}{dx}\left(\sqrt{x+1}\right)^5$$

Solution:

$$\frac{d}{dx}\left(\sqrt{x+1}\right)^5 = \frac{d}{dx}(x+1)^{\frac{5}{2}}$$
$$= \frac{5}{2}(x+1)^{\frac{3}{2}}$$
$$= \frac{5}{2}\left(\sqrt{x+1}\right)^3$$

Differentiating $(x + a)^n$ exercise   Go online

Q109: Differentiate:

a) $f(x) = (x-8)^9$

b) $f(x) = (x-9)^{-2}$

c) $f(x) = (x-3)^{\frac{8}{3}}$

d) $f(x) = \frac{1}{(x-6)^2}$

e) $f(x) = \left(\sqrt{x+2}\right)^9$

....

Q110: If $f(x) = (x+5)^5$ what is $f'(0) = ?$

....

Q111: If $f(x) = (x+5)^5$ what is $f'(3) = ?$

....

Q112: What is the gradient of the tangent to the curve $y = \frac{1}{x+1}$ when $x = 0$?

....

Q113: What is the equation of the tangent?

1.9.3   Differentiating $(ax + b)^n$

Example Problem:

Find the derivative when $y = (3x - 4)^5$.

Solution:

Step 1:	Bring down the power.	5
Step 2:	Write down the bracket.	$5(3x - 4)^{\cdot}$
Step 3:	Reduce the power by 1.	$5(3x - 4)^4$
Step 4:	Multiply by the derivative of the bracket.	$5(3x - 4)^4 \times 3$
Step 5:	Simplify the answer .	$15(3x - 4)^4$

Key point

When $f(x) = (ax + b)^n$ then

$$f'(x) = n(ax + b)^{n-1} \times a = an(ax + b)^{n-1}$$

Q114: Try differentiating these on paper then check your answers.

a) $y = (2x + 1)^4$

b) $y = (3x + 1)^4$

c) $y = (5x + 1)^4$

d) $y = (5x - 2)^8$

e) $y = (7x + 5)^4$

Differentiation examples   Go online

Examples

1. Problem:

Differentiate $f(x) = (9x - 4)^5$.

Solution:

$$f'(x) = 5(9x - 4)^4 \times 9 = 45(9x - 4)^4$$

. . . .

2. Problem:

Differentiate $y = \dfrac{1}{(6x - 5)^{\frac{1}{3}}}$

Solution:

First rewrite the expression for y.

$$y = \frac{1}{(6x - 5)^{\frac{1}{3}}}$$

$$= (6x - 5)^{-\frac{1}{3}}$$

Now differentiate using the rule.

$$\frac{dy}{dx} = -\frac{1}{3}(6x - 5)^{-\frac{4}{3}} \times 6$$

$$= -2(6x - 5)^{-\frac{4}{3}}$$

$$= -\frac{2}{(6x - 5)^{\frac{4}{3}}}$$

Differentiating (ax + b)^n exercise   Go online

Q115: Differentiate:

a) $f(x) = (8x + 5)^9$

b) $f(x) = (6 - 7x)^2$

c) $f(x) = (8x + 1)^{-2}$

d) $f(x) = \frac{1}{5x + 2}$

....

Q116: Differentiate $f(x) = (6x + 7)^{\frac{5}{2}}$

....

Q117: Differentiate $f(x) = \left(\sqrt{9x + 8}\right)^3$

....

Q118: Differentiate $f(x) = \frac{1}{\sqrt{8x + 7}}$

....

Q119: Differentiate $f(x) = \frac{1}{\left(\sqrt{4x + 5}\right)^5}$

1.9.4 Differentiating composite functions (The chain rule)

Key point

It is not essential for you to understand the theory to be able to use the chain rule.

If you are struggling as you read through it remember there are worked examples to follow which should make the method clear.

The Theory
Function notation

$h(x) = (ax + b)^n$ is an example of a composite function.
Let $f(x) = ax + b$ and $g(x) = x^n$ then

$h(x) = (ax + b)^n = (f(x))^n = g(f(x))$
When $f(x) = ax + b$ then $f'(x) = a$
When $g(x) = x^n$ then $g'(x) = nx^{n-1}$
Also when $g(f) = (f)^n$ then $g'(f) = n(f)^{n-1} = n(ax + b)^{n-1}$
However, when $y = (ax + b)^n$ then $dy/dx = an(ax + b)^{n-1}$
Writing this in function notation gives,
When $h(x) = g(f(x))$ then

$$h'(x) = an(ax + b)^{n-1} = n(ax + b)^{n-1} \times a = g'(f(x)) \times f'(x)$$

This result is known as **the chain rule**.

Leibniz notation

The chain rule can also be written in Leibniz notation.
Let $y = (ax + b)^n$ but this time let $u = ax + b$
so $y = u^n$
Since $u = ax + b$ then $du/dx = a$
Since $y = u^n$ then $dy/du = nu^{n-1} = n(ax + b)^{n-1}$
As before, when $y = (ax + b)^n$ then $dy/dx = an(ax + b)^{n-1}$
In Leibniz notation this is as follows
When $y = u^n$ then

$$dy/dx = an(x + a)^{n-1} = n(x + a)^{n-1} \times a = dy/du \times du/dx$$

It will be useful to remember both forms of the chain rule. (However, you are not required to be able to prove either of them.)

> **Key point**
>
> **Function notation:**
>
> $h'(x) = g'(f(x)) \times f'(x)$
>
> **Leibniz notation:**
>
> $dy/dx = dy/du \times du/dx$

Many types of composite functions can be differentiated using the chain rule.   Note that either function or Leibniz notation can be used.

Examples

1. Problem:

Find $\frac{dy}{dx}$ when $y = \sqrt{x^3 - 4x^2 - 5}$.

Solution:

It is often easier to follow these steps.

Step 1:   Turn the square root into a power. $y = \left(x^3 - 4x^2 - 5\right)^{\frac{1}{2}}$

Step 2:   Bring down the power. $\frac{1}{2}$

Step 3:   Write down the bracket. $\frac{1}{2}\left(x^3 - 4x^2 - 5\right)$

Step 4:   Reduce the power by 1. $\frac{1}{2}\left(x^3 - 4x^2 - 5\right)^{-\frac{1}{2}}$

Step 5:   Differentiate the bracket. $\frac{1}{2}\left(x^3 - 4x^2 - 5\right)^{-\frac{1}{2}} \times \left(3x^2 - 8x\right)$

Step 6:   Simplify the answer. $\frac{dy}{dx} = \frac{3x^2 - 8x}{2\sqrt{x^3 - 4x^2 - 5}}$

....

2. Problem:

Find $f'(x)$ when $f(x) = \cos(2x + 1)$.

Solution:

Step 1:   Differentiate cos. $-sin$

Step 2:   Write down the bracket. $-sin(2x + 1)$

Step 3:   Differentiate the bracket. $-sin(2x + 1) \times 2$

Step 4:   Simplify the answer. $-2sin(2x + 1) \times 2$

....

3. Problem:

Find the derivative of $\sin^2(3 - 2x)$.

Solution:

Step 1:   Remember: $\sin^2(3 - 2x) = (sin(3 - 2x))^2$

Step 2:   Bring down the power. 2

Step 3:   Write down the bracket. $2sin(3 - 2x)$

Step 4:   Reduce the power by 1. $2sin(3 - 2x)^1$

Step 5:   Differentiate the bracket.

    Now the bracket is: $sin(3 - 2x)$

    We have to use the chain rule here too. $\cos(3 - 2x) \times -2 = -2cos(3 - 2x)$

    Giving: $2sin(3 - 2x) \times -2cos(3 - 2x)$

Step 6:   Simplify the answer. $\frac{d}{dx} = -4\sin(3 - 2x)\cos(3 - 2x)$

The formula sheet gives the following derivatives which you should find useful.

$f(x)$	$f'(x)$
$\sin ax$	$a \cos ax$
$\cos ax$	$-a \sin ax$

Differentiating composite functions exercise   Go online

Q120: Find $h'(x)$ when $h(x) = \sqrt{x^2 + 6x}$

....

Q121: If $f(x) = \cos^3 x$, find $f'(x)$.

....

Q122: Differentiate $h(x) = (x^3 + 9x)^3$

....

Q123: Differentiate $y = \sqrt{4x^2 + 4}$

....

Q124: Differentiate $y = \cos\left(8x + \frac{\pi}{6}\right)$

....

Q125: Differentiate $y = \sin(x^4 + 5)$

....

Q126: Differentiate $h(x) = \sin^2 x$

....

Q127: Differentiate $y = \frac{1}{\sqrt{\cos x}}$

1.10   Learning points

Differentiation
The derivative

- The derived function represents:
  - the gradient of the tangent to the function;
  - the rate of change of the function.
- The gradient of a curve at a point is defined to be the gradient of the tangent to the curve at that point.
- Function notation
  - $f(x) = x^n \Rightarrow f'(x) = nx^{n-1}$
  - $f(x) = c \Rightarrow f'(x) = 0$ where c is a constant.
- Products and quotients must be simplified before differentiating.
- Simplify your derived expression if you can.
- Leibniz's notation
  - $y = x^n \Rightarrow \frac{dy}{dx} = nx^{n-1}$

Equation of a tangent

- To find the equation of a tangent at a point on a curve.
  - Identify or find the coordinates of the point of contact of the tangent
  - Find the derivative $\frac{dy}{dx}$.
  - Substitute the value of x into the derivative to get the gradient m.
  - Use $y - b = m(x - a)$ to get the equation.

Stationary points

- A stationary point could be one of the following:
  - A maximum turning point.
  - A minimum turning point.
  - A rising point of inflection.
  - A falling point of inflection.
- To determine stationary points and their nature:
  - find the derivative;
  - state that stationary points occur when $\frac{dy}{dx} = 0$;
  - solve for x when $\frac{dy}{dx} = 0$;
  - find the coordinates of the stationary points;

○ to determine the nature of the stationary points make a nature table;

x	$\to$	-1	$\to$	1	$\to$
$\frac{dy}{dx}$	+	0	-	0	+
shape	/	———	\	———	/

○ state the nature of the stationary points.

Curve sketching

- In order to make a good sketch of a curve some information about the curve is required:
  ○ The coordinates of the y-intercept.
  ○ The coordinates of the roots.
  ○ The coordinates of the stationary points and their nature.
  ○ The behaviour of the curve for large positive and negative values of x.

Sketching the graph of the derived function

- In order to sketch the graph of the derivative:
  ○ identify the stationary points;
  ○ make a nature table to identify where the function is increasing or decreasing;

x	$\to$	2	$\to$
shape	\	———	/
$f'(x)$	-	0	+
Derived function	below	on	above

  ○ sketch the derived function;
    ▪ Stationary points on $f(x)$ become x-intercepts for $f'(x)$.
    ▪ When $f(x)$ is increasing the graph of $f'(x)$ is above the x-axis.
    ▪ When $f(x)$ is decreasing the graph of $f'(x)$ is below the x-axis.
- If $f(x)$ is a quadratic then the derived function $f'(x)$ will be a straight line.
- If $f(x)$ is a cubic then the derived function $f'(x)$ will be a quadratic function.

Closed intervals

- To determine the maximum and minimum values in a closed interval:
  ○ identify the stationary points and their coordinates;
  ○ make a nature table to determine the shape of the function;
  ○ determine the coordinates of the end points;

- ○ make a sketch;
- ○ identify the maximum and minimum values.

Rates of change

- Velocity (or speed), v, is a rate of change of the distance (or displacement), s at time t, so $v = \frac{ds}{dt}$ or $s'(t)$.

- Acceleration, a, is a rate of change of the velocity (or speed), v at time t, so $a = \frac{dv}{dt}$ or $s''(t)$.

Optimisation

- Problems which involve finding a maximum or minimum value.

- The context is modelled by a function.

- The solution can be found by using differentiation to find stationary points.

Trigonometric derivatives

- $y = \sin x \Rightarrow \frac{dy}{dx} = \cos x$

- $y = \cos x \Rightarrow \frac{dy}{dx} = -\sin x$

- $f(x) = \sin ax \Rightarrow f'(x) = a \cos ax$

- $f(x) = \cos ax \Rightarrow f'(x) = -a \sin ax$

Derivatives of composite functions

- $f(x) = (x + a)^n \Rightarrow f'(x) = n(x + a)^{n-1}$

- $f(x) = (ax + b)^n \Rightarrow f'(x) = an(ax + b)^{n-1}$

- $h(x) = g(f(x)) \Rightarrow h'(x) = g'(f(x)) \times f'(x)$

- $y = y(u)$ and $u = u(x) \Rightarrow \frac{dy}{dx} = \frac{dy}{du} \times \frac{du}{dx}$

1.10.1   Sir Isaac Newton

- Born on 4th January 1643 in Woolsthorpe, England.
- Died on 31st March 1727 in London.

> "If I have been able to see further, it was only because I stood on the shoulders of giants."

Newton came from a family of farmers but never knew his father who died three months before he was born. Although a wealthy man, Newton's father was uneducated and could not sign his own name. His mother, Hannah Ayscough remarried when Newton was two years old. Newton was then left in the care of his grandmother and he had a rather unhappy childhood.

In 1653 he attended the Free Grammar School in Grantham. However, his school reports described him as idle and inattentive and he was taken away from school to manage his mothers estate. He showed little interest for this and, due to the influence of an uncle, he was allowed to return to the Free Grammar School in 1660. This time he was able to demonstrate his academic promise and passion for learning and on 5th June 1661 he entered Trinity College, Cambridge.

His ambition at Cambridge was to obtain a law degree but he also studied philosophy, mechanics and optics. His interest in mathematics began in 1663 when he bought an astrology book at a fair and found that he could not understand the mathematics in it. This spurred him on to read several mathematical texts and to make further deep mathematical studies.

Newton was elected a scholar at Cambridge on 28th April 1664 and received his bachelors degree in April 1665. In the summer of 1665 the University was closed due to the plague and Newton had to return to Lincolnshire. There, while still less than 25 years old, he made revolutionary advances in mathematics, physics, astronomy and optics. While at home, Newton established the foundations for differential and integral calculus, several years before the independent discovery by Leibniz. The method of fluxions as he named it was based on his crucial insight that integration is merely the inverse procedure to differentiating a function.

In 1672 he was elected a fellow of the Royal Society after donating a reflecting telescope. In that year he also published his first scientific paper on light and colour. However, he came in for some criticism from other academics who objected with some of his methods of proof and from then on Newton was torn between wanting fame and recognition and the fear of criticism. He found the easiest way to avoid this was to publish nothing.

Newton's greatest achievement was his work in physics and celestial mechanics that lead to his theory of universal gravitation. He was persuaded to write a full account of his new physics and its application to astronomy. In 1687 he published the *Philosophiae naturalis principia mathematica* or *Principia* as it is always known. This is recognised as the greatest scientific book ever written. It made him an international leader in scientific research.

On 15th January Newton was elected by the University of Cambridge as one of their two members to the Convention Parliament in London. This may have led him to see that there was a life in London which might appeal more to him than that of the academic world in Cambridge.

After suffering a nervous breakdown in 1693, Newton retired from research and decided to leave Cambridge to take up a government position in London as Warden and then later as Master of the Royal Mint. He made an effective contribution to the work of the Mint particularly on measures to prevent counterfeiting of the coinage.

In 1703 he was elected as president of the Royal Society, a position he retained until his death. He was knighted by Queen Anne in 1705, the first scientist to be honoured in this way for his work.

However, his last years were not easy, dominated in many ways over the controversy with Leibniz as to who had first invented calculus.

1.10.2 Gottfried Leibniz

- Born on 1st July 1646 in Leipzig, Germany.

- Died on 14th November 1716 in Hannover.

"The soul is the mirror of an indestructible universe."

His father Friedrich was a professor of moral philosophy and his mother Catharina Schmuck was Friedrich's third wife. Friedrich died when Leibniz was only six, so he was brought up by his mother and it was her influence that played an important role in his life and philosophy.

In 1661 Leibniz entered the University of Leipzig. He was only fourteen, which nowadays would be considered highly unusual, however at that time there would be others of a similar age. He studied philosophy and mathematics and graduated with a bachelors degree in 1663. Further studies took him on to a Masters Degree in philosophy and a bachelors degree and doctorate in Law.

By November 1667 Leibniz was living in Frankfurt where he investigated various different projects, scientific, literary and political. He also continued his law career.

In 1672 Leibniz went to Paris with the aim of contacting the French government and dissuading them from attacking German land. While there he made contact with mathematicians and philosophers and began construction of a calculating machine. On the January of the following year he went to England to try the same peace mission, the French one having failed and while there he visited The Royal Society of London and presented his incomplete calculating machine. The Royal Society elected him as a fellow on 19th April 1673 but by 1674 he had not kept his promise to finish his mechanical calculating machine and so he fell out of favour.

It was during his time in Paris that Leibniz developed his version of calculus. However, the English mathematician Sir Isaac Newton, several years before Leibniz had already laid the foundations for differential and integral calculus. This lead to much controversy over who had invented calculus and caused Newton to fly into an irrational temper directed against Leibniz. Neither Leibniz nor Newton thought in terms of functions, both always worked in terms of graphs. Leibniz concentrated on finding a good notation for calculus and spent a lot of time thinking about it, whereas Newton wrote more for himself and tended to use whatever notation he thought of on the day.

Amongst Leibniz's other achievements in mathematics were his development of the binary system of arithmetic and his work on determinants which arose from his developing methods to solve systems of linear equations. He also produced an important piece of work on dynamics.

Leibniz is described as:
"a man of medium height with a stoop, broad shouldered but bandy-legged, as capable of thinking for several days sitting in the same chair as of travelling the roads of Europe summer and winter. He was an indefatigable worker, a universal letter writer (he had more than 600 correspondents), a patriot and cosmopolitan, a great scientist, and one of the most powerful spirits of Western civilisation."

It was also said about him
"It is rare to find learned men who are clean, do not stink and have a sense of humour."!

1.11   End of topic test

Differentiating products and quotients

Q128: Differentiate $y = (2x + 9)(x - 3)$ with respect to x.

....

Q129: Differentiate $y = \frac{4x + 8}{\sqrt{x}}$ with respect to x.

....

Q130: Given $y = \frac{x^4 - 2x + 4}{\sqrt{x}}$ find $\frac{dy}{dx}$.

....

Q131:

a) If $g(x) = (x + 5)(4x - 1)$ $find$ $g'(x)$.
b) Find $g'(3)$.

....

Q132: Differentiate $y = \sqrt{x}\,(x + \sqrt{x})$.

....

Q133: Differentiate $y = \frac{x^3 - 2}{3x}$

Gradient of a tangent to a curve

Q134: Find the gradient of the tangent to the curve $y = (x - 5)^2$ at $x = 3$.

....

Q135: Find the gradient of the tangent to the curve $y = \frac{3}{x}$ at $x = 2$.

Equation of a tangent to a curve

Q136: Find the equation of the tangent to the curve $y = 9 + 4x - 3x^3$ at the point where $x = 2$.

a) If $x = 2$ then $y = ?$
b) Find $\frac{dy}{dx}$.
c) Find the gradient of the curve when $x = 2$.
d) What is the equation of the tangent?

Stationary points

Q137: Find the coordinates of the stationary points on the curve $y = x^3 + 3x^2 + 7$. Determine the nature of these stationary points and justify your answer.

a) Find $\frac{dy}{dx}$.

b) One stationary point exists at $x = 0$, what is the y-coordinate?

c) What are the coordinates of the other stationary point?

d) Determine the nature of these stationary points.

Curve sketching

Q138: Sketch the curve $f(x) = x^4 - 8x^3$ by answering these questions.

a) What are the coordinates of the y-intercept?

b) What are the roots?

c) What is the nature of the stationary point furthest to the left?

d) What are the coordinates of this stationary point?

e) What is the nature of the stationary point furthest to the right?

f) What are the coordinates of this stationary point?

g) Check the behaviour of the curve when x takes large positive and negative values then make a good sketch.
   Make sure you annotate your sketch fully then show it to your teacher or tutor.

. . . .

Q139: Which one of the following statements is true for the function $f(x) = x^3 + 3x^2 + 3x + 1$?

a) f is never increasing

b) f is never decreasing

c) f is increasing then decreasing

d) f is decreasing then increasing

Derived functions

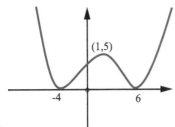

Q140:

Which of the following represents the derived function of the graph above?

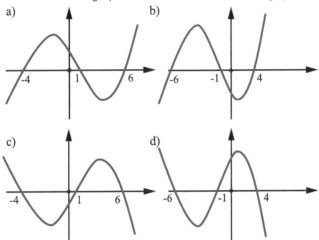

Closed intervals

Q141: Find the maximum and minimum values of the function $g(x) = x(x - 6)^2$ on the closed interval $-1 < x < 8$.

    a) Find $g(-1)$.

    b) Find $g(8)$.

    c) Find the maximum stationary value of $g(x)$.

    d) Find the minimum stationary value of $g(x)$.

    e) Find the maximum and minimum values within the closed interval $-1 < x < 8$.

Optimisation

A farmer wants to build a rectangular sheep pen in a triangular shaped field as shown in the diagram.
Find the maximum area that the farmer can make the sheep pen.

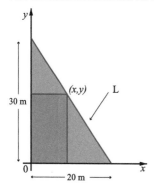

Q142: Find the equation of line L.

....

Q143: Find an expression for the area, A, in terms of x.

....

Q144: Find the width that gives maximum area for the sheep pen.

....

Q145: Find the maximum area, A, in m^2.

The minimum enclosure for a chicken run is $10\ m^2$.

Q146: For a rectangular enclosure of length x metres, give an expression for the perimeter, P, of the enclosure.

....

Q147: What is the length of the run which will give the minimum enclosure?

....

Q148: What is the breadth of the run which will give the minimum enclosure?

Differentiating sin x and cos x

Q149: Differentiate $8cos\ x$ with in terms of x.

....

Q150: If $y = 6sin\ x$ then what is $\frac{dy}{dx}$?

The chain rule

Q151: If $f(x) = (x + 9)^{-7}$ what is $f'(x)$?

....

Q152: Find $f'(x)$ when $f(x) = (x + 3)^{\frac{2}{3}}$.

....

Q153: Given $f(x) = 2(7 - 4x)^2$, find f'(2).

....

Q154: Find $\frac{dy}{dx}$ given that $y = \sqrt{3 - 7\sin\ x}$.

Topic 2

Trigonometry

Contents

Learning objective

By the end of this topic, you should be able to:

- convert between degrees and radians or between radians and degrees;
- sketch trigonometric graphs in degrees and radians;
- solve trigonometric equations in:
  - degrees or radians with a calculator;
  - degrees or radians as exact values;
- expand the
  - addition formulae for sin or cos;
  - double angle formulae for sin or cos;
- prove complex trigonometric identities;
- express the sum of two trig functions as a single trig function of the form $k \sin(x \pm a)$ or $k \cos(x \pm a)$
- solve equations using the wave function, $k \sin(x \pm a)$ or $k \cos(x \pm a)$;
- find maximum and minimum values using the wave function.

2.1   Looking back at National 5

Summary
Trigonometric rules
Area rule

- $Area = \frac{1}{2}ab \sin C$
- Two sides and the angle in-between are required.

Sine rule for a side

- $\frac{a}{\sin A} = \frac{b}{\sin B} = \frac{c}{\sin C}$
- Two angles and the side opposite one of the angles are required.

Sine rule for an angle

- $\frac{a}{\sin A} = \frac{b}{\sin B} = \frac{c}{\sin C}$
- Two sides and the angle opposite one of the sides are required.

Cosine rule for a side

- $a^2 = b^2 + c^2 - 2bc \cos A$
- Two sides and the angle in-between are required.

Cosine rule for an angle

- $\cos A = \frac{b^2 + c^2 - a^2}{2bc}$
- All three sides are required.

Bearings

- A bearing is measured clockwise from a north line and has three digits.

Angle properties

- Supplementary angles = $180°$.
- Angles round a point = $360°$.
- The sum of the angles in a triangle = $180°$.
- Alternate angles or "Z" angles are equal.
- Corresponding angles or "F" angles are equal.

Trigonometric equations, graphs and identities
Sketching and identifying trigonometric graphs

- The graph of $y = \sin x$ looks like this:

- The graph of $y = \cos x$ looks like this:

- The graph of $y = \tan x$ looks like this:

- The graph of $y = a \sin bx$ has:

    ◦ a maximum of a;
    ◦ a minimum of $-a$;
    ◦ b complete waves in 360°.

- The graph of $y = a \cos bx + c$ has:

    ◦ a maximum of a + c;
    ◦ a minimum of $-a + c$;
    ◦ b complete waves in 360°.

- The graph of $y = a \sin(x + b) + c$ has:

    ◦ a maximum of a + c;
    ◦ a minimum of $-a + c$;
    ◦ been moved left or right horizontally by **b**°.

- The amplitude of a graph is half of the distance between the maximum and minimum values of the graph.

- The period of a graph is the distance along the x-axis over which the graph completes one full wave pattern.
- When identifying a trig graph:
  - determine whether it is sin, cos or tan from its shape;
  - identify the maximum and minimum values;
  - determine the amplitude;
  - identify the number of complete waves in $360°$;
  - determine any vertical translation up or down;
  - determine any horizontal translation left or right.

Solving trigonometric equations

- Rearrange the equation to $\sin x° =$ or $\tan x° =$ or $\cos x° =$
- Draw a quadrant chart and tick the quadrants where the function has solutions.
- Use your calculator to find the acute angle
  - Use the $\sin^{-1}$ or $\tan^{-1}$ or $\cos^{-1}$ button.
  - Never enter a negative to find it's inverse trig value.
- Find the other solution(s):
  - for the sin quadrant use $180 - a$;
  - for the tan quadrant use $180 + a$;
  - for the cos quadrant use $360 - a$;
- Underline your solutions.

Exact trigonometric values

- Learn the table of exact values between $0°$ and $90°$ or remember how to construct the two special triangles.

angle	$0°$	$30°$	$45°$	$60°$	$90°$
$\sin x°$	0	$\frac{1}{2}$	$\frac{1}{\sqrt{2}}$	$\frac{\sqrt{3}}{2}$	1
$\cos x°$	1	$\frac{\sqrt{3}}{2}$	$\frac{1}{\sqrt{2}}$	$\frac{1}{2}$	0
$\tan x°$	0	$\frac{1}{\sqrt{3}}$	1	$\sqrt{3}$	undefined

Trigonometric identities

- $\sin^2 x + \cos^2 x = 1$
- $\tan x = \frac{\sin x}{\cos x}$

2.1.1   Solving trigonometric equations

Solving trigonometric equations   Go online

Solve sin x° = 0.2, for 0 ≤ x ≤ 360°.

We want to know where y = 0.2 cuts y = sin x° between 0° and 360°.

Use the controls to set up y = 0.2.

Check that the line crosses the curve at (12,0.2) and (168,0.2).

The solutions are x = 12 and x = 168 (sin 12° and sin 168° both equal 0.2).

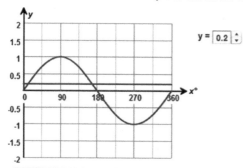

$$y = \boxed{0.2 \; \updownarrow}$$

> **NOTICE the symmetry of the sin curve.**
> **This means for the solution x = a, there is another solution at x = 180 - a.**

Solve tan x° = 0.6, for 0 ≤ x ≤ 360°.

We want to know where y = 0.6 cuts y = tan x° between 0° and 360°.

Use the controls to set up y = 0.6.

Check that the line crosses the curve at (31,0.6) and (211,0.6).

The solutions are x = 31 and x = 211 (tan 31° and tan 211° both equal 0.6).

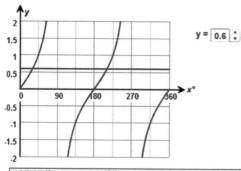

$$y = \boxed{0.6 \; \updownarrow}$$

> **NOTICE the symmetry of the tan curve.**
> **This means for the solution x = a, there is another solution at x = 180 + a.**

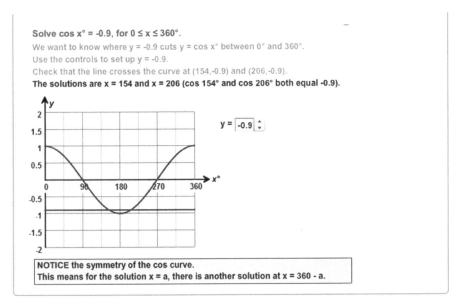

Solve cos x° = -0.9, for 0 ≤ x ≤ 360°.
We want to know where y = -0.9 cuts y = cos x° between 0° and 360°.
Use the controls to set up y = -0.9.
Check that the line crosses the curve at (154,-0.9) and (206,-0.9).
The solutions are x = 154 and x = 206 (cos 154° and cos 206° both equal -0.9).

y = ⌐-0.9⌐

NOTICE the symmetry of the cos curve.
This means for the solution x = a, there is another solution at x = 360 - a.

To summarise, when solving a trig equation there are two solutions for $0 \leq x \leq 360°$ due to the symmetry of the graphs.

Using the inverse trig functions on your calculator, you will get the acute angle a then:

- for a sin equation the second solution is $180 - a$;
- for a tan equation the second solution is $180 + a$.
- for a cos equation the second solution is $360 - a$;

This is often memorised by the aid of a diagram.

Sin	All
180 - a	a
Tan	Cos
180 + a	360 - a

Top tip

There are many ways to remember the quadrant diagram e.g.

- Going anti-clockwise round the quadrants this give ASTC ... All Sinners Take Care.
- Going anti-clockwise round the quadrants gives CAST.

Key point

You should draw a little quadrant chart every time you solve a trig equation to identify where you will find solutions.

Example

Problem:

Solve the equation $3 \sin x° = 2, 0 \leq x \leq 360°$

Solution:

Step 1:
Rearrange the equation $3 \sin x° = 2 \Rightarrow \sin x° = \frac{2}{3}$

Step 2:
Draw a quadrant chart and tick the quadrants where sin has solutions, i.e. all and sin.

Step 3:
Use your calculator to find the first solution [using the sin⁻¹ button] $\Rightarrow x = \sin^{-1}\left(\frac{2}{3}\right) = \underline{41 \cdot 8°}$

Step 4:
Find the second solution [for sin use $180 - a$] $\Rightarrow x = 180 - 41 \cdot 8 = \underline{138 \cdot 2°}$

Q1: Solve the equation $4 \sin x° = 1, 0 \leq x \leq 360°$

So far we have looked for solutions where sin x, cos x and tan x equal a positive number. If sin x, cos x and tan x equal a negative number we must look for solutions in the opposite quadrants.

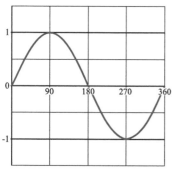

If we take the graph of $y = \sin x$ you will see that the graph is positive between $0°$ and $180°$ and that corresponds to the All and Sin quadrants. The graph is negative between $180°$ and $360°$ and that corresponds to the Tan and Cos quadrants.

You know that $\cos x$ is positive in the All and Cos quadrants so it follows that $\cos x$ is negative in the Sin and Tan quadrants.

You know that $\tan x$ is positive in the All and Tan quadrants so it follows that $\tan x$ is negative in the Sin and Cos quadrants.

Example

Problem:

Solve the equation $5 \sin x° + 4 = 0, 0 \leq x \leq 360°$

Solution:

Step 1:
Rearrange the equation $5 \sin x° + 4 = 0 \Rightarrow \sin x° = -\frac{4}{5}$.

Step 2:
Draw a quadrant chart and tick the quadrants where sin has negative solutions, i.e. tan and cos.

Step 3:
Use your calculator to find the solution for $\sin x = \frac{4}{5}$ [using the sin^{-1} button] $\Rightarrow x = \sin^{-1}\left(\frac{4}{5}\right) = 53 \cdot 1°$

Step 4:
Find the first solution [the one in the tan quadrant so use $180 + a$] $\Rightarrow x = 180 + 53 \cdot 1 = \underline{233 \cdot 1°}$

Step 5:
Find the second solution [the one in the cos quadrant so use $360 - a$] $\Rightarrow x = 360 - 53 \cdot 1 = \underline{306 \cdot 9°}$

Key point

It is ***extremely important*** to underline your two solutions in this type of questions.

Key point

Always find the acute angle in the ALL quadrant first. This means never putting a negative value into your calculator to find its inverse trig value.

Solving trigonometric equations exercise   Go online

Q2: Solve the equation $6 \sin x = 1, 0 \le x \le 360°$

....

Q3: Solve the equation $6 \cos x = -4, 0 \le x \le 360°$

....

Q4: Solve the equation $\tan x = -2, 0 \le x \le 360°$

....

Q5: Solve the equation $8 \sin x + 1 = 4, 0 \le x \le 360°$

....

Q6: Solve the equation $9 \cos x - 2 = 0, 0 \le x \le 360°$

....

Q7: Solve the equation $7 \tan x + 2 = 10, 0 \le x \le 360°$

....

Q8: Solve the equation $5 \sin x = -4, 0 \le x \le 360°$

....

Q9: Solve the equation $3 \cos x - 2 = -4, 0 \le x \le 360°$

....

Q10: Solve the equation $2 \tan x + 7 = 0, 0 \le x \le 360°$

2.1.2 Exact trigonometric values

The exact values of the trig. ratios (sin, cos and tan) for certain angles can also make calculations quicker and easier.

When $x = 0$ the values of $\sin x$, $\cos x$ and $\tan x$ are easily seen from their graphs. Also when $x = 90°$ the values of $\sin x$ and $\cos x$ can be taken from the graphs.

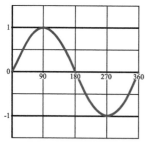 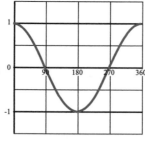 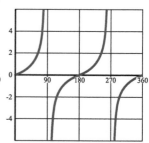

The table below shows all the exact values between $0°$ and $90°$.

angle	0°	30°	45°	60°	90°
sin x°	0	$\frac{1}{2}$	$\frac{1}{\sqrt{2}}$	$\frac{\sqrt{3}}{2}$	1
cos x°	1	$\frac{\sqrt{3}}{2}$	$\frac{1}{\sqrt{2}}$	$\frac{1}{2}$	0
tan x°	0	$\frac{1}{\sqrt{3}}$	1	$\sqrt{3}$	undefined

Construction of 30° and 60° angles   Go online

Sketch an equilateral triangle with side lengths of 2 units.

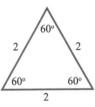

Draw in the perpendicular bisector from the apex to the base, focus on one of the triangles now formed.

The angles of this triangle are 30°, 60° and 90°. The sides of the triangle are 2 units, 1 unit (base halved by bisector) and $\sqrt{3}$ units (by Pythagoras).

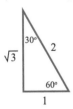

Read off the exact values for sin, cos and tan for the angles 30° and 60° using the SOH-CAH-TOA ratios.

$$\sin 30° = \frac{O}{H} = \frac{1}{2}$$

$$\sin 60° = \frac{O}{H} = \frac{\sqrt{3}}{2}$$

$$\cos 30° = \frac{A}{H} = \frac{\sqrt{3}}{2}$$

$$\cos 60° = \frac{A}{H} = \frac{1}{2}$$

$$\tan 30° = \frac{O}{A} = \frac{1}{\sqrt{3}}$$

$$\tan 60° = \frac{O}{A} = \sqrt{3}$$

Construction of 45° angles   Go online

Sketch a square with side length 1 unit.

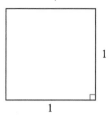

Draw in one of the diagonals, focus on one of the triangles now formed.

The angles of this triangle are 45° (twice) and 90°. The sides of the triangle are 1 unit, 1 unit and $\sqrt{2}$ units (by Pythagoras).

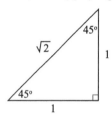

Read off the exact values for sin, cos and tan for the angles 30° and 60° using the SOH-CAH-TOA ratios.

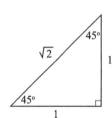

$$\sin 45° = \frac{1}{\sqrt{2}}$$

$$\cos 45° = \frac{1}{\sqrt{2}}$$

$$\tan 45° = 1$$

The table shows all the exact values between 0° and 90°.

angle	0°	30°	45°	60°	90°
$\sin x°$	0	$\frac{1}{2}$	$\frac{1}{\sqrt{2}}$	$\frac{\sqrt{3}}{2}$	1
$\cos x°$	1	$\frac{\sqrt{3}}{2}$	$\frac{1}{\sqrt{2}}$	$\frac{1}{2}$	0
$\tan x°$	0	$\frac{1}{\sqrt{3}}$	1	$\sqrt{3}$	undefined

These exact values for trig. ratios can be extended to angles in all four quadrants.

Recall the quadrant diagram:

This can be remembered easily as All Students Talk Constantly and depicts the quadrants in which the various ratios are positive.

The first has all ratios (A) positive.

The second has sine (S) positive.

The third has tangent (T) positive.

The fourth has cosine (C) positive.

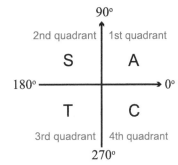

To find an exact value for an angle greater than $90°$, the angle is converted to the associated angle between 0 and $90°$ with the help of the following diagram.

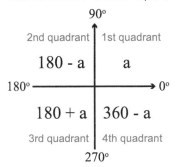

These examples show how to find the associated acute angle which will be needed to determine the exact value.

Examples

1. Problem:

Find the associated acute angle for 120°.

Solution:

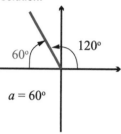

120° is in the sin quadrant.
The related angle is 60° because 180 - 60 = 120°.
So the associated acute angle $a = 60°$.

· ·

2. Problem:

Find the associated acute angle for 300°.

Solution:

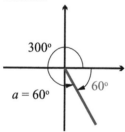

300° is in the cos quadrant.
The related angle is 60° because 360 - 60 = 300°.
So the associated acute angle $a = 60°$.

· ·

3. Problem:

Find the associated acute angle for 210°.

Solution:

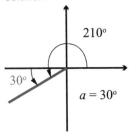

210° is in the tan quadrant.
The related angle is 30° because 180 + 30 = 210°.
So the associated acute angle $a = 30°$.

Exact values Go online

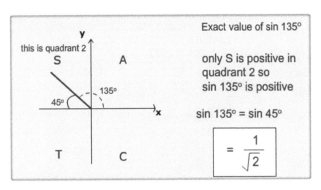

Exact value of sin 135°

only S is positive in
quadrant 2 so
sin 135° is positive

sin 135° = sin 45°

$$= \frac{1}{\sqrt{2}}$$

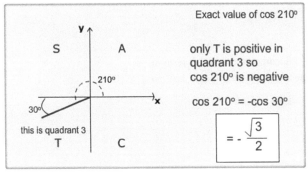

Exact value of cos 210°

only T is positive in
quadrant 3 so
cos 210° is negative

cos 210° = -cos 30°

$$= -\frac{\sqrt{3}}{2}$$

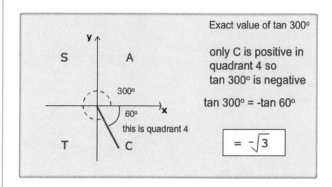

Exact value of tan 300°

only C is positive in quadrant 4 so tan 300° is negative

tan 300° = -tan 60°

$$= -\sqrt{3}$$

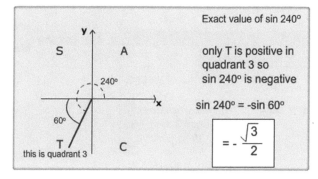

Exact value of sin 240°

only T is positive in quadrant 3 so sin 240° is negative

sin 240° = -sin 60°

$$= -\frac{\sqrt{3}}{2}$$

Examples

1. Problem:

Find the exact value of $\cos 300°$.

Solution:

300° is in quadrant 4.

Only cos is positive in the C quadrant so cos 300° is positive.

The associated acute angle is found by $360 - a = 300°$ so $a = 60°$

$$\cos 300° = \cos 60°$$
$$= \frac{1}{2}$$

....

2. Problem:

Find the exact value of $\sin 330°$.

Solution:

330° is in quadrant 4.

Only cos is positive in the C quadrant so sin $330°$ is negative.

The associated acute angle is found by $360 - a = 330°$ so $a = 30°$

$\sin 330° = -\sin 30°$

$\qquad = -\dfrac{1}{2}$

Exact trigonometric values exercise Go online

Q11: Find the exact value of sin $150°$.
Is sin $150°$ positive or negative?

a) Positive
b) Negative

....

Q12: What is the associated acute angle?

....

Q13: What is the exact value of sin $150°$?

a) $\frac{1}{\sqrt{2}}$
b) $\frac{1}{2}$
c) $-\frac{1}{2}$

....

Q14: Find the exact value of tan $150°$.
Is tan $150°$ positive or negative?

a) Positive
b) Negative

....

Q15: What is the associated acute angle?

....

Q16: What is the exact value of tan $150°$?

a) $-\frac{1}{\sqrt{3}}$
b) $\sqrt{3}$
c) $-\sqrt{3}$

2.1.3 Using trigonometric identities

There are two trigonometric formulae to learn.

From SOHCAHTOA we know that: $\sin x = \frac{O}{H}$ and $\cos x = \frac{A}{H}$

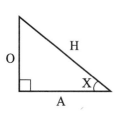

$$\begin{aligned}
\sin^2 x + \cos^2 x &= \left(\frac{O}{H}\right)^2 + \left(\frac{A}{H}\right)^2 \\
&= \frac{O^2}{H^2} + \frac{A^2}{H^2} \\
&= \frac{O^2 + A^2}{H^2} \\
&= \frac{H^2}{H^2} \quad \text{by the Theorem of Pythagoras} \\
&= 1
\end{aligned}$$

$$\begin{aligned}
\frac{\sin x}{\cos x} &= \frac{\frac{O}{H}}{\frac{A}{H}} \\
&= \frac{O}{H} \times \frac{H}{A} \\
&= \frac{O}{A} \\
&= \tan x
\end{aligned}$$

Key point

You will need to learn these trigonometric identities.

1. $\frac{\sin x}{\cos x} = \tan x$

2. $\sin^2 x + \cos^2 x = 1$

Examples

1. Problem:

Simplify $4\sin^2 x + 4\cos^2 x$

Solution:

$$\begin{aligned}
4\sin^2 x + 4\cos^2 x &= 4\left(\sin^2 x + \cos^2 x\right) \quad \text{we know that } \sin^2 x + \cos^2 x = 1 \\
&= 4 \times 1 \\
&= 4
\end{aligned}$$

....

2. Problem:

Solve $4\sin x - 5\cos x = 0$

Solution:

Divide each term by cos x.

$$\frac{4 \sin x}{\cos x} - \frac{5 \cos x}{\cos x} = \frac{0}{\cos x}$$

now $\frac{\sin x}{\cos x} = \tan x$, $\frac{\cos x}{\cos x} = 1$ and $\frac{0}{\cos x} = 0$ so,

$$4 \tan x - 5 = 0$$
$$4 \tan x = 5$$
$$\tan x = \frac{5}{4}$$
$$x = \tan^{-1}\left(\frac{5}{4}\right) = 51 \cdot 3°$$
$$x = 180 + 51 \cdot 3 = 231 \cdot 3°$$

....

3. Problem:

Prove that sin $A \sin^2 x$ + sin $A \ cox^2 x$ = sin A

Solution:

The aim is to start with the left hand side of the equation and end up with the right hand side of the equation.

$$LHS = \sin A \sin^2 x + \sin A \cos^2 x$$
$$= \sin A \left(\sin^2 x + \cos^2 x\right)$$
$$= \sin A \times 1$$
$$= \sin A$$
$$= RHS$$

This is called a mathematical proof.

Using trigonometric identities exercise　　　　　　　　　Go online

Q17: Using $\sin^2 x + \cos^2 x = 1$ and $\tan x = \frac{\sin x}{\cos x}$.

　a) What is $\sin^2 x$ equal to?
　b) What is $\cos^2 x$ equal to?
　c) What is sin x equal to?
　d) What is cos x equal to?

....

Q18: Simplify:

　a) $2 \cos^2 x + 2 \sin^2 x$
　b) $\frac{3 \sin A}{3 \cos A}$

....

Q19: Simplify:

a) $(1 + \cos x)(1 - \cos x)$

b) $2 - 2\sin^2 A$

....

Q20: Prove that:

a) $(\sin X + \cos X)^2 = 1 + 2\sin X \cos X$

b) $(\sin x - \cos x)^2 + (\sin x + \cos x)^2 = 2$

c) $\cos^2 A - \sin^2 A = 2\cos^2 A - 1$

2.2   Sketching trigonometric graphs

You will already know how to sketch the graphs of trigonometric functions from the National 5 course. In the following sections we will revisit, consolidate and extend these skills.

2.2.1   Angles in degrees and radians

There are two units of measurement which can be used for angles. Measuring in degrees will be familiar but it is also possible to measure in units called **radians**.

An angle subtended at the centre of a circle by an arc of length equal to the radius of the circle is called a radian.

There is no symbol for a radian. Therefore it is assumed that an angle with no units stated is measured in radians, otherwise if the angle is measured in degrees, it will have the degree symbol °.

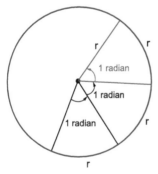

Key point

There are 2π radians in one complete turn. Since there are $360°$ in one complete turn it follows that 2π radians $= 360°$.

It is more common however, to remember that π radians $= 180°$.

Degrees to radians   Go online

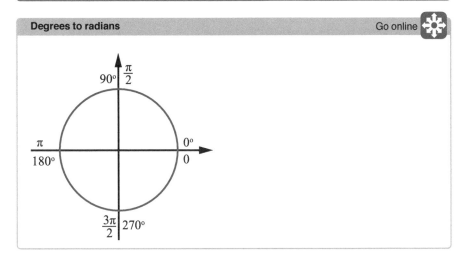

Sometimes it is necessary to convert angles from one form into the other.
If possible leave radian measurements in the form of a fraction of π.
This is an exact answer and is more accurate for problem solving.

Examples

1. Convert degrees to radians

Problem:

Convert into radians the following angle measurements given in degrees :

    a) $60°$

    b) $145°$

    c) $225°$

    d) $330°$

Solution:

To convert, since $180° = \pi$ radians, divide by 180 and multiply by π.

    a) $60° = \frac{60 \times \pi}{180} = \frac{\pi}{3}$
         Notice that: $\frac{60\pi}{180} = \frac{6\pi}{18} = \frac{1\pi}{3}$

b) $145° = \frac{145 \times \pi}{180} = \frac{29\pi}{36}$ *or* $2 \cdot 531$

   Note that it sometimes makes more sense to give the answer as a decimal. In this case it is good practice to give three decimal places for radians.

c) $225° = \frac{225 \times \pi}{180} = \frac{5\pi}{4}$

   Notice that 225 and 180 are both divisible by 45.

d) $330° = \frac{330 \times \pi}{180} = \frac{11\pi}{6}$

   Notice that 330 and 180 are both divisible by 30.

. . . .

2. Convert radians to degrees

Problem:

Convert into degrees, the following angle measurements given in radians:

a) $\frac{2\pi}{3}$

b) $\frac{\pi}{12}$

c) $\frac{5\pi}{2}$

d) 3π

Solution:

This time replace π with $180°$.

a) $\frac{2\pi}{3} = \frac{2 \times 180}{3} = \frac{360}{3} = 120°$

b) $\frac{\pi}{12} = \frac{180}{12} = \frac{90}{6} = \frac{45}{3} = 15°$

c) $\frac{5\pi}{2} = \frac{5 \times 180}{2} = 5 \times 90 = 450°$

d) $3\pi = 3 \times 180 = 540°$

Key point

To change degrees to radians multiply the degrees by π and divide by 180.

To change radians to degrees replace the π symbol with multiply by 180
or
multiply radians by 180 and divide by π.

Exact values can also be found for radians.

It is often easier to change radians to degrees first.

Construction of 30° and 60° angles Go online

Sketch an equilateral triangle with side lengths of 2 units.

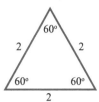

Draw in the perpendicular bisector from the apex to the base, focus on one of the triangles now formed.

The angles of this triangle are 30°, 60° and 90°. The sides of the triangle are 2 units, 1 unit (base halved by bisector) and $\sqrt{3}$ units (by Pythagoras).

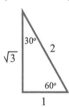

Read off the exact values for sin, cos and tan for the angles 30° and 60° using the SOH-CAH-TOA ratios.

$$\sin \frac{\pi}{6} = \frac{1}{2}$$

$$\cos \frac{\pi}{6} = \frac{\sqrt{3}}{2}$$

$$\tan \frac{\pi}{6} = \frac{2}{\sqrt{3}}$$

$$\sin \frac{\pi}{3} = \frac{\sqrt{3}}{2}$$

$$\cos \frac{\pi}{3} = \frac{1}{2}$$

$$\tan \frac{\pi}{3} = \sqrt{3}$$

Construction of 45° angles Go online

Sketch a square with side length 1 unit.

Draw in one of the diagonals, focus on one of the triangles now formed.

The angles of this triangle are 45° (twice) and 90°. The sides of the triangle are 1 unit, 1 unit and $\sqrt{2}$ units (by Pythagoras).

Read off the exact values for sin, cos and tan for the angles 30° and 60° using the SOH-CAH-TOA ratios.

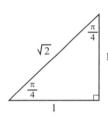

$$\sin \frac{\pi}{4} = \frac{1}{\sqrt{2}}$$

$$\cos \frac{\pi}{4} = \frac{1}{\sqrt{2}}$$

$$\tan \frac{\pi}{4} = 1$$

This gives us the table of exact values:

angle	0°	30°	45°	60°	90°
	0	$\frac{\pi}{6}$	$\frac{\pi}{4}$	$\frac{\pi}{3}$	$\frac{\pi}{2}$
$\sin x°$	0	$\frac{1}{2}$	$\frac{1}{\sqrt{2}}$	$\frac{\sqrt{3}}{2}$	1
$\cos x°$	1	$\frac{\sqrt{3}}{2}$	$\frac{1}{\sqrt{2}}$	$\frac{1}{2}$	0
$\tan x°$	0	$\frac{1}{\sqrt{3}}$	1	$\sqrt{3}$	undefined

Key point

You will have to learn the table or remember how to draw the two triangles in the activities.

These exact values can be extended to cover angles in all 4 quadrants.

Examples of exact values Go online

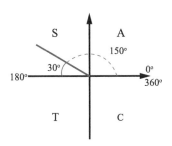

Exact value of sin 150°

only S positive in quadrant 2 so
sin 150° is positive.

sin 150° = sin 30°

$$= \frac{1}{2}$$

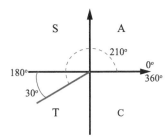

Exact value of cos 210°

only T positive in quadrant 3 so
cos 210° is negative.

cos 210° = -cos 30°

$$= -\frac{\sqrt{3}}{2}$$

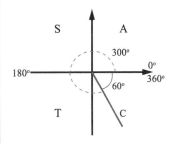

Exact value of tan 300°

only C positive in quadrant 4 so
tan 300° is negative.

tan 300° = -tan 60°

$$= -\sqrt{3}$$

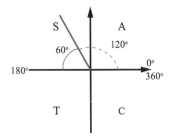

Exact value of $\sin \frac{2\pi}{3}$

$$\frac{2\pi}{3} = \frac{2 \times 180}{3} = 120°$$

only S positive in quadrant 2 so
sin 120° is positive.

sin 120° = sin 60°

$$\sin \frac{2\pi}{3} = \frac{\sqrt{3}}{2}$$

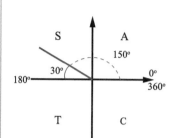

Exact value of $\cos \frac{2\pi}{3}$

$$\frac{5\pi}{6} = \frac{5 \times 180}{6} = 150°$$

only S positive in quadrant 2 so
cos 120° is negative.

cos 150° = -cos 30°

$$\cos \frac{5\pi}{6} = -\frac{\sqrt{3}}{2}$$

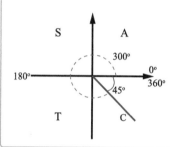

Exact value of $\tan \frac{7\pi}{4}$

$$\frac{7\pi}{4} = \frac{7 \times 180}{4} = 315°$$

only C positive in quadrant 4 so
tan 315° is negative.

tan 315° = -tan 45°

$$\tan \frac{7\pi}{4} = -1$$

Key point

It is easier to convert the angle from radians to degrees to find an exact value.

Angles in degrees and radians exercise   Go online

Converting degrees to radians

Q21: Convert these angles from degrees to radians.

a) 30°
b) 150°
c) 108°
d) 90°
e) 72°
f) 225°
g) 135°
h) 270°

Converting radians to degrees

Q22: Convert these angles from radians to degrees.

a) $\frac{3\pi}{5}$

b) $\frac{5\pi}{6}$

c) $\frac{\pi}{3}$

d) $\frac{\pi}{4}$

e) $\frac{4\pi}{5}$

f) $\frac{\pi}{2}$

g) $\frac{2\pi}{5}$

h) $\frac{\pi}{5}$

Exact values

Q23: What are the exact values of these angles?

a) cos 330°

b) sin 180°

c) $\tan \frac{5\pi}{4}$

d) tan 120°

e) $\sin \frac{7\pi}{6}$

f) $\cos \pi$

2.2.2   Graphs of trigonometric functions

It is important to be able to picture and sketch the three basic trigonometric functions, $y = \sin x$, $y = \cos x$ and $y = \tan x$.

Graphs of trigonometric functions practice	Go online

Try these three questions and compare your answers.

Q24: Sketch the graph of $y = \sin x$.

. . . .

Q25: Sketch the graph of $y = \cos x$.

. . . .

Q26: Sketch the graph of $y = \tan x$.

Graphs of trigonometric functions (1)

Go online

This activity allows you to investigate the graphs of various types of trigonometric functions. This will help you to be able to sketch the graphs of trigonometric functions from their equation.

Using the equation $y = a \sin bx°$ practice drawing graphs changing the values of a, b and the type of trigonometric function (sin, cos and tan).

Here are some examples when the trigonometric function is sin. Notice how the values of a and b change the graph of the function.

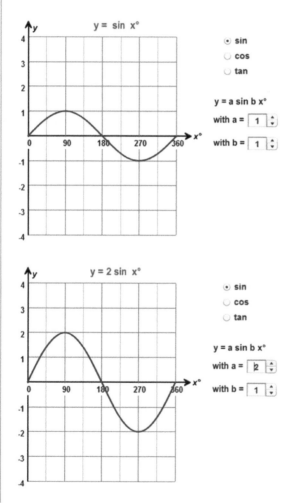

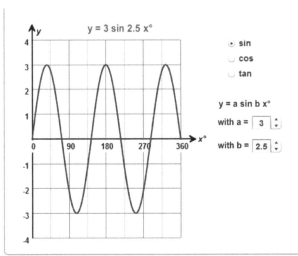

Key point

The Amplitude of a graph

The amplitude of a graph is half of the distance between the maximum and minimum values of the graph.

For example: In $y = a \sin x$ and $y = a \cos x$ the amplitude is represented by a.

Key point

The Period of a graph

The period of a graph is the distance along the x-axis over which the graph completes one full wave pattern.

Key point

$y = \tan x$ is different...

The graph is not a smooth curve.

The period of $y = \tan x$ is 180°.

Examples

1. Problem:

Sketch the graph of $y = \sin 3x°$ for $0 \le x \le 360$.

Solution:

Step 1:

We want a 'sin' wave which starts at the origin and rises to a maximum.

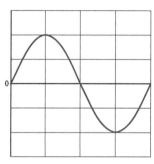

Step 2:

This maximum is 1 and the minimum is -1 since we want $y = 1\sin 3x°$.
The amplitude = 1.

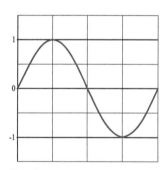

Step 3:

We need 3 waves in 360 degrees for $y = \sin 3x°$.

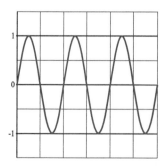

Step 4:

The period $= 360 \div 3 = 120°$ so each full wave covers a distance of 120°.

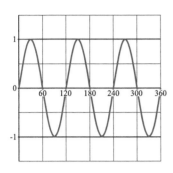

. . . .

2. Problem:

Sketch the graph of $y = 4 \cos 2x°$ for $0 \leq x \leq 360$.

Solution:

Step 1:

We want a 'cos' wave which starts at the maximum and drops through zero to the minimum.

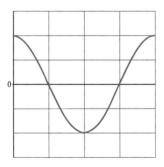

Step 2:

This maximum is 4 and the minimum is -4 since we want $y = 4\cos 2x°$.
The amplitude = 4

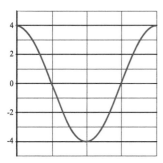

Step 3:

We need 2 waves in 360 degrees for $y = 4\cos 2x°$.

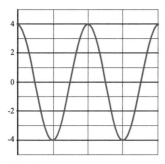

Step 4:

The period $= 360 \div 2 = 180°$ so each full wave covers a distance of $180°$.

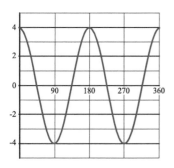

. . . .

3.

Problem:

Sketch the graph of $y = -\tan 2x°$ for $0 \leq x \leq 360$.

Solution:

Step 1:

We need a 'tan' graph which starts at the origin and has asymptotes at $x = 90$ and $x = 270$.

An asymptote is a line which the graph gets closer and closer to but never actually touches. The asymptotes will help us to make a better sketch.

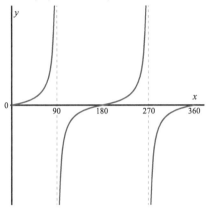

Step 2:

The negative reflects the graph in the x-axis.

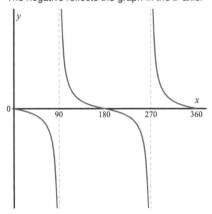

Step 3:

We require two copies of this tan graph in 360 for $y = -\tan 2x$.

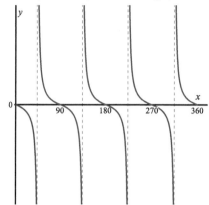

The period of $y = \tan x$ is 180°.
The period of $y = -\tan 2x$ is 180 ÷ 2 = 90°.
We now have asymptotes at x = 45, 135, 225 and 315.

Sketching trigonometric functions exercise 1   Go online

Q27: Sketch the graph of $y = 6\sin 4x°$, for $0 \leq x \leq 360°$

....

Q28: Sketch the graph of $y = 4\cos 2x°$, for $0 \leq x \leq 360°$

....

Q29: Sketch the graph of $y = 5\tan 3x°$, for $0 \leq x \leq 360°$

Graphs of trigonometric functions (2)   Go online

This activity allows you to investigate vertical translations of trigonometric functions.

Using the equation $y = a \sin bx° + c$ practice drawing graphs changing the values of a, b, c and the type of trigonometric function (sin, cos and tan).

Here are some examples when the trigonometric function is sin. Notice how the values of a, b and c change the graph of the function.

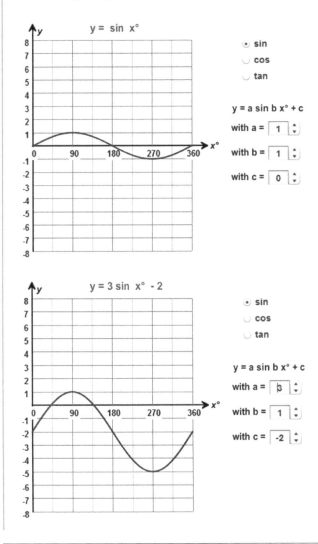

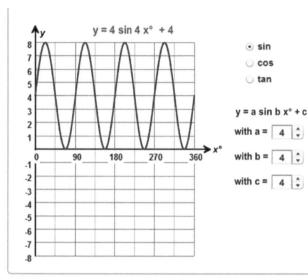

$y = 4 \sin 4 x° + 4$

- ⊙ **sin**
- ○ **cos**
- ○ **tan**

y = a sin b x° + c

with a = [4] ⬍

with b = [4] ⬍

with c = [4] ⬍

Examples

1. Problem:

Sketch the graph of $y = \sin 2x° - 1$, for $0 \le x \le 360°$.

Solution:

Step 1:

Start by sketching the graph of $y = \sin 2x°$.

The graph of $y = \sin 2x°$ starts at the origin and rises to a maximum.
The graph of $y = \sin 2x°$ has a maximum of 1 and a minimum of -1.
The amplitude = 1.
There are 2 waves in $y = \sin 2x°$.
The period $= 360 \div 2 = 180°$ so each full wave covers a distance of 180°.

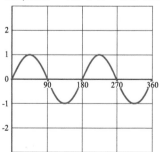

Step 2:

The graph of $y = \sin 2x° - 1$ is the graph of $y = \sin 2x°$ moved down vertically by 1 unit.

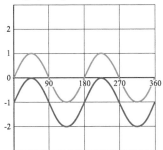

The maximum is 0 and the minimum is -2.
The amplitude = 1 as before.
The period $= 360 \div 2 = 180°$ as before.

....

2. Problem:

Sketch the graph of $y = 2\cos 3x° + 4$, for $0 \leq x \leq 360°$

Solution:

Step 1:

Start by sketching the graph of $y = 2\cos 3x°$.

The graph of $y = 2\cos 3x°$ starts at 2 and decreases to a minimum.
The graph of $y = 2\cos 3x°$ has a maximum of 2 and a minimum of -2.
The amplitude = 2.
There are 3 waves in $y = 2\cos 3x°$.
The period $= 360 \div 3 = 120°$ so each full wave covers a distance of 120°.

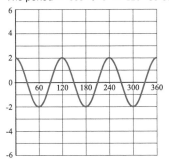

Step 2:

The graph of $y = 2\cos 3x° + 4$ is the graph of $y = 2\cos 3x°$ moved up vertically by 4 units.

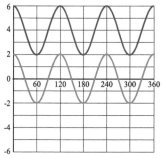

The maximum is 6 and the minimum is 2.
The amplitude = 2 as before.
The period $= 360 \div 3 = 120°$ as before.

....

3. Problem:

Sketch the graph of $y = \tan x° + 3$, for $0 \leq x \leq 360°$

Solution:

Step 1:

Start by sketching the graph of $y = \tan x°$.

The graph of $y = \tan x°$ starts at the origin and increases infinitely.
The graph of $y = \tan x°$ has no maximum or minimum.
There is no amplitude.
The tan graph is different from sin and cos. There are 2 waves in $y = \tan x°$.
The period $= 360 \div 2 = 180°$ so each full wave covers a distance of 180°.
The graph has asymptotes where the it tends to positive and negative infinity. $y = \tan x°$ has asymptotes at 90° and 270°.

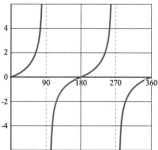

Step 2:

The graph of $y = \tan x° + 3$ is the graph of $y = \tan x°$ moved up vertically by 3 units.

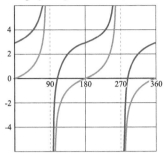

The period $= 360 \div 2 = 180°$ as before.
The asymptotes are at 90° and 270° as before.

Key point

An asymptote is a vertical line of the form $x = k$ at which the function is undefined. The graph gets closer and closer to the asymptote but never actually touches it.

Sketching trigonometric functions exercise 2   Go online

Q30: Sketch the graph of $y = 5 \sin 4x° + 1$, for $0 \le x \le 360°$

....

Q31: Sketch the graph of $y = \cos 2x° + 2$, for $0 \le x \le 360°$

....

Q32: Sketch the graph of $y = \tan 2x° - 4$, for $0 \le x \le 360°$

Graphs of trigonometric functions (3)   Go online

This activity allows you to investigate horizontal translations of trigonometric functions.

Using the equation $y = a \sin (x° + b) + c$ practice drawing graphs changing the values of a, b, c and the type of trigonometric function (sin, cos and tan).

Here are some examples when the trigonometric function is sin. Notice how the values of a, b and c change the graph of the function.

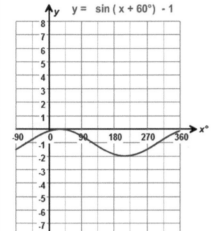

$y = \sin (x + 60°) - 1$

⊙ sin
○ cos
○ tan

y = a sin (x + b°) + c

with a = 1

with b = 60

with c = -1

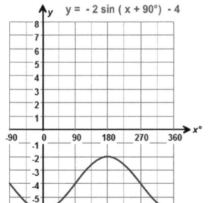

$y = -2 \sin (x + 90°) - 4$

⊙ sin
○ cos
○ tan

y = a sin (x + b°) + c

with a = -2

with b = 90

with c = -4

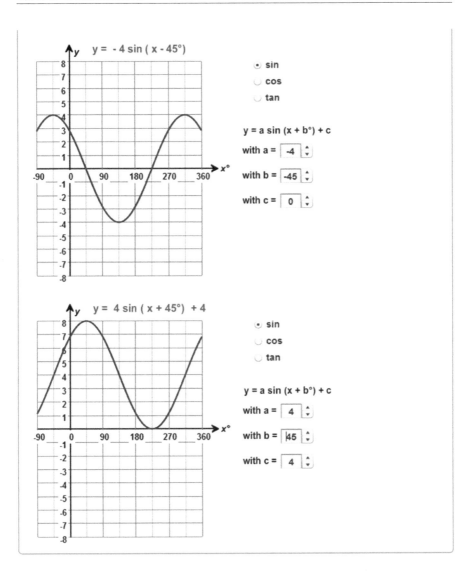

Examples

1. Problem:

Sketch the graph of $y = \sin(x° - 45)$, for $0 \le x \le 360°$

Solution:

Step 1:

Start by sketching the graph of $y = \sin x°$.

The graph of $y = \sin x°$ starts at the origin and rises to a maximum.
The graph of $y = \sin x°$ has a maximum of 1 and a minimum of -1.
The amplitude = 1.
There is 1 wave in $y = \sin x°$ so the period $= 360°$.

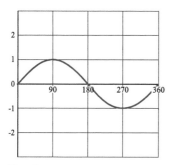

Step 2:

The graph of $y = \sin(x° - 45)$ is the graph of $y = \sin x°$ moved right by 45°.

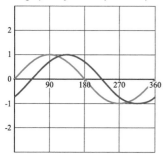

The maximum, minimum, amplitude and period are unchanged.
It is much easier to draw a faint version of the graph of $y = \sin x°$ first then make a copy 45°
to the right.

. . . .

2. Problem:

Sketch the graph of $y = 3\cos(x° + 30)$, for $0 \le x \le 360°$

Step 1:

Start by sketching the graph of $y = 3 \cos x°$.

The graph of $y = 3 \cos x°$ starts at 3 and decreases to a minimum.
The graph of $y = 3 \cos x°$ has a maximum of 3 and a minimum of -3.
The amplitude = 3.
There is 1 wave in $y = 3 \cos x°$ so the period $= 360°$.

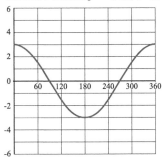

Step 2:

The graph of $y = 3 \cos (x° + 30)$ is the graph of $y = 3 \cos x°$ moved left by 30°.

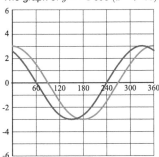

The maximum, minimum, amplitude and period are unchanged.
It is much easier to draw a faint version of the graph of $y = 3 \cos x°$ first then make a copy
30° to the left.

....

3. Problem:

Sketch the graph of $y = 2 \sin (x + 90°) + 1$, for $0 \leq x \leq 360°$

Solution:

Step 1:

Start by sketching the graph of $y = 2 \sin x°$.

The graph of $y = 2 \sin x°$ starts at the origin and increases to a maximum.
The graph of $y = 2 \sin x°$ has a maximum of 2 and a minimum of -2.

The amplitude = 2.

There is 1 wave in $y = 2 \sin x°$ so the period $= 360°$.

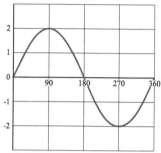

Step 2:

The graph of $y = 2 \sin x° + 1$ is the graph of $y = 2 \sin x°$ moved up vertically by 1 unit.

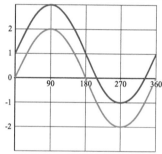

The graph of $y = 2 \sin x° + 1$ has a maximum of 3 and a minimum of -1.

The amplitude = 2 as before and the period is unchanged.

Step 3:

The graph of $y = 2 \sin (x + 90°) + 1$ is the graph of $y = 2 \sin x° + 1$ moved left by 90°.

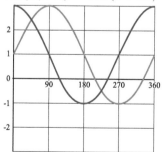

Note again that it is much easier to make faint copies of $y = 2 \sin x°$ and $y = 2 \sin x° + 1$ then make a copy 90° to the left.

Notice that the graph now looks like $y = 2 \cos x° + 1$.

Key point

For $y = \sin(x + c)$ then the graph of $y = \sin x$ moves **c** degrees to the **left**.

For $y = \sin(x - c)$ then the graph of $y = \sin x$ moves **c** degrees to the **right**.

The same changes will take place when $y = \cos x$ and $y = \tan x$.

Sketching trigonometric functions exercise 3   Go online

Q33: Sketch the graph of $y = 5\sin(x + 15°) - 2$, for $0 \leq x \leq 360°$. Remember the equation takes the form $y = a\sin(x + b) + c$.

. . . .

Q34: Sketch the graph of $y = 4\cos(x + 90°) + 4$, for $0 \leq x \leq 360°$. Remember the equation takes the form $y = a\cos(x + b) + c$.

. . . .

Q35: Sketch the graph of $y = -\tan(x - 75°) - 4$, for $0 \leq x \leq 360°$. Remember the equation takes the form $y = a\tan(x + b) + c$.

We can also draw trigonometric graphs in radians.

The period of trigonometric graphs   Go online

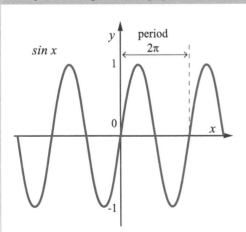

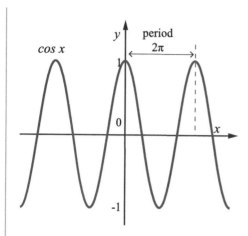

For the graph of tan x the period is 180° or π.

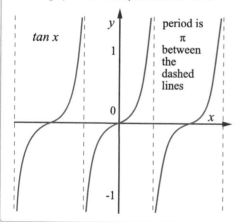

Key point

For the graphs of sin x and of cos x the period is 360° or 2π radians.

For the graph of tan x the period is 180° or π radians.

Examples

1. Finding the amplitude and period of a trig. graph

Problem:

Find the amplitude and the period (in radians) of the following graph:

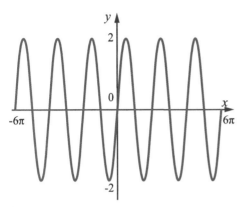

Solution:

The amplitude is half the distance between the maximum and the minimum.
That is, $\frac{1}{2}(2-(-2)) = 2$

The period is the length along the x-axis required to trace one full pattern.
Since there are three full patterns in 6π, one full pattern takes 2π. The period is 2π

. . . .

2. Finding the amplitude and period of a trig. function

Problem:

Find the amplitude and the period (in radians) of the function $3\cos\left(\frac{1}{2}x\right)$

Solution:

The graph of $y = 3\cos x$ has a maximum value of 3 and a minimum value of -3.
So the amplitude is, $\frac{1}{2}(3-(-3)) = 3$

The graph of $y = \cos(\frac{1}{2}x)$ is the same as the graph of $y = \cos x$ stretched horizontally by a factor of 2.

The period for $y = \cos x$ is 360° or 2π radians so the graph of $y = \cos(\frac{1}{2}x)$ will have a period twice as large as the period for $\cos x$.

So the period is 720° or 4π radians.

Graphs of trigonometric functions exercise   Go online

Q36: What is the period of $2 \cos (3x)$?

....

Q37: What is the amplitude of $2 \cos (3x)$?

....

Q38: What is the period of $3 \sin (6x)$?

....

Q39: What is the amplitude of $3 \sin (6x)$?

....

Q40: What is the period of $5 \cos \left(\frac{x}{3}\right)$?

....

Q41: What is the amplitude of $5 \cos \left(\frac{x}{3}\right)$?

Find the trigonometric equation represented by the following graph and hence find the amplitude and period.

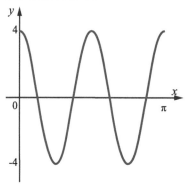

Q42: What is the equation represented by the graph?

....

Q43: What is the amplitude of the graph?

....

Q44: What is the period of the graph?

Find the trigonometric equation represented by the following graph and hence find the amplitude and period.

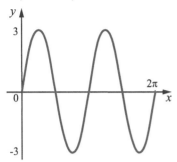

Q45: What is the equation represented by the graph?

....

Q46: What is the amplitude of the graph?

....

Q47: What is the period of the graph?

Find the trigonometric equation represented by the following graph and hence find the amplitude and period.

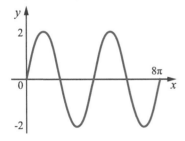

Q48: What is the equation represented by the graph?

....

Q49: What is the amplitude of the graph?

....

Q50: What is the period of the graph?

2.2.3   More complex trigonometric graphs

To sketch a more complicated function such as $f(x) = a \cos (bx + c) - d$
(e.g. $3 \cos (2x - 30)° - 4$) the technique is almost the same.

Combined trig function example   Go online

Example : Amplitude and period from the equation

Problem:

Sketch the graph of the function $f(x) = 2 \cos (5x - 60)° - 7$

Solution:

The maximum and minimum values of $y = 2cos(5x - 60)°$ are 2 and -2.

But the graph of $y = 2 \cos (5x - 60)° - 7$ has been moved down by 7 units so the maximum and minimum values are -5 and -9.

The period and horizontal movement of the graph is a little harder and we have to factorise the contents of the bracket to give $f(x) = 2 \cos 5(x - 12)° - 7$.

There are 5 repeats in 360° so the period is 72°.

The -12 tells us that the graph has been moved horizontally to the right by 12°.

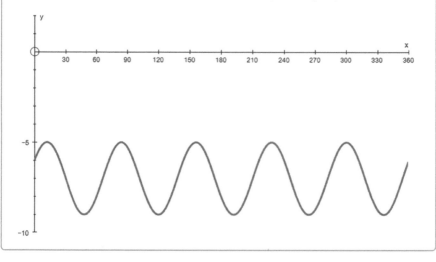

Two examples simpler than the previous activity are shown.

Examples

1. Problem:

Sketch the graph of the function $f\ (x)\ =\ \cos\ (3x\ -\ 30)°$

Solution:

First we must factorise the bracket to get $y\ =\ \cos 3(x\ -\ 10)°$

The 3 indicates that the graph will repeat itself every 120° (It has a period of $\frac{360}{3}\ =\ 120°$).

The -10 tells us that the graph moves 10° horizontally to the right.

The graph of $y\ =\ \cos x$ has important points i.e. the max, min and x-intercepts.

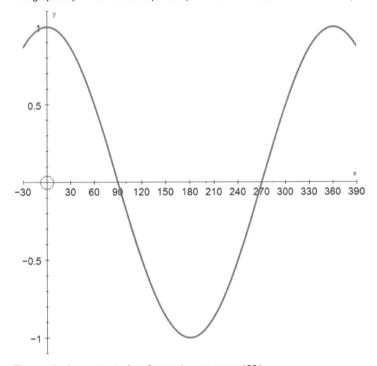

The graph of $y\ =\ \cos 3x$ has 3 repeats, one every 120°.

Notice the important points now,

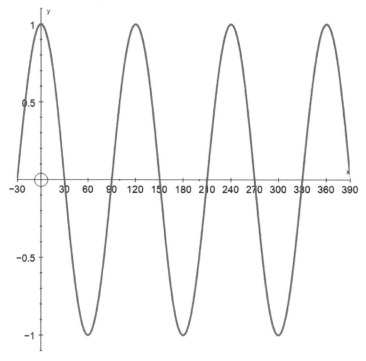

Now move the graph horizontally right by 10°.

A complete cos curve will now fit between 10° to 130° then 130° to 250° and lastly from 250° to 370°.

This gives the sketch,

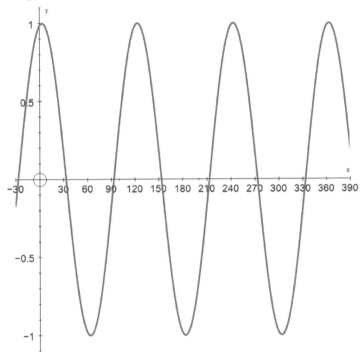

Notice the y-intercept.
We can find it by solving for $x = 0$.

$$y = \cos(3x - 30)°$$
$$y = \cos(3 \times 0 - 30)°$$
$$y = \cos(-30)° \quad \text{this will be the same as } y = \cos 30° \text{ so}$$
$$y = \frac{\sqrt{3}}{2}$$

. . . .

2. Problem:

Sketch the graph the function $f(x) = \sin(1/2 x + 30)°$

Solution:

First we must factorise the bracket to get $y = \sin 1/2 (x + 60)°$

The $1/2$ indicates that the graph will repeat every $720°$ (It has a period of $\frac{360}{\frac{1}{2}} = 720°$).

The +60 tells us that the graph moves $60°$ horizontally to the left.

Remember the graph of $y = \sin x$ looks like this,

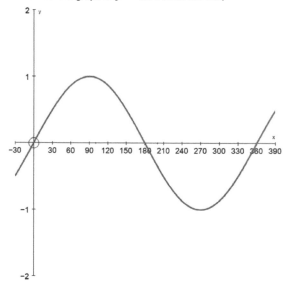

The graph of $y = \sin \frac{1}{2}x$ has a period of 720° and looks like this,

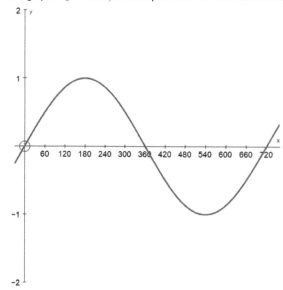

The graph of $y = \sin \frac{1}{2}(x + 60)°$ has a period of 720° and has been moved by 60° to the

left.

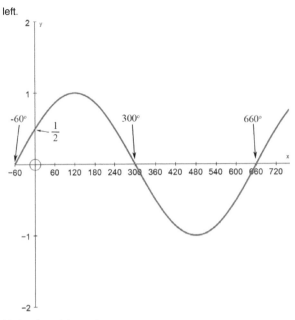

Notice the y-intercept.
We can find it by solving for $x = 0$.

$$y = \sin\left(\frac{1}{2}x + 30\right)^{\circ}$$

$$y = \sin\left(\frac{1}{2} \times 0 + 30\right)^{\circ}$$

$$y = \sin 30^{\circ}$$

$$y = \frac{1}{2}$$

....

3. Problem:

Identify the equation of the graph shown in the diagram below in the form $f(x) = a \cos (bx + c)$.

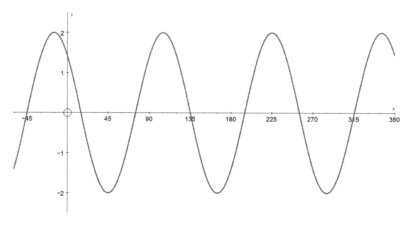

Solution:

The graph has a period of $120°$ so there are 3 repeats in $360°$.

The amplitude is 2.

For a basic cos curve the y-intercept is the maximum value but this graph has been moved to the left by $15°$.

A first attempt at the equation of this graph is $y = 2 \cos 3(x + 15)°$

This gives $f(x) = 2 \cos (3x + 45)°$.

. . . .

4. Problem:

Identify the equation of the function of the graph below in the form $f(x) = a \sin(bx + c) + d$.

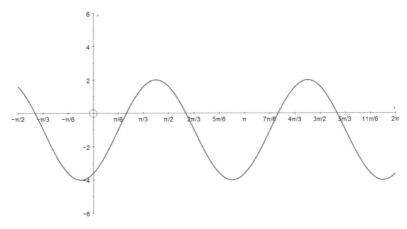

Solution:

The graph has a period of $\pi \ radians$ or $180°$ because there are 2 repeats in $2\pi \ radians$ or $360°$.

The amplitude is $\frac{1}{2}(2 - (-4)) = 3$.

The amplitude tells us that the maximum value should be 3 and the minimum value -3.
This graph has a max of 2 and a min of -4 so the basic sin curve has been move down by 1 unit.

For a basic sin curve the y-intercept is the origin but if we imagine this graph being moved back up by 1 unit we would be able to see that it has been moved to the right by $\frac{\pi}{6}$ or $30°$.

A first attempt at the equation of this graph is $y = 3\sin 2\left(x - \frac{\pi}{6}\right)° - 1$.

This gives $f(x) = 3\sin\left(2x - \frac{\pi}{3}\right)° - 1$.

More complex trigonometric graphs exercise   Go online

Trigonometric functions of the form sin(ax+b)

Q51: Find the equation of this trigonometric graph.

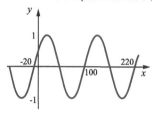

Trigonometric functions of the form cos(ax+b)

Q52: Find the equation of this trigonometric graph.

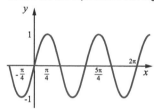

....

Identify cos/sin(ax+b)

Q53: Which of the following graphs represents the trigonometric equation
$y = \cos(2x + 60)$?

a)

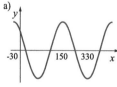

b)

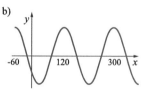

c)

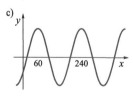

d)

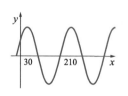

....

Q54: Which of the following graphs represents the trigonometric equation $y = \sin(4(x - 30))$?

a)

b)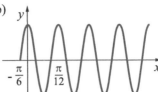

c)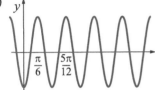

d)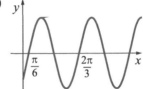

Consider the graph represented by the equation $y = 3\sin(2x - 120)°$.

Q55: What is the amplitude of the graph?

....

Q56: What is the period of the graph?

....

Q57: How many repeats are there in $360°$?

....

Q58: Has the basic sin curve been moved horizontally left or right?

....

Q59: How many degrees has the graph been moved horizontally?

Consider the graph represented by the equation $y = 5\cos\left(3x + \frac{\pi}{4}\right) + 1$.

Q60: What is the amplitude of the graph?

....

Q61: What is the period of the graph in radians?

....

Q62: How many repeats are there in $360°$?

....

Q63: Has the basic sin curve been moved vertically up or down?

....

Q64: By how many units has the basic curve been moved up or down?

....

Q65: Has the basic sin curve been moved horizontally left or right?

....

Q66: How many radians has the graph been moved horizontally?

2.3   Solving trigonometric equations

You will already be able to solve trigonometric equations from the National 5 course.

Sometimes recalling the graph of the function can help.

Example

Problem:

Solve $\sin 2x° + 1 = 0, 0 \leq x \leq 360$

Solution:

$$\sin 2x° + 1 = 0$$
$$\sin 2x° = -1$$

Make a sketch of the graph of $y = \sin 2x°$.
It has 2 cycles or repeats in 360° so the period is 180°.
The amplitude is 1 so the maximum is 1 and the minimum is -1.

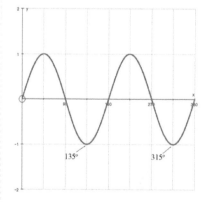

Identify for which angles the graph reaches -1

$x = 135°$ and $315°$

It is important to check that our solutions lie between 0 and 360° as specified in the question by $0 \leq x \leq 360$.

It is often the case that we have to solve trigonometric equations algebraically.

Example Problem:

Solve $2 \cos x + 1 = 0, 0 \leq x \leq 2\pi$

Solution:

$$2 \cos x + 1 = 0$$
$$2 \cos x = -1$$
$$\cos x = -\frac{1}{2}$$

From our exact values we know that $\cos 60° = \frac{1}{2}$ so when $\cos x = -\frac{1}{2}$,

$x = 180 - 60 = 120°$ $\qquad\qquad$ $x = 180 + 60 = 240°$

Again we must check that our solutions lie in the range $0 \leq x \leq 2\pi$.

Since $2\pi = 360°$, we know that our solutions lie in the range $0 \leq x \leq 2\pi$ but our solutions must be in radians so,

$120° = \frac{120 \times \pi}{180} = \frac{2\pi}{3}$ $\qquad\qquad$ $240° = \frac{240 \times \pi}{180} = \frac{4\pi}{3}$

$x = \frac{2\pi}{3}$ and $\frac{4\pi}{3}$ radians

Not all questions have exact values for their answers.

Examples

1. Problem:

Solve $3 \sin 2x° - 1 = 0, 0 \leq x \leq 360$

Solution:

$$3 \sin 2x - 1 = 0$$
$$3 \sin 2x = 1$$
$$\sin 2x = \frac{1}{3}$$

$$2x = \sin^{-1}\left(\frac{1}{3}\right) = 19 \cdot 5°$$

$$x = 9 \cdot 75°$$

$$2x = 180 - 19 \cdot 5 = 160 \cdot 5\circ$$

$$x = 80 \cdot 25\circ$$

But remember the period of the graph of $y = \sin 2x$ is 180° then the graph repeats itself so there are more solutions to be found.

$$x = 9 \cdot 75 + 180$$

$$x = 189 \cdot 75°$$

$$x = 80 \cdot 25 + 180$$

$$x = 260 \cdot 25°$$

Hence, there are 4 solutions and $x = 9 \cdot 75°,\ 80 \cdot 25°,\ 189 \cdot 75°$ and $260 \cdot 25°$

Notice that all our solutions lie between 0 and 360°

Look at the graph of $y = \sin 2x°$ and the points of intersection with the line $y = {}^1/_3$ to double check your solutions.

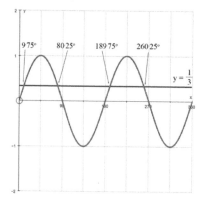

. . . .

2. Problem:

Solve $2 \tan 2x = 3,\ 0 \leq x \leq 2\pi$

Solution:

$$2 \tan 2x = 3$$

$$\tan 2x = \frac{3}{2}$$

$$2x = \tan^{-1}\left(\frac{3}{2}\right) = 56 \cdot 3°$$

$$x = 28 \cdot 15°$$

$$2x = 180 + 56 \cdot 3 = 236 \cdot 3°$$

$$x = 118 \cdot 15°$$

The period of the graph of $y = \tan x$ is 180° so there are more solutions to be found.

$$x = 28 \cdot 15 + 180 = 208 \cdot 15°$$

$$x = 118 \cdot 15 + 180 = 298 \cdot 15°$$

Hence the solutions are $x = 28 \cdot 15°,\ 118 \cdot 15°,\ 208 \cdot 15°$ and $298 \cdot 15°$ and all our solutions lie in the range $0 \leq x \leq 360$.

But our solutions must lie in the range $0 \leq x \leq 2\pi$ so we must change our solutions to radians.

We do this on the calculator by multiplying each solution by π and dividing by 180 then rounding each answer to 3 decimal places.

$$\underline{\underline{x = 0 \cdot 491,\ 2 \cdot 062,\ 3 \cdot 633 \text{ and } 5 \cdot 204 \text{ radians}}}$$

Key point

It is easier to work in degrees but you **must** remember to change your final answers to radians to gain full marks.

Example

Problem:

Solve $5cos(3x + 20)° - 2 = 0, 0 \leq x \leq 360$

Solution:

$$5\cos(3x + 20) = 2$$

$$\cos(3x + 20) = \frac{2}{5}$$

S	A ✓
T	C ✓

$$3x - 20 = \cos^{-1}\left(\frac{2}{5}\right) = 66 \cdot 4°$$

$$3x = 86 \cdot 4°$$

$$x = 28 \cdot 8°$$

$$3x - 20 = 360 - 66 \cdot 4 = 293 \cdot 6°$$

$$3x = 313 \cdot 6°$$

$$x = 104 \cdot 53°$$

The period of the graph of $y = \cos 3x$ is 120° so there are more solutions to be found.

$$x = 28 \cdot 8 + 120 = 148 \cdot 8°$$

$$x = 104 \cdot 53 + 120 = 224 \cdot 53°$$

There are 2 more solutions to be found.

$$x = 148 \cdot 8 + 120 = 368 \cdot 8°$$

$$x = 224 \cdot 53 + 120 = 344 \cdot 53°$$

Hence, the solutions are $x = 28 \cdot 8°,\ 104 \cdot 53°,\ 148 \cdot 8°,\ 224 \cdot 53°,\ 268 \cdot 8°$ and $344 \cdot 53°$

It is good practice to put your solutions in ascending order.

Notice that all our solutions lie in the range $0 \leq x \leq 360$.

Sometimes the domain is not $0 \leq x \leq 360$ or $0 \leq x \leq 2\pi$.

Examples

1. Problem:

Solve $2 \tan 2x° = 4,\ -90 \leq x \leq 90$

Solution:

$$2 \tan 2x = 4$$
$$\tan 2x = 2$$

S	A ✓
✓ T	C

$$2x = \tan^{-1}(2) = 63 \cdot 4° \qquad\qquad 2x = 180 + 63 \cdot 4 = 243 \cdot 4°$$
$$x = 31 \cdot 7° \qquad\qquad\qquad\qquad x = \cancel{121 \cdot 7°}$$

We are looking for solutions which lie in the range $-90 \leq x \leq 90$ but $121 \cdot 7$ is outside that range so we must put a line through that solution.

Draw a line to show that we know it is not a solution but keep it visible for the marker to be able to check it.

The period of the graph of $y = \tan 2x$ is $90°$ so there could be more solutions to be found.

However if we add $90°$ the two solutions they will both be bigger than $90°$ so we must try subtracting $90°$.

$$x = 31 \cdot 7 - 90 = -58 \cdot 3°$$

Our solutions are,

$x = -58 \cdot 3°$ and $31 \cdot 7°$

Notice that $121 \cdot 7 - 90 = 31 \cdot 7°$ and we already know that $31 \cdot 7°$ is a solution.

....

2. Problem:

Solve $3\tan^2 x - 1 = 0, 0 \leq x \leq \pi$

Solution:

$$3\tan^2 x - 1 = 0$$
$$3\tan^2 x = 1$$
$$\tan^2 x = \frac{1}{3}$$
$$\tan x = \sqrt{\frac{1}{3}}$$
$$\tan x = \pm\frac{1}{\sqrt{3}}$$

✓S	A✓
✓T	C✓

$x = 30°$ $\begin{aligned}x &= 180 - 30\\ &= 150°\end{aligned}$ $\begin{aligned}x &= 180 + 30\\ &= \cancel{210°}\end{aligned}$ $\begin{aligned}x &= 360 - 30\\ &= \cancel{330°}\end{aligned}$

We are looking for solutions which lie in the range $0 \leq x \leq \pi$ which is $0 \leq x \leq 180$ in degrees. That means that 210° and 330° are not solutions so score them out.

To change from degrees to radians we multiply each solution by π and divide by 180 giving,

$x = \frac{\pi}{6}$ and $\frac{5\pi}{6}$

This question could appear in the non-calculator paper.

Sometimes we have to factorise to solve trig equations.

Example Problem:

Solve $12\sin^2 x - 5\sin x - 2 = 0, 0 \leq x \leq 2\pi$

Solution:

This expression looks like the quadratic $12x^2 - 5x - 2$ which can be factorised as $(3x - 2)(4x + 1)$ so,

$$12\sin^2 x - 5\sin x - 2 = 0$$
$$(3\sin x - 2)(4\sin x + 1) = 0$$

$3\sin x - 2 = 0$ $4\sin x + 1 = 0$

$\sin x = \frac{2}{3}$ $\sin x = -\frac{1}{4}$

When $\sin x = \frac{1}{4}$, $x = 14 \cdot 5°$

$x = 41 \cdot 8°, 138 \cdot 2°$

$x = 194 \cdot 5°, 345 \cdot 5°$

All solutions lie between 0 and 360° but we must change them to radians.

We are looking for solutions which lie in the range $0 \leq x \leq 2\pi$ which is $0 \leq x < 360$ in degrees so we must change all our solutions to radians.

$x = 0 \cdot 730, 2 \cdot 412, 3 \cdot 395, 6 \cdot 030$ **radians**

Solving trigonometric equations exercise   Go online

Solve $4 \sin 3x = 1, 0 \leq x \leq 360$

Q67: How many solutions does the equation $\cos 2x° - 1 = 0, 0 \leq x \leq 360$, have?

....

Q68: Solve $2 + 3 \sin (2x - 30)° = 4, 180° < x < 225°$ giving your answer correct to 1 decimal place.

....

Q69: What is the value of $3x$ in quadrant A?

....

Q70: In which other quadrant is there a solution? Where solutions may lie in A, S, T or C.

....

Q71: What is the value of $3x$ in the quadrant given as the answer to the previous question?

Solve $3 \sin 4x = 2, 0 \leq x \leq 360$

Q72: What is the first solution?

....

Q73: What is the second solution?

....

Q74: What is the third solution?

....

Q75: What is the last solution?

Solve $-4 \cos 5x = 2, 0 \leq x \leq 360$

Q76: What is the first solution?

....

Q77: What is the second solution?

....

Q78: How many other solutions are there?

Solve $\sqrt{2} \cos x + 1 = 0, 0 \leq x \leq 2\pi$. Give your solutions as exact values.

Q79: What is the first solution?

....

Q80: What is the second solution?

Solve $3 \sin^2 x° - 7sin\, x° - 6 = 0, 0 \leq x \leq 360$

Q81: How many solutions are there?

....

Q82: What is the first solution?

....

Q83: What is the second solution?

Solve $3 \tan^2 x - 4 = 0, \pi \leq x \leq 2\pi$

Q84: How many solutions are there?

....

Q85: What is the first solution, correct to 3 decimal places?

....

Q86: What is the second solution, correct to 3 decimal places?

2.4   The addition formula

The addition formula for sin is:

$$\sin(A + B) = \sin A \cos B + \cos A \sin B$$

Examples

1. Problem:

Expand $\sin(x + 30)°$

Solution:

Find the exact value of $\cos 30°$ and $\sin 30°$

$$\sin(x + 30)° = \sin x \cos 30° + \cos x \sin 30°$$

$$= \sin x \times \frac{\sqrt{3}}{2} + \cos x \times \frac{1}{2}$$

$$= \frac{\sqrt{3}}{2} \sin x + \frac{1}{2} \cos x$$

....

2. Problem:

Find the exact value of $\sin(p + q)$.

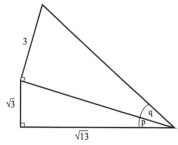

Solution:

Step 1: Use Pythagoras to calculate the size of the unknown sides in the diagram.

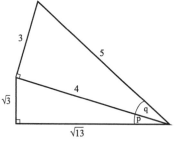

Step 2: Expand $\sin(p + q)$.

$$\sin(p + q) = \sin p \cos q + \cos p \sin q$$

Step 3: Use $SOHCAHTOA$ to find sin p, cos q, cos p and sin q.

$$\sin p \, \cos q \, + \, \cos p \, \sin q \, = \, \tfrac{\sqrt{3}}{4} \times \tfrac{4}{5} + \tfrac{\sqrt{13}}{4} \times \tfrac{3}{5}$$

We get these answers by:

$$\sin p \; = \; \frac{O}{H} \; = \; \frac{\sqrt{3}}{4}$$

$$\cos q \; = \; \frac{A}{H} \; = \; \frac{4}{5}$$

$$\cos p \; = \; \frac{O}{H} \; = \; \frac{3}{5}$$

$$\sin q \; = \; \frac{A}{H} \; = \; \frac{\sqrt{13}}{4}$$

Step 4: Simplify your answer.

$$\frac{\sqrt{3}}{4} \times \frac{4}{5} + \frac{\sqrt{13}}{4} \times \frac{3}{5} \; = \; \frac{4\sqrt{3}}{20} + \frac{3\sqrt{13}}{20}$$

$$= \; \frac{4\sqrt{3} \, + \, 3\sqrt{13}}{20}$$

$\sin(A - B) \; = \; \sin A \, \cos B \, - \, \cos A \, \sin B$

Examples

1. Problem:

Expand $\sin(x \, - \, 45)^\circ$

Solution:

Find the exact value of cos 45° and sin 45°.

$$\sin(x \, - \, 45)^\circ \; = \; \sin x \, \cos 45^\circ \, - \, \cos x \, \sin 45^\circ$$

$$= \; \sin x \times \frac{1}{\sqrt{2}} \, - \, \cos x \times \frac{1}{\sqrt{2}}$$

$$= \; \frac{1}{\sqrt{2}} \sin x \, - \, \frac{1}{\sqrt{2}} \cos x$$

....

2. Problem:

Find the exact value of sin AOB.

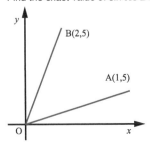

Solution:

Step 1: Make 2 right-angled triangles and calculate the unknown sides.

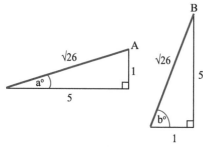

Step 2: Identify that $\sin AOB = \sin(b - a)°$ and expand.

$\sin(b - a)° = \sin b \cos a - \cos b \sin a$

Step 3: use SOHCAHTOA to find $\sin a$, $\cos b$, $\cos a$ and $\sin b$.

$\sin b \cos a - \cos b \sin a = \frac{5}{\sqrt{26}} \times \frac{5}{\sqrt{26}} - \frac{1}{\sqrt{26}} \times \frac{1}{\sqrt{26}}$

Step 4: Simplify your answer.

$$\frac{5}{\sqrt{26}} \times \frac{5}{\sqrt{26}} - \frac{1}{\sqrt{26}} \times \frac{1}{\sqrt{26}} = \frac{25}{26} - \frac{1}{26}$$
$$= \frac{24}{26}$$
$$= \frac{12}{13}$$

The addition formula for cos is:

$$\cos(A + B) = \cos A \cos B - \sin A \sin B$$

Examples

1. Problem:

Expand $\cos(2x + y)$.

Solution:

$\cos(2x + y) = \cos 2x \cos y - \sin 2x \sin y$

. . . .

2. Problem:

Find the exact value of $\cos 75°$

Solution:

This does not look like an addition formula question and $\cos 75°$ is not one of the exact values that we have learned.

However we do know that $45 + 30 = 75$ so,

$\cos 75° = \cos(45 + 30)°$

$$\cos(45 + 30)° = \cos 45° \cos 30° - \sin 45° \sin 30°$$

$$= \frac{1}{\sqrt{2}} \times \frac{\sqrt{3}}{2} - \frac{1}{\sqrt{2}} \times \frac{1}{2}$$

$$= \frac{\sqrt{3}}{2\sqrt{2}} - \frac{1}{2\sqrt{2}}$$

$$= \frac{\sqrt{3} - 1}{2\sqrt{2}}$$

$\cos(A - B) = \cos A \cos B + \sin A \sin B$

Examples

1. Problem:

Find the exact value of $\frac{\pi}{12}$.

Solution:

$\cos \frac{\pi}{12} = \cos 15° = \cos(60 - 45)°$

$$\cos(60 - 45)° = \cos 60 \cos 45 + \sin 60 \sin 45$$

$$= \frac{1}{2} \times \frac{1}{\sqrt{2}} + \frac{\sqrt{3}}{2} \times \frac{1}{\sqrt{2}}$$

$$= \frac{1}{2\sqrt{2}} + \frac{\sqrt{3}}{2\sqrt{2}}$$

$$= \frac{1 + \sqrt{3}}{2\sqrt{2}}$$

. . . .

2. Problem:

$\sin A = \frac{5}{13}$ and $\cos B = \frac{4}{5}$, where A and B are acute angles.

Find the exact value of $\cos(A - B)$.

Solution:

Start by sketching two right-angled triangles.

Remember $\sin A = \frac{5}{13} = \frac{O}{H}$ and $\cos B = \frac{4}{5} = \frac{A}{H}$ giving,

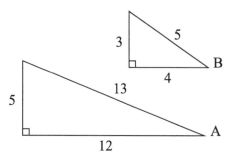

Pythagoras helps us to find the missing sides.

Now we can find $\sin B$ and $\cos A$, $\sin B = \frac{3}{5}$ and $\cos A = \frac{12}{13}$

Next expand the addition formula and substitute the exact values.

$$
\begin{aligned}
\cos(A - B) &= \cos A \cos B + \sin A \sin B \\
&= \frac{12}{13} \times \frac{4}{5} + \frac{5}{13} \times \frac{3}{5} \\
&= \frac{48}{65} + \frac{15}{65} \\
&= \frac{63}{65}
\end{aligned}
$$

Key point

The addition formulae will appear on the formula sheet like this:

- $\sin(A \pm B) = \sin A \cos B \pm \cos A \sin B$

- $\cos(A \pm B) = \cos A \cos B \mp \sin A \sin B$

The addition formula exercise   Go online

Q87: Expand $\sin(x - 5y)$

....

Q88: Expand $\cos(\pi - x)$, give your answer in fully simplified form.

....

Q89: Expand $\cos(5a)$, in terms of the angles $2a$ and $3a$.

....

Q90: Find the exact value of $\cos 15°$

....

Q91: Find the exact value of $\cos 105°$

....

Q92: Find the exact value of sin $75°$

....

Q93: Find the exact value of sin $315°$

Q94: What is the exact value of sin$(e + f)$?

....

Q95: What is the exact value of cos$(e + f)$?

$\tan A = \frac{1}{3}$, where A is an acute angle.

Q96: What is the exact value of cos$(A - 90)°$?

....

Q97: What is the exact value of sin$(A - 90)°$?

2.5 The double angle formula

The expressions sin $2A$ and cos $2A$ are easier to deal with when expanded using the double angle formulae.

The formulae are:

$$\sin 2A = 2 \sin A \cos A$$

$$\cos 2A = \cos^2 A - \sin^2 A$$
$$= 2\cos^2 A - 1$$
$$= 1 - 2\sin^2 A$$

Key point

The three versions of cos $2A$ can be useful in different situations.

If cos A and sin A appear in the equation, the first version (cos $2A = \cos^2 A - \sin^2 A$) is appropriate.

If only cos A appears in the equation to be solved then cos $2A = 2\cos^2 A - 1$ is probably the best to use.

Finally if the equation contains sin A then try cos $2A = 1 - 2\sin^2 A$ first.

Examples

1. Problem:

If tan $x = {}^3/_4$ in a right angled triangle, give the exact values for:

a) sin $2x$

b) cos $2x$

c) tan $2x$

Solution:

Draw a right-angled triangle and mark on the lengths of all the sides.

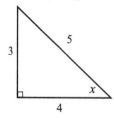

Using Pythagoras the hypotenuse is 5, $\sin x = \frac{3}{5}$ and $\cos x = \frac{4}{5}$

a)
$$\begin{aligned}
\sin 2x &= 2 \sin x \, \cos x \\
&= 2 \times \frac{3}{5} \times \frac{4}{5} \\
&= \frac{24}{25}
\end{aligned}$$

b)
$$\begin{aligned}
\cos 2x &= \cos^2 x - \sin^2 x \\
&= \left(\frac{4}{5}\right)^2 - \left(\frac{3}{5}\right)^2 \\
&= \frac{16}{25} - \frac{9}{25} \\
&= \frac{7}{25}
\end{aligned}$$

c)
$$\tan 2x \; = \; \frac{\sin 2x}{\cos 2x} \qquad \text{Remember} \; \tan x \; = \; \frac{\sin x}{\cos x}$$

$$= \; \frac{\frac{24}{25}}{\frac{7}{25}}$$

$$= \; \frac{24}{25} \; \times \; \frac{25}{7}$$

$$= \; \frac{24}{7}$$

. . . .

2. Problem:

Write down a formula for $\sin 4x$ in terms of $2x$.

Solution:

$\sin 4x \; = \; \sin 2(2x) \; = \; 2 \sin 2x \cos 2x$

Key point

The double angle formulae will appear on the formula sheet like this:

$$\text{sin2A} \; = \; 2 \, \text{sinA cosA}$$

$$\text{cos2A} \; = \; \text{cos}^2\text{A - sin}^2\text{A}$$

$$= \; 2 \, \text{cos}^2\text{A - 1}$$

$$= \; 1 - 2 \, \text{sin}^2\text{A}$$

The double angle formula exercise   Go online

Q98: If $\sin A \; = \; \frac{3}{5}$, what is the value of $\cos 2A$?

. . . .

Q99: If $\sin x \; = \; \frac{2}{3}$, what is the exact value of $\cos 2x$?

. . . .

Q100: If $\tan x \; = \; \frac{1}{2}$, what is the exact value of $\sin 2x$?

. . . .

Q101: Evaluate $\sin 4A$ when $\cos 2A \; = \; \frac{12}{13}$.

. . . .

Q102: Evaluate $\tan 4A$ when $\sin 2A \; = \; \frac{3}{5}$.

. . . .

Q103: If $\sin A \; = \; \frac{12}{13}$ what is the value of $\sin 2A$?

. . . .

Q104: Assuming that sin A is positive evaluate sin A when $\cos 2A = \frac{1}{2}$.

....

Q105: What is the value of $2\cos^2 15° - 1$ correct to 2 d.p.?

....

Q106: Simplify sin $x(cos\ x - sin\ x) + \cos x(sin\ x - \cos x)$.

Q107: Solve sin $2x = 10\cos x, 0 \leq x \leq 180$. What is the solution closest to 0°?

....

Q108:

$\angle ACB = \angle ACE = x°$
$\angle DCE = \angle ABC = 90°$
AB = 2 units
BC = 3 units

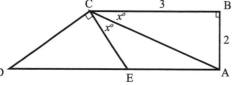

What is the exact value of $\sin\left(B\hat{C}D\right)$?

....

Q109: If $\sin x = \frac{2}{3}$, what is the exact value of sin $3x$?

2.6 Trigonometric identities

We now have several trigonometric identities in our toolkit:

$\cos^2 A + \sin^2 A = 1$

$\tan A = \frac{\sin A}{\cos A}$

$\sin(A + B) = \sin A \cos B + \cos A \sin B$

$\sin(A - B) = \sin A \cos B - \cos A \sin B$

$\cos(A + B) = \cos A \cos B - \sin A \sin B$

$\cos(A - B) = \cos A \cos B + \sin A \sin B$

$\sin 2A = 2sin\ A \cos A$

$$\begin{aligned}
\cos 2A &= \cos^2 A - \sin^2 A \\
&= 2\cos^2 A - 1 \\
&= 1 - 2\sin^2 A
\end{aligned}$$

These identities are useful whenever expressions involving trigonometric functions need to be simplified or proved.

Examples

1. Problem:

Show that $\frac{2\tan A}{1+\tan^2 A} = \sin 2A$

Solution:

$$\frac{2\tan A}{1+\tan^2 A} = \frac{\dfrac{2\sin A}{\cos A}}{\dfrac{\cos^2 A}{\cos^2 A} + \dfrac{\sin^2 A}{\cos^2 A}} \qquad \textit{remember } \tan A = \frac{\sin A}{\cos A}, \; 1 = \frac{\cos^2 A}{\cos^2 A} \textit{ and } \tan^2 A = \frac{\sin^2 A}{\cos^2 A}$$

$$= \frac{\dfrac{2\sin A}{\cos A}}{\dfrac{\cos^2 A + \sin^2 A}{\cos^2 A}} \qquad \textit{add the fractions on the denominator}$$

$$= \frac{2\sin A}{\cos A} \times \frac{\cos^2 A}{\cos^2 A + \sin^2 A} \qquad \textit{simplify the fractions}$$

$$= \frac{2\sin A}{\cancel{\cos A}} \times \frac{\cancel{\cos^2 A}}{\cos^2 A + \sin^2 A} \qquad \textit{cancel out } \cos A$$

$$= \frac{2\sin A \cos A}{\cos^2 A + \sin^2 A} \qquad \textit{simplify again}$$

$$= \frac{2\sin A \cos A}{1} \qquad \textit{remember } \cos^2 A + \sin^2 A = 1$$

$$= \sin 2A \qquad \textit{remember } \sin 2A = 2\sin A \cos A$$

· ·

2. Problem:

Prove that $\cos^2 x = \frac{1}{2}(1 + \cos 2x)$

Solution:

We know that $\cos 2x = 2\cos^2 x - 1$.

$$\begin{aligned}
2\cos^2 x - 1 &= \cos 2x \\
2\cos^2 x &= \cos 2x + 1 \\
\cos^2 x &= \frac{1}{2}(\cos 2x + 1) \\
\cos^2 x &= \frac{1}{2}(1 + \cos 2x)
\end{aligned}$$

· ·

3. Problem:

Show that $\cos 4x = \cos^4 x - 6\sin^2 x \cos^2 x + \sin^4 x$

Solution:

$$
\begin{aligned}
\cos 4x &= \cos 2\,(2x) && \text{express in the form } \cos 2A \\
&= \cos^2 2x - \sin^2 2x && \text{expand as for } \cos 2A \\
&= (\cos 2x)^2 - (\sin 2x)^2 \\
&= (\cos^2 x - \sin^2 x)^2 - (2\sin x \cos x)^2 && \text{expand for } \cos 2A \text{ and } \sin 2A \\
&= \cos^4 x - 2\sin^2 x \cos^2 x + \sin^4 x - 4\sin^2 x \cos^2 x && \text{collect like terms} \\
&= \cos^4 x - 6\sin^2 x \cos^2 x + \sin^4 x
\end{aligned}
$$

....

4. Problem:

Find the value of $\cos 2x$ if $2\cos^2 x - 4\sin^2 x + 1 = 3$

Solution:

$$
\begin{aligned}
2\cos^2 x - 4\sin^2 x + 1 &= 3 && \text{Recall:} 2\cos^2 x - 1 = \cos 2x \,\&\, 1 - 2\sin^2 x = \cos 2x \\
2\cos^2 x - 1 + 2 - 4\sin^2 x &= 3 && \text{Notice that } -1 + 2 = 1 \\
(2\cos^2 - 1) + 2(1 - 2\sin^2 x) &= 3 && \text{Recall: } 1 - 2\sin^2 x = \cos 2x \\
\cos 2x + 2\cos 2x &= 3 \\
3\cos 2x &= 3 \\
\cos 2x &= 1
\end{aligned}
$$

....

5. Problem:

Show that $\sin 3\theta = 3\sin\theta - 4\sin^3\theta$

Solution:

This is a tricky question but let's start by expressing 3θ as $2\theta + \theta$!

$$
\begin{aligned}
\sin 3\theta &= \sin(2\theta + \theta) && \text{expand } \sin(A + B) \\
&= \sin 2\theta \cos\theta + \cos 2\theta \sin\theta && \text{expand } \sin 2A \text{ and } \cos 2A \\
&= (2\sin\theta \cos\theta)\cos\theta + (1 - 2\sin^2\theta)\sin\theta && \text{multiply out the brackets} \\
&= 2\sin\theta \cos^2\theta + \sin\theta - 2\sin^3\theta && \sin\theta \text{ is a common factor} \\
&= \sin\theta(2\cos^2\theta + 1 - 2\sin^2\theta) && \text{rearrange the bracket} \\
&= \sin\theta(2\cos^2\theta - 2\sin^2\theta + 1) && \text{2 is a common factor of the first 2 terms in the bracket} \\
&= \sin\theta(2(\cos^2\theta - \sin^2\theta) + 1) && \text{replace } \cos^2\theta - \sin^2\theta \\
&= \sin\theta(2(1 - 2\sin^2\theta) + 1) && \text{expand the inner bracket} \\
&= \sin\theta(2 - 4\sin^2\theta + 1) && \text{collect like terms} \\
&= \sin\theta(3 - 4\sin^2\theta) && \text{expand the bracket} \\
&= 3\sin\theta - 4\sin^3\theta
\end{aligned}
$$

Trigonometric identities exercise Go online

Q110: Show that $(\cos x + \sin x)^2 = 1 + \sin 2x$.

....

Q111: Prove that $\sin^2 x = \frac{1}{2}(1 - \cos 2x)$.

....

Q112: Show that if $\frac{\cos x + \sin x}{\cos 2x} = 1$ then $\cos x = 1 + \sin x$.

....

Q113: Prove that $2\cos 2A - \cos^2 A = 1 - 3\sin^2 A$

....

Q114: Now solve $2\sin A = 2\cos 2A - \cos^2 A$, $0 \le A \le 360$.
There are 3 solutions a, b and c where $a < b < c$.

2.7 The wave function

Let's start by looking at the graphs of two wave functions that you already know ($y = \sin x$ and $y = \cos x$) then consider the wave function $y = \sin x + \cos x$.

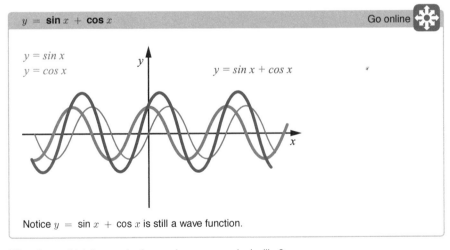

$y = \sin x + \cos x$ Go online

$y = \sin x$
$y = \cos x$

$y = \sin x + \cos x$

Notice $y = \sin x + \cos x$ is still a wave function.

What do you think the graph of $y = \sin x + \cos x$ looks like?

There are four possible answers but the two most likely answers are:

1. $y = k\cos(x - a)°$ where the graph of $y = \cos x$ has been stretched vertically by a factor of k and shifted horizontally to the right by $a°$

2. $y = k\sin(x + a)°$ where the graph of $y = \sin x$ has been stretched vertically by a factor of k and shifted horizontally to the left by $a°$

The other two are:

1. $y = k\cos(x + a)°$ where the graph of $y = \cos x$ has been stretched vertically by a factor of k and shifted horizontally to the left by $a°$

2. $y = k\sin(x - a)°$ where the graph of $y = \sin x$ has been stretched vertically by a factor of k and shifted horizontally to the right by $a°$

In fact it turns out that the wave function, $y = \sin x + \cos x$, has an amplitude of $1 \cdot 414$ or $\sqrt{2}$ so $k = \sqrt{2}$. The graph $y = \sin x$ has moved horizontally to the left by 45° or to the right of the graph of $y = \cos x$ by 45°.

This is known as a phase angle of 45°. This means that the graph of $y = \sin x + \cos x$ could also be described as $y = \sqrt{2}\cos(x - 45)°$ or $y = \sqrt{2}\sin(x + 45)°$.

There are strategies for finding the equation of combined trigonometric functions as single trig functions.

Strategy for combining trig equations: $k\sin(x + \alpha)°$ Go online

Express $2\sin x + 3\cos x$ in the form $k\sin(x + \alpha)°$, where $k > 0$ and $0 \leq \alpha \leq 360°$

Step 1: Expand $k\sin(x + \alpha)$ and write your expression underneath it.

$k\sin(x + \alpha) = k(sin\,x\cos\alpha + \cos x\sin\alpha)$
$k\sin(x + \alpha) = k\sin x\cos\alpha + k\cos x\sin\alpha$

$$2\sin x + 3\cos x$$

Step 2: Identify the value of $k\sin\alpha$ and $k\cos\alpha$.

$k\sin(x + \alpha) = k(sin\,x\cos\alpha + \cos x\sin\alpha)$
$k\sin(x + \alpha) = k\sin x\cos\alpha + k\cos x\sin\alpha$

$$2\sin x + 3\cos x$$

$k\cos\alpha = 2$
$k\sin\alpha = 3$

Step 3: Find the value of k.

$k\sin(x + \alpha) = k(sin\,x\cos\alpha + \cos x\sin\alpha)$
$k\sin(x + \alpha) = k\sin x\cos\alpha + k\cos x\sin\alpha$

$$2\sin x + 3\cos x$$

$k\cos\alpha = 2$
$k\sin\alpha = 3$

$$k = \sqrt{2^2 + 3^2}$$
$$k = \sqrt{13}$$

We can do this because:

$$\sqrt{(k\cos \alpha)^2 + (k\sin \alpha)^2} = \sqrt{k^2\cos^2\alpha + k^2\sin^2\alpha}$$
$$= \sqrt{k^2 (\cos^2\alpha + \sin^2\alpha)}$$
$$= \sqrt{k^2 \times 1}$$
$$= \sqrt{k^2}$$
$$= k$$

Remember that $\cos^2 x + \sin^2 x = 1$.

Step 4: Find the value of the phase angle $\alpha°$.

$$k\sin(x + \alpha) = k(\sin x \cos \alpha + \cos x \sin \alpha)$$
$$k\sin(x + \alpha) = k \sin x \cos \alpha + k \cos x \sin \alpha$$

$$2 \sin x + 3 \cos x$$

$$k \cos \alpha = 2$$
$$k \sin \alpha = 3$$

$$k = \sqrt{2^2 + 3^2}$$
$$k = \sqrt{13}$$

$$\frac{k\sin \alpha}{k\cos \alpha} = \frac{3}{2}$$
$$\tan \alpha = \frac{3}{2} \qquad \text{Remember that } \frac{\sin \alpha}{\cos \alpha} = \tan \alpha$$

$k \sin \alpha = 3$ is positive

$k \cos \alpha = 2$ is positive

2 ticks tells us that the solution is in the ALL quadrant so
$$\alpha = 56 \cdot 3°$$

$$\tan^{-1}\left(\tfrac{3}{2}\right) = 56 \cdot 3°$$

Step 5: Express the answer to the question.

$$2 \sin x + 3 \cos x = \sqrt{13} \sin (x + 56 \cdot 3)°$$

Express $3 \sin x - 4 \cos x$ in the form $k \sin(x - \alpha)^\circ$, where $k > 0$ and $0 \le \alpha \le 360°$

Step 1: Expand $k \sin(x - \alpha)$ and write your expression underneath it.

$k \sin(x - \alpha) = k(sin\, x \cos \alpha - \cos x \sin \alpha)$
$k \sin(x - \alpha) = k \sin x \cos \alpha - k \cos x \sin \alpha$

$$3 \sin x - 4 \cos x$$

Step 2: Identify the value of $k \sin \alpha$ and $k \cos \alpha$.

$k \sin(x - \alpha) = k(sin\, x \cos \alpha - \cos x \sin \alpha)$
$k \sin(x - \alpha) = k \sin x \cos \alpha - k \cos x \sin \alpha$

$$3 \sin x - 4 \cos x$$

$k \cos \alpha = 3$
$k \sin \alpha = 4$

Step 3: Find the value of k.

$k \sin(x - \alpha) = k(sin\, x \cos \alpha - \cos x \sin \alpha)$
$k \sin(x - \alpha) = k \sin x \cos \alpha - k \cos x \sin \alpha$

$$3 \sin x - 4 \cos x$$

$k \cos \alpha = 3$
$k \sin \alpha = 4$

$$k = \sqrt{3^2 + 4^2}$$
$$k = \sqrt{25} = 5$$

We can do this because:

$$\sqrt{(k \cos\, \alpha)^2 + (k \sin\, \alpha)^2} = \sqrt{k^2 \cos^2\alpha + k^2 \sin^2\alpha}$$
$$= \sqrt{k^2 \left(\cos^2\alpha + \sin^2\alpha\right)}$$
$$= \sqrt{k^2 \times 1}$$
$$= \sqrt{k^2}$$
$$= k$$

Remember that $\cos^2 x + \sin^2 x = 1$.

Step 4: Find the value of the phase angle $\alpha°$.

$k \sin(x - \alpha) = k(sin\, x \cos \alpha - \cos x \sin \alpha)$
$k \sin(x - \alpha) = k \sin x \cos \alpha - k \cos x \sin \alpha$

$$3 \sin x - 4 \cos x$$

$k \cos \alpha = 3$
$k \sin \alpha = 4$

$$k = \sqrt{3^2 + 4^2}$$
$$k = \sqrt{25} = 5$$

$$\frac{k \sin \alpha}{k \cos \alpha} = \frac{4}{3}$$

$$\tan \alpha = \frac{4}{3} \qquad \text{Remember that } \frac{\sin \alpha}{\cos \alpha} = \tan \alpha$$

✓S	A✓✓
T	C✓

$k \sin \alpha = 4$ is positive

$k \cos \alpha = 3$ is positive

2 ticks tells us that the solution is in the ALL quadrant so
$\alpha = 53 \cdot 1°$

$\tan^{-1}\left(\frac{4}{3}\right) = 53 \cdot 1°$

Step 5: Express the answer to the question.

$3 \sin x - 4 \cos x = 5 \sin(x - 53 \cdot 1)°$

Strategy for combining trig equations: $k \cos(x - \alpha)°$ Go online

Express $7 \cos x - 4 \sin x$ in the form $k \cos(x - \alpha)°$, where $k > 0$ and $0 \leq \alpha \leq 360°$

Step 1: Expand $k \cos(x - \alpha)$ and write your expression underneath it.

$k \cos(x - \alpha) = k(\cos x \cos \alpha + \sin x \sin \alpha)$
$k \cos(x - \alpha) = k \cos x \cos \alpha + k \sin x \sin \alpha$

$\qquad\qquad\qquad\qquad\qquad 7 \cos x - 4 \sin x$

The signs don't match up so change $-4 \sin x$ into $+ (-4) \sin x$.

$k \cos(x - \alpha) = k(\cos x \cos \alpha + \sin x \sin \alpha)$
$k \cos(x - \alpha) = k \cos x \cos \alpha + k \sin x \sin \alpha$

$\qquad\qquad\qquad\qquad\qquad 7 \cos x + (-4) \sin x$

Step 2: Identify the value of $k \sin \alpha$ and $k \cos \alpha$.

$k \cos(x - \alpha) = k(\cos x \cos \alpha + \sin x \sin \alpha)$
$k \cos(x - \alpha) = k \cos x \cos \alpha + k \sin x \sin \alpha$

$\qquad\qquad\qquad\qquad\qquad 7 \cos x + (-4) \sin x$

$k \cos \alpha = 7$
$k \sin \alpha = -4$

Step 3: Find the value of k.

$k \cos(x - \alpha) = k(\cos x \cos \alpha + \sin x \sin \alpha)$
$k \cos(x - \alpha) = k \cos x \cos \alpha + k \sin x \sin \alpha$

$\qquad\qquad\qquad\qquad\qquad 7 \cos x + (-4) \sin x$

$k \cos \alpha = 7$
$k \sin \alpha = -4$

$$k = \sqrt{7^2 + (-4)^2}$$
$$k = \sqrt{65}$$

Remember that $\cos^2 x + \sin^2 x = 1$.

Step 4: Find the value of the phase angle $\alpha°$.

$k \cos(x - \alpha) = k(\cos x \cos \alpha + \sin x \sin \alpha)$
$k \cos(x - \alpha) = k \cos x \cos \alpha + k \sin x \sin \alpha$

$$7 \cos x + (-4) \sin x$$

$k \cos \alpha = 7$
$k \sin \alpha = -4$

$$k = \sqrt{7^2 + (-4)^2}$$
$$k = \sqrt{65}$$

$$\frac{k \sin \alpha}{k \cos \alpha} = \frac{-4}{7}$$
$$\tan \alpha = \frac{-4}{7}$$

$k \sin \alpha = -4$ is negative

$k \cos \alpha = 7$ is positive

2 ticks tells us that the solution is in the COS quadrant so $\alpha = 360 - 29 \cdot 7° = 330 \cdot 3°$

$\tan^{-1}\left(\frac{4}{7}\right) = 29 \cdot 7°$

Step 5: Express the answer to the question.

$$\underline{\underline{7 \cos x - 4 \sin x = \sqrt{65} \cos(x - 330 \cdot 3)°}}$$

Strategy for combining trig equations: $k \cos(x + \alpha)°$ Go online

Express $5 \sin x + 2 \cos x$ in the form $k \cos(x + \alpha)°$, where $k > 0$ and $0 \le \alpha \le 360°$

Step 1: Expand $k \cos(x + \alpha)$ and write your expression underneath it.

$k \cos(x + \alpha) = k(\cos x \cos \alpha - \sin x \sin \alpha)$
$k \cos(x + \alpha) = k \cos x \cos \alpha - k \sin x \sin \alpha$

$$5 \sin x + 2 \cos x$$

Step 2: We have to swap the terms around.

$k\cos(x + \alpha) = k(\cos x \cos \alpha - \sin x \sin \alpha)$

$k\cos(x + \alpha) = k \cos x \cos \alpha - k \sin x \sin \alpha$

$$2\cos x + 5\sin x$$

The signs don't match up so make the add a double negative.

$k\cos(x + \alpha) = k(\cos x \cos \alpha - \sin x \sin \alpha)$

$k\cos(x + \alpha) = k \cos x \cos \alpha - k \sin x \sin \alpha$

$$2\cos x - (-5)\sin x$$

Step 3: Identify the value of $k \sin \alpha$ and $k \cos \alpha$.

$k\cos(x + \alpha) = k(\cos x \cos \alpha - \sin x \sin \alpha)$

$k\cos(x + \alpha) = k \cos x \cos \alpha - k \sin x \sin \alpha$

$$2\cos x - (-5)\sin x$$

$k \cos \alpha = 2$

$k \sin \alpha = -5$

Step 4: Find the value of k.

$k\cos(x + \alpha) = k(\cos x \cos \alpha - \sin x \sin \alpha)$

$k\cos(x + \alpha) = k \cos x \cos \alpha - k \sin x \sin \alpha$

$$2\cos x - (-5)\sin x$$

$k \cos \alpha = 2$

$k \sin \alpha = -5$

$$k = \sqrt{2^2 + (-5)^2}$$
$$k = \sqrt{29}$$

Step 5: Find the value of the phase angle α°.

$k\cos(x + \alpha) = k(\cos x \cos \alpha - \sin x \sin \alpha)$

$k\cos(x + \alpha) = k \cos x \cos \alpha - k \sin x \sin \alpha$

$$2\cos x - (-5)\sin x$$

$k \cos \alpha = 2$

$k \sin \alpha = -5$

$$k = \sqrt{2^2 + (-5)^2}$$
$$k = \sqrt{29}$$

$$\frac{k \sin \alpha}{k \cos \alpha} = \frac{-5}{2}$$
$$\tan \alpha = \frac{-5}{2}$$

S	A ✓
✓ T	C ✓✓

$k \sin \alpha = -5$ is negative

$k \cos \alpha = 2$ is positive

2 ticks tells us that the solution is in the COS quadrant so $\alpha = 360 - 68 \cdot 2° = 291 \cdot 8°$

$\tan^{-1}\left(\frac{5}{2}\right) = 68 \cdot 2°$

Step 6: Express the answer to the question.

$$5 \sin x + 2 \cos x = \sqrt{29} \cos (x + 291 \cdot 8)°$$

Key point

The wave function strategy

Step 1: Expand the addition formula and write your expression underneath it.

Step 2: Identify the value of $k \sin \alpha$ and $k \cos \alpha$, you may have to swap terms around or change signs.

Step 3: Find the value of k.

Step 4: Find the value of the phase angle $\alpha°$.

Step 5: Express the answer to the question.

Note:
When $\tan \alpha$ is negative always find the angle in the ALL quadrant then use it to find the angle in the required quadrant.

We can work in radians too...

Examples

1. Problem:

Express $\sqrt{3} \sin \theta - \cos \theta$ in the form $k \cos(\theta + \alpha)$, where $k > 0$ and $0 \le \alpha \le 2\pi$.

Solution:

$k \cos (\theta + \alpha) = k \cos \theta \cos \alpha - k \sin \theta \sin \alpha$

$\sqrt{3} \sin \theta - \cos \theta$ we have to swap the terms around

$- \cos \theta + \sqrt{3} \sin \theta$ make the add a double negative

$- \cos \theta - \left(- \sqrt{3} \right) \sin \theta$ cancel out matching terms

$$k \cos(\theta + \alpha) = k \cancel{\cos \theta} \cos \alpha \cancel{-} k \cancel{\sin \theta} \sin \alpha$$

$$-\cancel{\cos \theta} \cancel{-} \left(-\sqrt{3} \right) \cancel{\sin \theta}$$

$k \cos \alpha = -1$

$k \sin \alpha = -\sqrt{3}$

$k = \sqrt{(-1)^2 + \left(-\sqrt{3}\right)^2}$

$k = \sqrt{4} = 2$

$\dfrac{k \sin \alpha}{k \cos \alpha} = \dfrac{-\sqrt{3}}{-1}$

$\tan \alpha = \sqrt{3}$ Remember that $\dfrac{\sin \alpha}{\cos \alpha} = \tan \alpha$

$k \sin \alpha$ is negative

$k \cos \alpha$ is negative

2 ticks tells us that the solution is in the TAN quadrant so $\alpha = 180 + 60 = 240°$

$\tan^{-1}\left(\sqrt{3}\right) = 60°$

We know from the question that $0 \leq \alpha \leq 2\pi$ so our angle must be in radians.

$240° = \dfrac{240 \times \pi}{180} = \dfrac{4\pi}{3}$

$\sqrt{3} \sin \theta - \cos \theta = 2 \cos\left(\theta + \dfrac{4\pi}{3}\right)$

....

2. Problem:

a) Express $8 \sin x - 16 \cos x$ in the form $k \sin(x - \alpha)°$, where $k > 0$ and $0 \leq \alpha \leq 360°$

b) Hence find algebraically the values of x for which $8 \sin x - 16 \cos x = 15$, $0 \leq x \leq 360°$

Solution:

a)

$k \sin(x - \alpha) = k \sin x \cos\alpha - k \cos x \sin\alpha$

$8 \sin x - 16 \cos x$

$k \cos \alpha = 8$

$k \sin \alpha = 16$

$k = \sqrt{8^2 + 16^2}$

$k = \sqrt{320} = 8\sqrt{5}$

$\dfrac{k \sin \alpha}{k \cos \alpha} = \dfrac{16}{8}$

$\tan \alpha = 2$

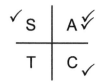

$k \sin \alpha$ is positive

$k \cos \alpha$ is positive

2 ticks tells us that the solution is in the ALL quadrant so $\alpha = 63 \cdot 4°$

$\tan^{-1}(2) = 63 \cdot 4°$

$8 \sin x - 16 \cos x = 8\sqrt{5} \sin (x - 63 \cdot 4)°$

b)

$8 \sin x - 16 \cos x = 15$ which is the same as. . .

$8\sqrt{5} \sin (x - 63 \cdot 4)° = 15$

$\sin (x - 63 \cdot 4)° = \dfrac{15}{8\sqrt{5}}$

$x - 63 \cdot 4 = 57$ $\qquad\qquad\qquad$ $x - 63 \cdot 4 = 123$

$x = 57 + 63 \cdot 4 = 120 \cdot 4$ $\qquad$ $x = 123 + 63 \cdot 4 = 186 \cdot 4$

$x = 120 \cdot 4°$ and $186 \cdot 4°$

. . . .

3. Problem:

a) Express $2\sin 3x + \cos 3x$ in the form $k \sin(3x + \alpha)°$, where $k > 0$ and $0 \leq \alpha \leq 360°$.

b) Hence or otherwise, find algebraically the points of intersection of the graph of $y = 2\sin 3x + \cos 3x$ with the x-axis, for $0 \leq \alpha \leq 360°$.

Solution:

a)

$k \sin (3x + \alpha) = k \sin 3x \cos \alpha + k \cos 3x \sin \alpha$

$2 \sin 3x + \cos 3x$

$k \cos \alpha = 2$

$k \sin \alpha = 1$

$k = \sqrt{2^2 + 1^2}$

$k = \sqrt{5}$

$\dfrac{k \sin \alpha}{k \cos \alpha} = \dfrac{1}{2}$

$\tan \alpha = \dfrac{1}{2}$

$k \sin \alpha$ is positive

$k \cos \alpha$ is positive

2 ticks tells us that the solution is in the ALL quadrant so $\alpha = 26 \cdot 6°$

$2 \sin 3x + \cos 3x = \sqrt{5} \sin (3x + 26 \cdot 6)°$

b)

Since the graph of $y = 2\sin 3x + \cos 3x$ crosses the x-axis when $y = 0$ it follows that we should solve $2\sin 3x + \cos 3x = 0$ which is the same as solving:

$$\sqrt{5} \sin (3x + 26 \cdot 6)° = 0$$
$$\sin (3x + 26 \cdot 6)° = 0$$
$$3x + 26 \cdot 6 = 0, \ 180, \ 360$$
$$3x = -26 \cdot 6, \ 153 \cdot 4, \ 333 \cdot 4$$
$$x = -8 \cdot 9°, \ 51 \cdot 1°, \ 111 \cdot 1°$$

But remember the domain is $0 \leq x \leq 360°$ and the period of the graph of $y = \sin 3x$ is $120°$ then the graph repeats itself so there are more solutions to be found.

$x = 51 \cdot 1 + 120 = 171 \cdot 1°$ $\qquad\qquad\qquad$ $x = 111 \cdot 1 + 120 = 231 \cdot 1°$

and

$x = 171 \cdot 1 + 120 = 291 \cdot 1°$ $\qquad\qquad\qquad$ $x = 231 \cdot 1 + 120 = 351 \cdot 1°$

Hence there are 6 solutions and $x = 51 \cdot 1°, \ 111 \cdot 1°, \ 171 \cdot 1°, \ 231 \cdot 1°, \ 291 \cdot 1°$ and $351 \cdot 1°$.

The wave function exercise   Go online

Express $5 \sin x - 2 \cos x$ in the form $k \sin(x - \alpha)°$, where $k > 0$ and $0 \leq \alpha \leq 360°$

Q115: What is the value of k?

....

Q116: What is the value of $\alpha°$?

Express $3 \sin x - 4 \cos x$ in the form $k \sin(x - \alpha)°$, where $k > 0$ and $0 \leq \alpha \leq 360°$

Q117: What is the value of k?

....

Q118: What is the value of $\alpha°$?

Express $6 \sin x + 3 \cos x$ in the form $k \sin(x - \alpha)°$, where $k > 0$ and $0 \leq \alpha \leq 360°$

Q119: What is the value of k?

....

Q120: What is the value of $\alpha°$?

Express $9 \sin x + 2 \cos x$ in the form $k \sin(x - \alpha)°$, where $k > 0$ and $0 \leq \alpha \leq 360°$

Q121: What is the value of k?

....

Q122: What is the value of $\alpha°$?

Express $-4 \sin \theta + 4 \cos \theta$ in the form $k \cos(\theta - \alpha)°$, where $k > 0$ and $0 \leq \alpha \leq 2\pi$

Q123: What is the value of k?

....

Q124: What is the value of α?

Express $-3 \sin \theta - 8 \cos \theta$ in the form $k \cos(\theta - \alpha)°$, where $k > 0$ and $0 \leq \alpha \leq 2\pi$

Q125: What is the value of k?

....

Q126: What is the value of α?

Express $\sqrt{3} \cos x + \sin x$ in the form $k \cos(x - \alpha)°$, where $k > 0$ and $0 \leq \alpha \leq 2\pi$

Q127: What is the value of k?

....

Q128: What is the value of α?

Hence or otherwise solve $\sqrt{3} \cos x + \sin x = 1$ where $0 \leq \alpha \leq 2\pi$.

Q129: What is the solution closest to 0?

....

Q130: What is the other solution?

2.8 Maximum and minimum values of the wave function

From the work covered in this topic, it should now be straightforward to express $a \sin x + b \cos x$ in terms of a single cosine or sine function.

The form of this new function has two variables, say k and α, although it is important to realise that other symbols can be used.
(r instead of k and θ instead of x are very common.)

We know from sketching graphs of trigonometric equations of the form $k \sin(x + \alpha)^\circ$ and $k \cos(x + \alpha)^\circ$ that the amplitude is k.

By definition, the amplitude of a wave function is half of the distance between the maximum and the minimum values.

It follows that for a combined wave function, the maximum value is k and the minimum value is $-k$.

Key point

$k \sin(x + \alpha)^\circ$ and $k \cos(x + \alpha)^\circ$

have a maximum value of k and a minimum value of $-k$.

Examples

1. Problem:

If $3 \sin x + \cos x$ can be expressed as $\sqrt{10} \sin (x + 18)^\circ$, find the maximum and minimum values of the function and the values of x at which they occur?

Solution:

It has been stated that the maximum is k so the maximum is $\sqrt{10}$.

Similarly the minimum is $-k$ so the minimum is $-\sqrt{10}$.

If we were to sketch the graph of $y = \sqrt{10} \sin (x + 18)^\circ$ we would get,

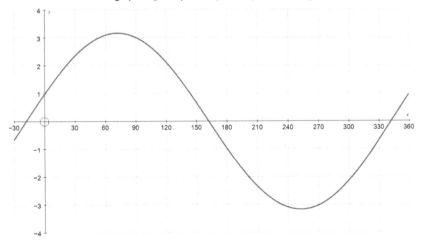

Remember $\sqrt{10} = 3 \cdot 162$.

The maximum and minimum values are clearly the values $\pm k$, and the amplitude is confirmed as half the distance between the maximum and the minimum.

The maximum value occurs when,

$$\sqrt{10}\sin(x + 18)° = \sqrt{10}$$

$$\sin(x + 18)° = \frac{\sqrt{10}}{\sqrt{10}}$$

$$\sin(x + 18)° = 1$$

$$x + 18 = 90°$$

$$x = 72°$$

The minimum occurs when,

$$\sqrt{10}\sin(x + 18)° = -\sqrt{10}$$

$$\sin(x + 18)° = \frac{-\sqrt{10}}{\sqrt{10}}$$

$$\sin(x + 18)° = -1$$

$$x + 18 = 270°$$

$$x = 252°$$

. . . .

2. Problem:

What are the maximum and minimum values of the expression $4 + 5\cos(x - 37)°$? What are the values of x at which the maximum and minimum occur?

Solution:

Remember that $4 + 5cos(x - 37)° = 5cos(x - 37)° + 4$ where the graph of $y = \cos x$ has been shifted to the right by 37°, stretched vertically by a factor of 5 then moved up by 4 units.

Since $k = 5$, the maximum and minimum values are $4 \pm k$.

The maximum is $4 + 5 = 9$ and occurs when,

$$5\cos(x - 37)° + 4 = 9$$

$$\cos(x - 37)° = 1$$

$$x - 37 = 0 \ or \ 360$$

$$x = 37° \ or \ 397°$$

(We would reject the second value if the domain was given as $0 \le x \le 360°$)

The minimum is $4 - 5 = -1$ and occurs when,

$$5\cos(x - 37)° + 4 = -1$$

$$\cos(x - 37)° = -1$$

$$x - 37 = 180$$

$$x = 217°$$

Some care is needed though when the expression is slightly different.

Example Problem:

What are the maximum and minimum values of the expression $3 - 7\sin(x - 20)°$ and the values of x at which they occur?

Solution:

It can be useful to make a quick sketch of the graph first. Remembering that

$$3 - 7\sin(x - 20)° = -7\sin(x - 20)° + 3$$

The graph of $y = \sin x$ is reflected in the x-axis, shifted right by $20°$, stretched vertically by a factor of 7 then moved up by 3 units.

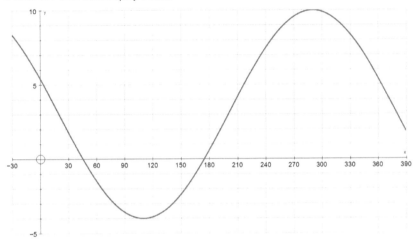

Since $k = -7$, the maximum and minimum values are $3 \pm k$.

$3 + -7 = -4$ and we can see from the graph that this is the minimum and it occurs when,

$$3 - 7\sin(x - 20)° = -4$$
$$\sin(x - 20)° = -1$$
$$x - 20 = 90$$
$$x = 110°$$

It follows that the maximum is $3 - (-7) = 10$ and it occurs when,

$$3 - 7\sin(x - 20) = 10$$
$$\sin(x - 20)° = -1$$
$$x - 20 = 270$$
$$x = 290°$$

Using the techniques of this topic it is now possible to find the maximum and minimum of expressions such as $-2 + 3\sin x - 5\cos x$ and the value of x at which these maxima and minima occur.

Example

Problem:

What are the maximum and minimum values of the expression $-3 \sin x + 4 + 5 \cos x$ and the values of x at which they occur?

Solution:

Step 1: Isolate the combination of trig functions: $-3 \sin x + 5 \cos x$

Step 2: Express $-3 \sin x + 5 \cos x$ as $k \sin(x + \alpha)°$

Note that you can choose any of $k \sin(x \pm \alpha)°$ or $k \cos(x \pm \alpha)°$.

However $k \sin(x + \alpha)°$ is the best choice as the terms and signs match up.

$$k \sin(x + \alpha) = k \sin x \cos \alpha + k \cos x \sin \alpha$$
$$-3 \sin x + 5 \cos x$$

$$k \cos \alpha = -3$$
$$k \sin \alpha = 5$$

$$k = \sqrt{(-3)^2 + 5^2}$$
$$k = \sqrt{34}$$

$$\frac{k \sin \alpha}{k \cos \alpha} = \frac{5}{-3}$$

$$\tan \alpha = \frac{5}{-3} \qquad \text{Remember that } \frac{\sin \alpha}{\cos \alpha} = \tan \alpha$$

$k \sin \alpha$ is positive and $k \cos \alpha$ is negative.

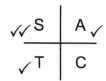

Two ticks tells us that the solution is in the SIN quadrant so when $\tan \alpha = \frac{5}{3}$, $\alpha = 59°$
but in the SIN quadrant $\alpha = 180 - 59 = 121°$

$$-3 \sin x + 5 \cos x = \sqrt{34} \sin(x + 121)°$$

Step 3: Find the maximum and minimum values and the corresponding values of x.

$-3 \sin x + 4 + 5 \cos x = 4 - 3 \sin x + 5 \cos x = 4 + \sqrt{34} \sin(x + 121)°$

Since $k = \sqrt{34}$, the maximum and minimum values are $4 \pm k$.

The maximum is $4 + \sqrt{34}$ and occurs when,

$$\sin(x + 121)° = 1$$
$$x + 121 = 90$$
$$x = -31°$$

... since this solution is < 0 we add $360°$ and $x = 329°$ ($0 \leq x \leq 360°$)

The minimum is $4 - \sqrt{34}$ and occurs when,

$$\sin(x + 121)° = -1$$
$$x + 121 = 270$$
$$x = 149°$$

Maximum and minimum values of the wave function exercise   Go online

Maximum and minimum values of trig functions

Q131: What is the minimum value of $-5 + \sqrt{2}\sin(x + 236)$ in surd form?

....

Q132: What is the minimum value of $-8 + \sqrt{4}\sin(x + 194)$ in surd form?

....

Q133: What is the minimum value of $-7 + \sqrt{7}\sin(x + 267)$ in surd form?

....

Q134: What is the minimum value of $5 + \sqrt{3}\cos(x - 165)$ in surd form?

....

Q135: What is the minimum value of $8 + \sqrt{5}\cos(x - 77)$ in surd form?

....

Q136: What is the minimum value of $7 + \sqrt{5}\cos(x - 13)$ in surd form?

....

Q137: What is the minimum value of $-1 + 3\cos(x - 165)$?

....

Q138: What is the minimum value of $-1 + 5\cos(x - 77)$?

....

Q139: What is the minimum value of $-1 + 5\cos(x - 13)$?

Find the minimum and maximum values of $9\sin(x) + 4\cos(x)$ and determine the corresponding values of x for $0 \leq x \leq 360°$ at which this occurs.

Q140: What is the minimum value of the function?

....

Q141: State the value of x, in degrees, at which the minimum value occurs for $0 \leq x \leq 360°$.

....

Q142: What is the maximum value of the function?

....

Q143: What is the value of x, in degrees, at which the maximum value occurs?

Given $-6 - 9 \sin x + 2 \cos x$

Q144: What is the maximum value in surd form?

....

Q145: What is the corresponding value of x, where $0 \leq x \leq 360$?

....

Q146: What is the minimum value in surd form?

....

Q147: What is the corresponding value of x, where $0 \leq x \leq 360$?

Given $9 + 9 \cos x - 9 \sin x$

Q148: What is the maximum value in surd form?

....

Q149: What is the corresponding value of x, where $0 \leq x \leq 360$?

....

Q150: What is the minimum value in surd form?

....

Q151: What is the corresponding value of x, where $0 \leq x \leq 360$?

2.9   Learning points

Trigonometry
Degrees and radians

- π radians = 180° and 2π radians = 360°.

- To change degrees to radians multiply the degrees by π and divide by 180.

- To change radians to degrees replace the π symbol with multiply by 180 or multiply radians by 180 and divide by π.

- It is much easier to work in degrees then change your final answer into radians.

- Learn the table of exact values or remember how to sketch the two triangles.

Sketching trigonometric graphs

- To sketch trigonometric graphs of the form $y = a\sin(bx + c) + d$ or $y = a\cos(bx + c) + d$:

  1. identify the amplitude a and vertical shift d.
  2. identify the maximum and minimum values $a \pm d$.
  3. identify the number of cycles b and the period $360 \div b$.
  4. factorise the bracket $b\left(x + \frac{c}{b}\right)$.
  5. identify the horizontal shift $\frac{c}{b}$.
  6. evaluate the y-intercept let $x = 0$.
  7. remember to keep the basic shape of sin or cos.

Solving trigonometric equations

- When solving trigonometric equations make a quadrant chart to determine where solutions lie.

- Identify the period and make sure that you find all the solutions. The domain is usually $0 \leq x \leq 360°$ or $0 \leq x \leq 2\pi$ but not always so be careful.

Trigonometric identities

- $\cos^2 A + \sin^2 A = 1$

- $\tan A = \frac{\sin A}{\cos A}$

Addition formula

- $\sin(A + B) = \sin A \cos B + \cos A \sin B$

- $\sin(A - B) = \sin A \cos B - \cos A \sin B$

- $\cos(A + B) = \cos A \cos B - \sin A \sin B$

- $\cos(A - B) = \cos A \cos B + \sin A \sin B$

Double angle formula

- $\sin 2A = 2\sin A \cos A$

    $$\cos 2A = \cos^2 A - \sin^2 A$$
-
    $$= 2\cos^2 - 1$$
    $$= 1 - 2\sin^2 A$$

The wave function

- Expand the addition formula and write your expression underneath it.

- Identify the value of $k \sin \alpha$ and $k \cos \alpha$, you may have to swap terms around or change signs.

- Find the value of k.

- Find the value of the phase angle $\alpha°$.

- Express the answer to the question.

- The maximum and minimum values are $\pm k$.

2.10 End of topic test

End of topic 6 test   Go online

Sketch the graph of $y = 4\sin(2x - 50)^\circ + 1$

Q152: What is the amplitude?

....

Q153: What is the maximum value?

....

Q154: What is the minimum value?

....

Q155: What is the period of the graph?

....

Q156: Has the basic sin curve been moved horizontally left or right?

....

Q157: What is the horizontal shift?

The equation of the graph below takes the form $y = a\cos(bx + c)$ and has turning points at $\left(-\frac{\pi}{4}, 5\right)$ and $\left(\frac{\pi}{4}, -5\right)$.

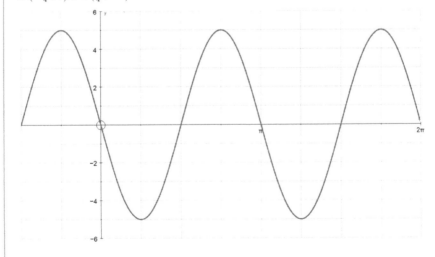

Q158: What is the value of a?

....

Q159: What is the value of b?

....

Q160: What is the value of c?

Q161: Solve $2 \cos x = \sqrt{3}$ for $0 \leq x \leq \pi$

....

Q162: Solve $\tan x + \sqrt{3} = 0$ for $\pi \leq x \leq 2\pi$

....

Q163: Solve $5 \sin (3x - 10)^\circ - 1 = 0$ for $270 \leq x \leq 360^\circ$

Q164: What is the exact value of $\cos 2x$?

....

Q165: What is the exact value of $\sin 2x$?

Q166: Using the fact that $\frac{\pi}{6} + \frac{\pi}{4} = \frac{5\pi}{12}$, what is the exact value of $\sin \frac{5\pi}{12}$?

....

Q167: Express $\frac{\pi}{12}$ in terms of $\frac{\pi}{6}$, $\frac{\pi}{4}$

....

Q168: What is the exact value of $\sin \frac{\pi}{12}$?

Express $3 \sin x^\circ - 5 \cos x^\circ$ in the form $R \sin(x - \alpha)^\circ$, where $R > 0$ and $0 \leq x \leq 360^\circ$ and solve $3 \sin x^\circ - 5 \cos x^\circ + 1 = 0$.

Q169: What is the value of R?

....

Q170: What is the value of α°?

....

Q171: What is the solution closest to 180°?

$15 \cos x^\circ - 8 \sin x^\circ$ can be expressed as $k \cos(x + a)^\circ$, where $k > 0$ and $0 \leq x \leq 360^\circ$

Q172: What is the maximum value of $15 \cos x^\circ - 8 \sin x^\circ$?

....

Q173: What is the value of x in the interval $180 \leq x \leq 360^\circ$ at which the maximum value occurs?

....

Q174: What is the minimum value of $15 \cos x^\circ - 8 \sin x^\circ$?

....

Q175: What is the value of x in the interval $0 \leq x \leq 360°$ at which the minimum value occurs?

Q176: Show that $\dfrac{\sin 2x}{\cos 2x + 1} = \tan x$

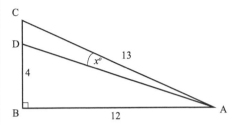

Q177: What is the exact value of $\cos x°$?

Topic 3

Recurrence relations

Contents

Learning objective

By the end of this topic, you should be able to:

- identify:
    - a geometric sequence;
    - an arithmetic sequence;
- determine a linear recurrence relation;
- use a recurrence relation to calculate terms;
- identify when a recurrence relation has a limit;
- find the limit of a converging recurrence relation;
- solve recurrence relations;
- interpret recurrence relations in context.

3.1 Looking back at National 5

Summary
Solving simultaneous equations algebraically
Solving by elimination

- The method of elimination requires the same quantity of one letter in both equations.

- One of them should be positive and the other negative.

- One or both of the equations may have to be multiplied to achieve this.

- Add the two equations together to eliminate one of the variables.

Solving by substitution

- The method of substitution requires one or both of the equations to be in the form $y = \ldots$ or $x = \ldots$

- This allows you to substitute for x or y in the other equation.

3.1.1 Solving simultaneous equations algebraically

Solving equations algebraically	Go online

Let's find out how to solve simultaneous linear equations algebraically.

We can use balancing and multiplying to solve systems of equations - in other words to find the values of x and y.

Look at these equations:
$$x + 2y = 10 \quad (1)$$
$$-5x + y = -6 \quad (2)$$

Start by getting the y's to cancel. Notice that equation 1 has '$+2y$' and equation 2 has '$+y$'. So we multiply equation 2 by -2,
$$10x - 2y = 12 \quad (3)$$

Next, add equation 1 to equation 3 to cancel y:

$$
\begin{array}{rrcll}
x & + \ 2y & = & 10 & (1) \\
10x & - \ 2y & = & 12 & (3) \\
\hline
11x & & = & 22 &
\end{array}
$$

Now divide both sides by 11, giving $x = 2$.

We now know the value of x so we can substitute x into equation 1 to find the value of y:
$$x + 2y = 10 \quad (1)$$
$$x = 2$$
$$2 + 2y = 10 \qquad \text{substitute in x = 2}$$
$$2y = 8 \qquad \text{this tidies to become}$$
$$y = 4 \qquad \text{divide both sides by 2}$$

The solution to the system is known: $x = 2$ and $y = 4$

To solve the simultaneous equations above we eliminated y. The method we used is called the Elimination Method.

3.1.2 Solving simultaneous equations by the method of elimination

Example

Problem:

Solve the simultaneous equations,

1. $a + 4b = 22$

2. $a - 4b = -18$

Solution:

$$a + 4b = 22 \quad (1) \quad \textit{add the equations to eliminate b}$$
$$+ \quad a - 4b = -18 \quad (2)$$
$$2a = 4 \quad \textit{divide by 2}$$
$$a = 2$$

Substitute $a = 2$ into equation 1:

$$a + 4b = 22 \quad (1)$$
$$2 + 4b = 22 \qquad \text{subtract 2}$$
$$4b = 20 \qquad \text{divide by 4}$$
$$b = 5$$

We can check our solution by substituting $a = 2$ and $b = 5$ into equations 1 and 2

$\Rightarrow 2 + 20 = 22\checkmark$ and $2 - 20 = -18\checkmark$

The solution is $a = 2$ and $b = 5$.

When solving simultaneous equations by elimination we often have to multiply one or both of the equations before we can add the equations. Our aim is to have the same quantity of one letter in both equations where one of them is positive and the other negative.

Examples

1. Problem:

Solve the simultaneous equations,

$$s + t = 9 \quad (1)$$
$$2s + t = 17 \quad (2)$$

Solution:

Unlike all the previous examples both equations have 2 terms which are being added so we have an extra step to make one of the t terms negative:

$$s + t = \ 9 \quad (1) \quad \textit{leave this equation alone}$$
$$2s + t = 17 \quad (2) \quad \textit{multiply this one by -1}$$

$$s + t = \ 9 \quad (1)$$
$$+ \ -2s - t = -17 \quad (3) \quad \textit{call equation 3 and add}$$
$$\overline{-s = -8} \quad \textit{divide by -1}$$
$$s = 8$$

Substitute $s = 8$ into equation 1:

$$s + t = 9$$
$$8 + t = 9 \quad \text{subtract 8}$$
$$t = 1$$

We can check our solution by substituting $s = 8$ and $t = 1$ into equations 1 and 2
$$\Rightarrow 8 + 1 = 9\checkmark \text{ and } 2 \times 8 + 1 = 17\checkmark$$

The solution is $s = 8$ and $t = 1$.

. . . .

2. Problem:

Solve the simultaneous equations,

$$v + w = 1 \quad (1)$$
$$3v + 2w = 4 \quad (2)$$

Solution:

This time we need to make the first equation have $-2w$ so we have an extra step:

$$v + w = 1 \quad (1) \quad \textit{multiply this equation by -2}$$
$$3v + 2w = 4 \quad (2) \quad \textit{leave this equation alone}$$

$$-2v - 2w = -2 \quad (3) \quad \textit{call equation 3 and add}$$
$$+ \ 3v + 2w = 4 \quad (2)$$
$$\overline{v = 2}$$

Substitute $v = 2$ into equation 1:

$$v + w = 1$$
$$2 + w = 1 \quad \text{subtract 2}$$
$$w = -1$$

We can check our solution by substituting $v = 2$ and $w = -1$ into equations 1 and 2
$$\Rightarrow 2 + (-1) = 1\checkmark \text{ and } 3 \times 2 + 2 \times (-1) = 4\checkmark$$

The solution is $v = 2$ and $w = -1$.

. . . .

3. Problem:

Solve the simultaneous equations,

$7y + 2z = 12$ (1)

$2y - 3z = 7$ (2)

Solution:

This time we need to find a common multiple of 2 and 3 so we have 2 extra steps:

$7y + 2z = 12$ (1)   *multiply this equation by 3*

$2y - 3z = 7$ (2)   *multiply this equation by 2*

$21y + 6z = 36$ (3)   *call equation 3*

$+ \quad 4y - 6z = 14$ (4)   *call equation 4 and add*

$\overline{}$

$25y = 50$ *divide by 25*

$y = 2$

Substitute $y = 2$ into equation 1:

$7y + 2z = 12$

$14 + 2z = 12$ subtract 14

$2z = -2$ divide by 2

$z = -1$

We can check our solution by substituting $y = 2$ and $z = -1$ into equations 1 and 2

$\Rightarrow 7 \times 2 + 2 \times (-1) = 12\checkmark$ *and* $2 \times 2 - 3 \times (-1) = 7\checkmark$

The solution is $y = 2$ and $z = -1$.

Key point

The aim is always to have the same quantity of one of the letters and make it positive in one equation and negative in the other.

One of the letters should have the same size of coefficient in both equations.

Solving simultaneous equations by elimination exercise   Go online

Q1: Solve $6x + 5y = 81$

$3x - y = 9$

  a) What is the value of x?

  b) What is the value of y?

. . . .

Q2: Solve $4a + 2b = 36$

$7a - b = 45$

  a) What is the value of a?

  b) What is the value of b?

Q3: Solve
$$7c - 3d = 5$$
$$4c + d = 11$$

a) What is the value of c?

b) What is the value of d?

....

Q4: Solve
$$e + 2f = 2$$
$$5e + f = 1$$

a) What is the value of e?

b) What is the value of f?

....

Q5: Solve
$$4g - 3h = 10$$
$$3g + 4h = 20$$

a) What is the value of g?

b) What is the value of h?

....

Q6: Solve
$$3m + 5n = 23$$
$$5m + 2n = 13$$

a) What is the value of m?

b) What is the value of n?

....

Q7: Solve
$$5p - 4q = -1$$
$$4p - 3q = 0$$

a) What is the value of p?

b) What is the value of q?

3.1.3   Solving simultaneous equations by the method of substitution

Sometimes equations are presented in the form $y = mx + c$ and in this case the method of solving simultaneous equations by substitution is easier.

Examples

1. Problem:

Solve,
$$y = 2x$$
$$y = x + 8$$

Solution:

$$y = x + 8 \quad (1)$$
$$y = 2x \quad (2)$$

Replace y in equation 1 with $2x$ and solve.

$$2x = x + 8 \qquad \text{subtract x}$$
$$x = 8$$

Replace x in equation 2 with 8.

$$y = 2x$$
$$y = 2 \times 8 = 16 \checkmark$$

If we substitute x in equation 1 with 8 we should also get $y = 16$.

$$y = x + 8$$
$$y = 8 + 8 = 16 \checkmark$$

The solution is $x = 8$ and $y = 16$.

....

2. Problem:

Solve,

$$y = 2x$$
$$3x + y = 5$$

Solution:

$$y = 2x \quad (1)$$
$$3x + y = 5 \quad (2)$$

Replace y in equation 2 with $2x$ and solve.

$$3x + 2x = 5 \qquad \text{simplify}$$
$$5x = 5 \qquad \text{divide by 5}$$
$$x = 1$$

Replace x in equation 1 with 1. We should get the value of $y = 2$.

$$y = 2x$$
$$y = 2 \times 1 = 2 \checkmark$$

Replace x in equation 2 with 1. We should get the value of $y = 2$.

$$3x + y = 5$$
$$3 \times 1 + y = 5$$
$$3 + y = 5$$
$$y = 2 \checkmark \qquad \text{y = 2 in both equations}$$

The solution is $x = 1$ and $y = 2$.

Solving simultaneous equations by substitution exercise — Go online

Q8: Solve
$$y = x$$
$$y = -2x + 9$$

a) What is the value of x?

b) What is the value of y?

. . . .

Q9: Solve
$$y = x + 4$$
$$y = -4x - 6$$

a) What is the value of x?

b) What is the value of y?

. . . .

Q10: Solve
$$-x + 7 = y$$
$$y = x - 7$$

a) What is the value of x?

b) What is the value of y?

. . . .

Q11: Solve
$$4x + y = 12$$
$$y = -x + 6$$

a) What is the value of x?

b) What is the value of y?

. . . .

Q12: Solve
$$y = -x + 6$$
$$3x + y = 8$$

a) What is the value of x?

b) What is the value of y?

3.2 Simple recurrence relations

A **sequence** is a series of terms with a definite pattern. A sequence can be defined by a rule or a formula for the nth term.

A **recurrence relation** describes a sequence in which each term is a function of the previous term or terms.

Examples

1.

2, 5, 8, 11, ...

The next two terms would be 14 and 17.

A rule for this sequence would be to start with 2 then add on 3 each time.

A formula to find the nth term would be $3n - 1$.

This is because our sequence goes up in 3s so we think of the multiples of 3, i.e. 3, 6, 9, 12, ...

You should be able to see that if we subtract 1 from each term we would get our sequence 2, 5, 8, 11, ...

....

2.

1, 1, 2, 3, 5, 8, ...

This is a **Fibonacci** sequence.

The next two terms would be 13 and 21.

A rule for this sequence would be to add the previous two terms to get the next term.

A formula to find the nth term for this sequence is much harder and would be $\approx \frac{1}{\sqrt{5}}\left(\frac{1+\sqrt{5}}{2}\right)^{n+1}$, where the "$\approx$" is close enough that you can round to the nearest integer.

You may have also spotted that $\frac{1+\sqrt{5}}{2}$ is the golden ratio.

It can be difficult to describe a formula to find the nth term so we will focus mainly on constructing a recurrence relation.

Just as we did when describing a formula for a sequence, we need some notation to describe recurrence relations.

Key point

u_0 defines the initial value.

u_1 defines the first term.

u_n defines the nth term.

u_{n-1} defines the term before the nth term.

u_{n+1} defines the term after the nth term.

Simple recurrence relations   Go online

Consider the sequence of numbers:

$u_1, \quad u_2, \quad u_3, \quad u_4, \quad u_5, \quad u_6, \quad \ldots$

$\downarrow \quad \downarrow \quad \downarrow \quad \downarrow \quad \downarrow \quad \downarrow$

$5, \quad 8, \quad 11, \quad 14, \quad 17, \quad 20, \quad \ldots$

Notice that given $u_1 = 5$ it is possible to calculate $u_2, u_3, u_4, u_5, u_6, \ldots$ by repeatedly adding 3.

$u_1 = 5$
$u_2 = u_1 + 3 = 8$
$u_3 = u_2 + 3 = 11$
$u_4 = u_3 + 3 = 14$
$u_5 = u_4 + 3 = 17$
$u_6 = u_5 + 3 = 20$

This sequence can then be defined in another way as $u_{n+1} = u_n + 3$

A sequence defined in this way is known as a recurrence relation because the pattern +3 recurs.

Special recurrence relations   Go online

Under certain laboratory conditions a bamboo plant grows at a rate of 20% per day. At the start of the experiment the height of the bamboo plant is $B_0 = 30 \; cm$.

   a) Write down a recurrence relation that describes the growth of the plant.

   b) Calculate how tall the plant is after five days.

   c) Find a formula for the height of the plant after n days giving your answer in terms of B_0

(Notice that the notation is slightly different in this question B_0 is used here for the initial height of the plant. Indeed, it makes sense that B_1 represents the height of the plant after one day and similarly for $B_2, B_3, B_4, \ldots$).

   a) $B_0 = 30$
      Since the plant grows by 20% each day, the height will be $120\% = 1 \cdot 2$ times its height from the previous day.
      The recurrence relation is therefore $B_{n+1} = 1.2B_n$ with $B_0 = 30$.

   b) $B_0 = 30$
      $B_1 = 1 \cdot 2 \times B_0 = 1 \cdot 2 \times 30 = 36$
      $B_2 = 1 \cdot 2 \times B_1 = 1 \cdot 2 \times 36 = 43 \cdot 2$
      $B_3 = 1 \cdot 2 \times B_2 = 1 \cdot 2 \times 43 \cdot 2 = 51 \cdot 84$
      $B_4 = 1 \cdot 2 \times B_3 = 1 \cdot 2 \times 51 \cdot 84 = 62 \cdot 208$
      $B_5 = 1 \cdot 2 \times B_4 = 1 \cdot 2 \times 62 \cdot 208 = 74 \cdot 6496$

      Thus after five days the plant will be 75 cm tall (to the nearest cm).

c) The preceding working can be written in another way as shown here

$$B_0 = 30$$
$$B_1 = 1 \cdot 2 \times B_0$$
$$B_2 = 1 \cdot 2 \times B_1 = 1 \cdot 2 \times (1 \cdot 2 \times B_0) = 1 \cdot 2^2 \times B_0$$
$$B_3 = 1 \cdot 2 \times B_2 = 1 \cdot 2 \times (1 \cdot 2^2 \times B_0) = 1 \cdot 2^3 \times B_0$$
$$B_4 = 1 \cdot 2 \times B_3 = 1 \cdot 2 \times (1 \cdot 2^3 \times B_0) = 1 \cdot 2^4 \times B_0$$
$$B_5 = 1 \cdot 2 \times B_4 = 1 \cdot 2 \times (1 \cdot 2^4 \times B_0) = 1 \cdot 2^5 \times B_0$$

A pattern develops and in general:

$$B_n = 1 \cdot 2^n B_0$$

Example

Problem:

Bacteria increase at a rate of 30% every hour.

Write down a recurrence relation to describe the growth of bacteria.

Solution:

Each hour the number of bacteria will be 130% of the previous hour where u_n is the number of bacteria after n hours.

$$u_{n+1} = 1.3u_n$$

Key point

A geometric sequence is a special type of recurrence relation that takes the form: $u_{n+1} = au_n$, where a is a scalar or multiple.

It is worth noting that a formula for the nth term is given by $u_n = a^n u_0$

Example

Problem:

A car depreciates at a rate of 15% per annum.

In 2010 a car cost £9500.

a) Describe the price each year by a recurrence relation in the form $V_{n+1} = aV_n$ where V_n is the value of the car after n years.

b) Calculate V_1, V_2, and V_3.

c) Write down a formula for V_n.

d) How long will it take for the car to half its value?

Solution:

(a)
The value is 85% of its value the previous year.
$V_{n+1} = 0 \cdot 85 V_n, V_0 = 9500$

(b)
Use the recurrence relation from part (a).
$V_1 = 0 \cdot 85 \times 9500 = 8075$
$V_2 = 0 \cdot 85 \times 8075 = 6863 \cdot 75$
$V_3 = 0 \cdot 85 \times 6863 \cdot 75 = 5834 \cdot 19$

(c)
This example uses the method for compound interest.
$V_n = (0 \cdot 85)^n \times 9500$

(d)
Using trial and error is often the easiest way.

Half of 9500 = £4750
$V_3 = 5834 \cdot 19$
$V_4 = 0 \cdot 85 \times 5834 \cdot 19 = 4959 \cdot 06$
This value is close but not yet half.

$V_5 = 0 \cdot 85 \times 4959 \cdot 06 = 4215 \cdot 20$
This value is below half so it will take five years to half its value.

Key point

Remember a recurrence relation describes how to find the next term in a sequence whereas a rule describes how to find the nth term.

Example Problem:

John saves £15 each month. Initially he had £35.

   a) If a_n is the amount he has saved after n months, construct a recurrence relation for a_{n+1} and state the value of a_0.

   b) Calculate a_1, a_2, a_3.

   c) Write down a formula for a_n.

   d) How much had John saved after 10 months?

Solution:

(a)
$a_{n+1} = a_n + 15, a_0 = 35$

(b)
$a_1 = 35 + 15 = 50$
$a_2 = 50 + 15 = 65$
$a_3 = 65 + 15 = 80$

(c)

The sequence so far is 50, 65, 80.

It is easier to ignore the initial value when $n = 0$.

Our sequence goes up in 15s so we think of the multiples of 15, i.e. 15, 30, 45, ...

You should be able to see that if we add 35 to each term we would get our sequence 50, 65, 80, ...

The formula is $a_n = 15n + 35$

(d)

When $n = 10$, $a_{10} = 15 \times 10 + 35 = 185$

He has saved £185.

An alternative solution would be to use the recurrence relation to find a_4, a_5, a_6, a_7, a_8, a_9 and finally a_{10}.

Key point

An *arithmetic sequence* is a special type of recurrence relation that takes the form

$u_{n+1} = u_n + b$

A formula for the nth term is given by $u_n = u_0 + bn$

Example

Problem:

Given the recurrence relation: $u_{n+1} = {}^1/2u_n - 3$ and $u_1 = 10$

List the first four terms of the sequence.

Solution:

$u_1 = 10$
$u_2 = {}^1/2 \times 10 - 3 = 5 - 3 = 2$
$u_3 = {}^1/2 \times 2 - 3 = 1 - 3 = -2$
$u_4 = {}^1/2 \times (-2) - 3 = -1 - 3 = -4$

Key point

A linear recurrence relation is defined by:

$u_{n+1} = au_n + b, a \neq 0$

Notice that the equation looks like the equation of a straight line i.e. $y = mx + c$.

Example

Problem:

During an epidemic a hospital claims that a new drug will cure 40% of patients with a virus each day.

Currently 3 new patients will be admitted with the virus each day.

If there were 22 patients with the virus last night find a recurrence relation for the number of patients in the hospital with the virus.

Solution:

We need to know about the number of patients with the virus so if 40% are cured then 60% still have the virus and 3 new patients must be added each day.

$v_{n+1} = 0 \cdot 6v_n + 3, v_0 = 22$ where v_n is the number of patients with the virus on day n.

Remember the initial value is part of the recurrence relation and must be included.

Example

Problem:

A farmer grows a variety of plum tree which ripens during the months of July and August.

On the last day in July there was 2000 kg of ripe fruit ready to be picked.

At the beginning of August the farmer hires some fruit pickers who manage to pick 75% of the ripe fruit each day.

Also, each day 60 kg more of the plums become ripe.

a) Find a recurrence relation for the weight of ripe plums left in the orchard.

b) What is the estimated weight of ripe plums left in the orchard at the end of the day on the 7th August ?

Solution:

a) Let P_0 represent the weight of ripe plums available at the start then $P_0 = 2000$
P_1 represents the amount of ripe plums left in the orchard at the end of the day on the 1st August and similarily for $P_2, P_3, P_4, \ldots$

Since 75% of the ripe fruit is picked each day then 25% of the ripe fruit is left in the orchard for the next day.
Also, each day 60 kg more of the plums ripen.

Thus the recurrence relation is:
$P_{n+1} = 0 \cdot 25 \, P_n + 60$

---

b) With $P_0 = 2000$ and $P_{n+1} = 0 \cdot 25P_n + 60$ then, using a calculator, you can check that

$$P_1 = 0 \cdot 25 \times 2000 + 60 = 560$$
$$P_2 = 200$$
$$P_3 = 110$$
$$P_4 = 87 \cdot 5$$
$$P_5 = 81 \cdot 875$$
$$P_6 = 80 \cdot 46875$$
$$P_7 = 80 \cdot 1171875$$

Thus after the 7th of August there is approximately 80 kg of ripe fruit in the orchard.

Occasionally it is useful to be able to identify specific terms in a recurrence relation.

Further linear recurrence relations   Go online

A sequence is defined by the recurrence relation $u_{n+1} = 0 \cdot 8u_n + 500$, $u_0 = 10$.

Calculate the value of u_4 and find the smallest value of n for which $u_n > 2000$.

The recurrence relation gives (to two decimal places):

$u_0 = 10$
$u_1 = 0 \cdot 8 \times 10 + 500 = 508$
$u_2 = 0 \cdot 8 \times 508 + 500 = 906 \cdot 4$
$u_3 = 0 \cdot 8 \times 906 \cdot 4 + 500 = 1225 \cdot 12$
$u_4 = 0 \cdot 8 \times 1225 \cdot 12 + 500 = 1480 \cdot 10$
$u_5 = 0 \cdot 8 \times 1480 \cdot 10 + 500 = 1684 \cdot 08$
$u_6 = 0 \cdot 8 \times 1684 \cdot 08 + 500 = 1847 \cdot 26$
$u_7 = 0 \cdot 8 \times 1847 \cdot 26 + 500 = 1977 \cdot 81$
$u_8 = 0 \cdot 8 \times 1977 \cdot 81 + 500 = 2082 \cdot 25$
$u_9 = 0 \cdot 8 \times 2082 \cdot 81 + 500 = 2165 \cdot 80$

So $u_4 = 1480 \cdot 10$ (to 2 d.p.) and $n = 8$ for $u_n > 2000$.

Key point

You may round your answers to write them down but you must keep and use all decimal places to calculate the next value in the sequence.

Simple recurrence relations exercise   Go online

Special recurrence relations

The value of a new car depreciates by 40% each year.
The value of the car was initially $C_0 = £16000$.

Q13: Find the recurrence relation that describes the value of the car.
....

Q14: Is this a geometric sequence or an arithmetic sequence?
....

Q15: How much will the car be worth after 5 years?
....

Q16: Find a formula for c_n giving your answer in terms of c_0.

Recurrence relations

At the start of a week a farmer has 20 apple trees in a small orchard.
He plants 14 more trees in the orchard each day for the next 6 days.

Q17: Find a recurrence relation that describes the number of trees T_{n+1} in the orchard.
....

Q18: How many trees does the farmer have in his orchard after 6 days?

Special recurrence relations

Joe bought a compact DVD player on hire purchase and paid a deposit of $P_0 = £10$.
He makes a payment of £18 at the end of each month to repay the balance.

Q19: Find the recurrence relation to describe the payments that Joe makes.
....

Q20: Is this a geometric sequence or an arithmetic sequence?
....

Q21: Joe has completed the payments after 12 months. How much did the DVD player cost him?
....

Q22: Find a formula for P_n, giving your answer in terms of P_0.

Recurrence relations

Due to global warming, it is estimated that an iceberg is melting at a rate of 7% per year. At the start of the year 2000 the volume of the iceberg was approximately $V_0 = 3200 \, km^3$.

Q23: Find the recurrence relation that describes the volume of the iceberg.

....

Q24: What will the volume of the iceberg be after 6 years?

....

Q25: Find a formula for V_n in terms of V_0.

....

Q26: If the iceberg continues to melt at the same rate, how many years it will take until the volume of the iceberg is less than 1000 km^3?

Using the recurrence relation $u_{n+1} = 3u_n + 1$ with $u_1 = 4$ calculate the values of the next three terms in the sequence, as well as u_{10}.

Q27: What is the value of u_2?

....

Q28: What is the value of u_3?

....

Q29: What is the value of u_4?

....

Q30: What is the value of u_{10}?

Using the recurrence relation $u_{n+1} = 0 \cdot 2u_n + 4$ with $u_1 = 300$ calculate the next four terms in the sequence, as well as u_{10}.

Q31: What is the value of u_2?

....

Q32: What is the value of u_3?

....

Q33: What is the value of u_4?

....

Q34: What is the value of u_5?

....

Q35: What is the value of u_{10}?

....

Q36: Consider the following sequence: 8, 32, 128, 512, 2048, . . .

Which is the correct recurrence relation?

a) $u_{n+1} = u_n + 4$

b) $u_{n+1} = 8u_n$

c) $u_{n+1} = 4u_n$

d) $u_{n+1} = 8u_n + 4$

Use the recurrence relation $u_{n+2} = u_{n+1} + u_n + 4$ with $u_1 = 1$ and $u_2 = 1$ calculate the next four terms in the sequence, as well as u_{10}.

Q37: What is the value of u_3?

. . . .

Q38: What is the value of u_4?

. . . .

Q39: What is the value of u_5?

. . . .

Q40: What is the value of u_6?

. . . .

Q41: What is the value of u_7?

. . . .

Q42: What is the value of u_8?

. . . .

Q43: What is the value of u_9?

. . . .

Q44: What is the value of u_{10}?

Linear recurrence relations

Ben is given a gift of £90 by a rich relative on his 15th birthday and on each birthday after that.

He saves this money in a savings account which pays 7% annual interest.

Q45: A recurrence relation for the amount of money that Ben has in his account is?

. . . .

Q46: How much should Ben have in his account by his 21st birthday?

Recurrence relations

A large shoal of 250 fish are observed and it is noticed that every minute 2 % of the fish leave the shoal and another 20 return.

Q47: Find a recurrence relation for the size of the shoal of fish.

....

Q48: How many fish are in the shoal after 8 minutes?

Linear recurrence relations

A pharmaceutical company is given permission to discharge 50 kg of chemical waste into a section of river each day.
Due to the natural tide of the river 90% of the chemical is washed away each day.

Q49: A recurrence relation for the amount of chemical waste in the river is?

....

Q50: How many kg of chemical waste are there in the river after 5 days?

....

Q51: How many kg of chemical waste are there in the river after 9 days?

A patient is injected with 50 units of a drug in hospital.
Every 6 hours, 20% of the drug passes out of the bloodstream.
The patient is therefore given a further dose of 50 units of the drug at 6 hourly intervals

Q52: Find a recurrence relation for the amount of the drug in the bloodstream.

....

Q53: How many units of the drug are in the patient's bloodstream after 36 hours?

Further linear recurrence relations

A sequence is defined by the recurrence relation $u_{n+1} = 0 \cdot 6u_n - 10$, $u_0 = 100$.

Q54: Calculate the value of u_2 .

....

Q55: What is the smallest value of n such that u_n is less than zero?

Recurrence relations

A sequence is defined by the recurrence relation $u_{n+1} = 1 \cdot 6u_n + 70$, $u_0 = 100$.

Q56: What is the value of u_2?

....

Q57: What is the value of u_5?

....

Q58: How many terms in the sequence have value less than 1000?

3.3 Finding a limit

Some recurrence relations tend toward a limit or settle around a particular value. Remember the orchard example from the previous sub-section 'Simple recurrence relations', it looks like the amount of fruit may settle around 80 kg.

Compare the following two recurrence relations.

Investigating recurrence relations   Go online

$u_{n+1} = 0 \cdot 6u_n + 20$, $u_0 = 10$ generates the following sequence (to 2 decimal places).

$u_0 = 10$
$u_1 = 26$
$u_2 = 35 \cdot 6$
$u_3 = 41 \cdot 36$
$u_4 = 44 \cdot 82$
$u_5 = 46 \cdot 89$
$u_6 = 48 \cdot 13$
$u_7 = 48 \cdot 88$
$u_8 = 49 \cdot 33$
$u_9 = 49 \cdot 60$
$u_{10} = 49 \cdot 76$
$u_{11} = 49 \cdot 85$
$u_{12} = 49 \cdot 91$

This can be represented on a graph as shown here.

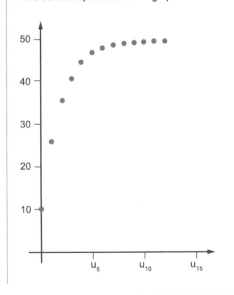

This shows that $u_n \rightarrow 50$ as $n \rightarrow \infty$. The terms become closer and closer to 50. This is a **convergent sequence**.

$u_{n+1} = 2u_n + 20$, $u_0 = 10$ generates the following sequence (to 2 decimal places).

$u_0 = 10$
$u_1 = 40$
$u_2 = 100$
$u_3 = 220$
$u_4 = 460$
$u_5 = 940$
$u_6 = 1900$
$u_7 = 3820$
$u_8 = 7660$
$u_9 = 15340$

This is represented on a graph as shown here.

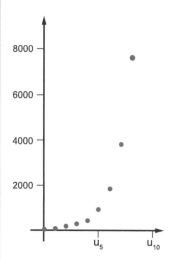

Notice that this time the **sequence is divergent**. Subsequent terms continue getting bigger and bigger.

Key point

A convergent recurrence relation tends toward a limit, L as $n \rightarrow \infty$.

A divergent recurrence relation does not have a limit.

The limit of a recurrence relation   Go online

Proof

The above formula for L can be derived from the following.
In general if $u_{n+1} \Rightarrow L$ as $n \to \infty$ then we also have that $u_n \to L$ as $n \to \infty$

Thus, as $n \Rightarrow \infty$, the formula $u_{n+1} = au_n + b$ tends to the following:

$$L \quad\quad = aL + b$$
$$L - aL = b$$
$$L(1 - a) = b$$
$$L = \frac{b}{1 - a}$$

Key point

For the linear recurrence relation $u_{n+1} = au_n + b$

A limit exists if $-1 < a < 1$ and the limit L is given by the formula:

$$L = \frac{b}{1 - a}$$

Some students find it difficult to remember this formula so there is an alternative.
For the recurrence relation $u_{n+1} = mu_n + c$:

A limit exists if $-1 < m < 1$ and the limit L is given by the formula:

$$L = \frac{c}{1 - m}$$

Examples

1. Problem:

a) Find the first six terms of the recurrence relation $u_{n+1} = 0 \cdot 8u_n + 4$ with $u_0 = 2$

b) Give a reason why this recurrence relation generates a sequence which has a limit.

c) Calculate the value of the limit.

Solution:

a) The first six terms in the sequence are:

$u_0 = 2$
$u_1 = 5 \cdot 6$
$u_2 = 8 \cdot 48$
$u_3 = 10 \cdot 784$
$u_4 = 12 \cdot 6272$
$u_5 = 14 \cdot 10176$

b) $-1 < 0 \cdot 8 < 1$ so a limit exists.

Note that it is essential that you make this statement to gain full marks.

c) As $n \Rightarrow \infty$ the recurrence relation $u_{n+1} = 0 \cdot 8u_n + 4$ tends to

$$L = \frac{b}{1 - a}$$

$$L = \frac{4}{1 - 0 \cdot 8}$$

$$L = \frac{4}{0 \cdot 2}$$

$$L = \frac{40}{2} = 20$$

Thus the sequence tends towards 20.

This type of question is often asked in the non-calculator paper. Be sure that you can calculate the limit without a calculator.

. . . .

2. Problem:

Fish, like all animals need oxygen to survive. The fish in a certain tank use up 15% of the oxygen in the water each hour.

However, due to the action of a pump, oxygen is added to the water at a rate of 1 part per metre^3 each hour.

The oxygen level in the tank should be between 5 and 7 parts per metre^3 for the survival of the fish.

Initially the concentration of oxygen in the tank is 6 ppm^3

1. Write down a recurrence relation to describe the oxygen level in the water.

2. Say whether or not a limit exists, giving a reason.

3. Determine, in the long term, whether the fish will survive.

Solution:

a) Let F_n represent the oxygen level in the water after n hours then

$F_{n+1} = 0 \cdot 85F_n + 1$ with $F_0 = 6$

b) $-1 < 0 \cdot 85 < 1$ so a limit exists.

c) The fish will survive because when $n \Rightarrow \infty$ then $u_n \Rightarrow L$ and $u_{n+1} \Rightarrow L$ thus

$$L = \frac{b}{1-a}$$
$$= \frac{1}{1-0\cdot85}$$
$$= \frac{1}{0\cdot15}$$
$$L = 6\cdot667$$

so oxygen levels in the tank will tend towards 6·667 ppm^3.

Since $5 < 6\cdot667 < 7$ the fish will survive.

. . . .

3. Problem:

You may remember the orchard problem from sub-topic 7.2.

A farmer grows a variety of plum tree which ripens during the months of July and August.

On the last day in July there was 2000 kg of ripe fruit ready to be picked.
At the beginning of August the farmer hires some fruit pickers who manage to pick 75% of the ripe fruit each day.

Also, each day 60 kg more of the plums become ripe.

a) Find a recurrence relation for the weight of ripe plums left in the orchard.

b) What is the estimated weight of ripe plums left in the orchard in the long term during the picking season?

Solution:

a) The recurrence relation is $P_{n+1} = 0\cdot25\, P_n + 60$

b)
$$L = \frac{c}{1-m}$$
$$= \frac{60}{1-0\cdot25}$$
$$= \frac{60}{0\cdot75}$$
$$= 60 \div \frac{3}{4}$$
$$= 60 \times 4 \div 3$$
$$L = 80$$

During the picking season the amount of fruit left unpicked in the orchard will settle around 80 kg.

> **Key point**
>
> It is important to remember that the limit is the value that a recurrence relation will tend towards or settle around. It will never actually be that value it will just get very close to it as $n \to \infty$.

Recurrence relations

Q59: Find the next four terms in the recurrence relation $u_{n+1} = -0 \cdot 7u_n + 50$ with $u_0 = 0$.

a) $u_1 = ?$

b) $u_2 = ?$

c) $u_3 = ?$

d) $u_4 = ?$

....

Q60: The recurrence relation has a limit as n tends to infinity because:

a) $50 > 1$

b) $0 < 10$

c) $-1 < -0 \cdot 7 < 1$

....

Q61: What is the limit as n tends to infinity?

....

Q62: Find the next four terms in the recurrence relation $u_{n+1} = -1 \cdot 5u_n + 60$ with $u_0 = 4$.

a) $u_1 = ?$

b) $u_2 = ?$

c) $u_3 = ?$

d) $u_4 = ?$

....

Q63: Explain why this recurrence relation does not have a limit as n tends to infinity.

Recurrence relations (Limits)

A sequence is defined by the recurrence relation $u_{n+1} = 0 \cdot 7u_n + 8$ with first term u_1.

Q64: Does this sequence have a limit as n tends to infinity?

....

Q65: What is the exact value of this limit?

Limits of recurrence relations

Trees are spayed weekly with the pesticide, 'Killpest', whose manufacturers claim it will destroy 61% of all pests.
Between the weekly sprayings it is estimated that 600 new pests invade the trees.

A new pesticide, 'Pestkill', comes onto the market. The manufacturers claim it will destroy 79% of existing pests but it is estimated that 720 new pests per week will invade the trees.

Which pesticide will be more effective in the long term?

Q66: Using "Killpest", how many pests will remain in the trees in the long term?

....

Q67: Using "Pestkill", how many pests will remain in the trees in the long term?

....

Q68: Which pesticide will be more effective in the long term?

Recurrence relations

An office worker has 50 folders on his desk ready to be filed. Each hour he manages to file 76 percent of the folders.
However, another 40 are also added to his pile each hour.

How many folders does he have on his desk after 5 hours and how many folders can he expect to have on his desk in the long term?

Q69: Letting F_n represent the number of folders on his desk after n hours, what is the recurrence relation that models this situation?

....

Q70: How many folders does he have on his desk after 5 hours?

....

Q71: In the long term, how many folders should he expect to have on his desk?

3.4 Solving recurrence relations

Example

Problem:

The recurrence relation $A_{n+1} = kA_n + 6$ has the same limit as the recurrence relation $B_{n+1} = -0 \cdot 8B_n + 18$ as $n \Rightarrow \infty$.

Find the value of k.

Solution:

We know that a limit exists so we can find the limit for B because $-1 < -0 \cdot 8 < 1$.

$$L_B = \frac{b}{1 - a}$$

$$L_B = \frac{18}{1 - (-0\cdot8)}$$

$$L_B = \frac{18}{1\cdot8} = 10$$

The formula for the limit of A is:

$$L_A = \frac{6}{1 - k} \quad but\ we\ know\ that\ L_A = 10\ so$$

$$10 = \frac{6}{1 - k}$$

$$10(1 - k) = 6$$

$$10 - 10k = 6$$

$$-10k = -4$$

$$k = 0\cdot4$$

Be sure you can do this calculation without a calculator.

Notice that $-1 < k < 1$ so we know that our answer lies in the range of values for which there is a limit.

Examples

1. Problem:

Given the recurrence relation $u_{n+1} = au_n + b$ with $u_1 = 2$, $u_2 = 7$ and $u_3 = 17$:

a) Find the values of a and b.

b) Calculate u_5.

Solution:

a) From the recurrence relation $u_{n+1} = au_n + b$ we can write an equation for u_2 using u_1 and an equation for u_3 using u_2.

$$u_2 = au_1 + b \qquad\qquad u_3 = au_2 + b$$

$$7 = 2a + b \qquad\qquad 17 = 7a + b$$

This gives us a pair of simultaneous equations to solve.

$$2a + b = 7 \quad \times\ -1$$

$$7a + b = 17$$

$$-2a - b = -7$$

$$+ \quad 7a + b = 17$$

$$\overline{\qquad\qquad\qquad}$$

$$5a = 10$$

$$a = 2$$

Let $a = 2$ in $2a + b = 7$ gives,

$2 \times 2 + b = 7$

$4 + b = 7$

$b = 3$

Hence, the recurrence relation is $u_{n+1} = 2u_n + 3$

b) Given the recurrence relation $u_{n+1} = 2u_n + 3$ and $u_3 = 17$ then

$u_4 = 2 \times 17 + 3 = 37$

$u_5 = 2 \times 37 + 3 = 77$

Thus $u_5 = 77$

. . . .

2. Problem:

Garry saved the same amount each month to a fixed rate savings account where no withdrawals were allowed during a fixed term.

The fixed rate of interest was paid monthly and the amount in his bank at the end of three consecutive months were £402, £642·20, £906·32.

What was the interest rate and the amount that he saved each month?

Solution:

The recurrence relation can be expressed as $u_{n+1} = au_n + b$ where a is the compound interest as a decimal and b is his monthly savings.

We can make $u_1 = 402$, $u_2 = 642 \cdot 20$ and $u_3 = 906 \cdot 42$.

From the recurrence relation $u_{n+1} = au_n + b$ we can write an equation for u_2 using u_1 and an equation for u_3 using u_2.

$$u_2 = au_1 + b \qquad\qquad u_3 = au_2 + b$$
$$642 \cdot 20 = 402a + b \qquad\qquad 906 \cdot 42 = 642 \cdot 20a + b$$

This gives us a pair of simultaneous equations.

$402a + b = 642 \cdot 20 \quad \times \;\; -1$

$642 \cdot 20a + b = 906 \cdot 42$

$-402a - b = -642 \cdot 20$

$+ \quad 642 \cdot 20a + b = 906 \cdot 42$

$\overline{\qquad 240 \cdot 20a = 264 \cdot 22}$

$a = 1 \cdot 1$

Let $a = 1 \cdot 1$ in $402a + b = 642 \cdot 20$ gives,

$402 \times 1 \cdot 1 + b = 642 \cdot 20$

$442 \cdot 20 + b = 642 \cdot 20$

$b = 200$

Since $a = 1 \cdot 1$ that equates to compound interest of 110% and an increase of 10%.

Hence his monthly savings are £200 and the interest rate is 10%.

Solving recurrence relations exercise   Go online

Finding a and b

Given the recurrence relation $u_{n+1} = au_n + b$ with $u_1 = -2$, $u_2 = -17$ and $u_3 = -92$ find a and b.

Q72: Let $n = 1$ then $u_{n+1} = au_n + b$ becomes $u_2 = au_1 + b$ hence $-17 = ?$
Give your answer in terms of a and b.

. . . .

Q73: Let $n = 2$ then $u_{n+1} = au_n + b$ becomes $u_3 = au_2 + b$ hence $-92 = ?$

. . . .

Q74: Using your answers to the previous questions solve the simultaneous equations to find a and b.

Recurrence relations

Given the recurrence relation $u_{n+1} = au_n + b$

Q75: Find a and b when $u_1 = 9200$, $u_2 = 7400$ and $u_3 = 6050$.

. . . .

Q76: Hence what is $u_0 = ?$

. . . .

Q77: What is the limit L of the sequence as n tends to infinity?

. . . .

Q78:
A recurrence relation is given as $u_{n+1} = 2u_n + b$ with $u_0 = 1$ and $u_2 = 58$.
What is the value of b?

A mushroom bed contains 6000 mushrooms on the first morning.
Each day x percent of the mushrooms are picked and each night another y mushrooms are ready for picking.
On the second and third days there are 1600 then 720 mushrooms ready to be picked.

Q79:
The recurrence relation that describes the number of mushrooms that are ready to be picked is $u_{n+1} = au_n + b$
What are the values of a and b?

. . . .

Q80: If x percent of mushrooms are picked each day.
What is the value of x?

. . . .

Q81: Each night another y mushrooms become ready to be picked.
What is the value of y?

Solving recurrence relations

Two sequences are defined by the recurrence relations:

1. $u_{n+1} = 0 \cdot 5u_n + x$ with $u_0 = 20$
2. $v_{n+1} = 0 \cdot 1v_n + y$ with $v_0 = 10$

Q82: What is the limit of sequence 1 in terms of x?

. . . .

Q83: What is the limit of sequence 2 in terms of y?

. . . .

Q84: Express x in terms of y.

3.5   Learning points

- A sequence is a series of numbers or terms with a definite pattern. A sequence can be defined by a rule or a formula for the nth term.

- A recurrence relation describes a sequence in which each term is a function of the previous term or terms.

- A geometric sequence takes the form $u_{n+1} = au_n$

  ◦ The nth term can be written as $u_n = a^n u_0$

- An arithmetic sequence takes the form $u_{n+1} = u_n + b$

  ◦ The nth term can be written as $u_n = u_0 + nb$

- A linear recurrence relation is a sequence defined by $u_{n+1} = au_n + b, a \neq 0$

- For the linear recurrence relation $u_{n+1} = au_n + b$, a limit exists if $-1 < a < 1$

- The limit is given by the formula $L = \frac{b}{1-a}$ or $L = \frac{c}{1-m}$

3.5.1 Leonardo Pisano Fibonacci

You may remember we saw a Fibonacci sequence earlier in the section Simple Recurrence Relations.

Fibonacci was born in 1170 and died in 1250 in Italy. Fibonacci is actually a nickname, his real name being Leonardo Pisano. He also sometimes called himself Bigollo, which may mean either a traveller or a good-for-nothing.

Although born in Italy he was educated in North Africa where his father held a diplomatic post. He travelled extensively with his father and grew to appreciate the different mathematical counting systems in the countries they visited.

When Fibonacci was about 30 he returned to Pisa and began writing a number of important texts. These include *Liber abbaci*(1202), *Practica geometriae*(1220), *Flos*(1225) and *Liber quadratorium*. It is remarkable that copies of these texts still exist, as Fibonacci lived in the days before printing, so his books were handwritten and the only way to have a copy was to have another handwritten version made.

Liber abbaci was based on the arithmetic and algebra that Fibonacci had observed during his travels. This book introduced the decimal system and the use of Arabic numerals into Europe. Linear simultaneous equations were presented in this text. It contains problems related to the price of goods and how to calculate profit. It detailed how to convert between various Mediterranean currencies. It also introduced the Fibonacci sequence which arises from the following problem and for which Fibonacci is probably best remembered today.

"A certain man put a pair of rabbits in a place surrounded on all sides by a wall. How many pairs of rabbits can be produced from that pair if it is supposed that every month each pair begets a new pair which from the second month on becomes productive?"

Practica geometriae contains a large collection of geometry problems. It also includes practical information for surveyors and demonstrates how to calculate the height of tall objects using similar triangles.

Flos provides an account of Fibonacci's solution to the root of the equation:

$10x + 2x^2 + x^3 = 20$, which comes from a book by Omar Khayyam on algebra. Fibonacci gives an approximate solution in sexagesimal notation as $1.22.7.42.33.4.40$ (this is $1 + \frac{22}{60} + \frac{7}{60^2} + \frac{42}{60^3} + \cdots$) which converts to the decimal $1 \cdot 3688081075$. This is correct to nine decimal places and was a remarkable achievement at that time.

Liber quadratorium means the book of squares and is considered as Fibonacci's most impressive work. It is a number theory book and includes methods for finding Pythagorean triples.

3.6 End of topic test

End of topic 7 test   Go online

A store replenishes 15% of it's stock at the end of each month.
During the course of each month 2500 items are sold.
At the end of this month there are 12000 items in the store.

Q85: Which of these is the correct recurrence relation for the number of items in stock after stock has been replenished at the end of each month?

a) $u_{n+1} = 0 \cdot 15u_n + 2500, u_0 = 12000$

b) $u_{n+1} = 1 \cdot 15u_n + 2500, u_0 = 12000$

c) $u_{n+1} = 0 \cdot 85u_n - 2500, u_0 = 12000$

d) $u_{n+1} = 1 \cdot 15u_n - 2500, u_0 = 12000$

. . . .

Q86: How many items will be in stock after 6 months?

A "pick your own" soft fruit grower estimates that during the summer 60 kg of strawberries will ripen each day and that 72% of the ripe strawberries will be picked.
It was estimated that on the first day of fruit picking, 5000 kg of strawberries were ripe and ready for picking.

Q87: Which of these is the correct recurrence relation for the weight of ripe fruit?

a) $u_{n+1} = 0 \cdot 72u_n + 60, u_0 = 5000$

b) $u_{n+1} = 1 \cdot 72u_n + 60, u_0 = 5000$

c) $u_{n+1} = 0 \cdot 28u_n + 60, u_0 = 5000$

d) $u_{n+1} = 1 \cdot 72u_n - 60, u_0 = 5000$

. . . .

Q88: What is the estimated weight of ripe strawberries available for picking after one week?

A gardener feeds her geraniums with "Growtall" plant food.
Each week the amount of plant food in the geraniums drops by about 65% and each week the gardener applies another 4 grams of "Growtall" to each plant.

Q89: If G_n represents the amount of "Growtall" plant food present in the plant after n weeks, what is the recurrence relation for G_{n+1}?

a) $G_{n+1} = 0 \cdot 96G_n + 65$

b) $G_{n+1} = 0 \cdot 35G_n + 4$

c) $G_{n+1} = 0 \cdot 04G_n + 65$

d) $G_{n+1} = 0 \cdot 65G_n + 4$

. . . .

Q90: What is the limit of this recurrence relation?
Give your answer correct to 1 d.p

. . . .

Q91: Explain what the limit means in the context of this question.

At a university students form a queue to buy food at the canteen.
Every 10 minutes 70% of the queue are served.
Also, every 10 minutes another 17 students join the queue.

Q92: If S_n represents the number of students in the queue after $10n$ minutes, what is the recurrence relation for S_{n+1}?

   a) $S_{n+1} = 0 \cdot 3S_n + 17$
   b) $S_{n+1} = 0 \cdot 17S_n + 70$
   c) $S_{n+1} = 0 \cdot 83S_n + 70$
   d) $S_{n+1} = 0 \cdot 7S_n + 17$

. . . .

Q93: What is the limit of this recurrence relation?
Give your answer correct to 1 d.p

. . . .

Q94: Explain what the limit means in the context of this question.

Two sequences are defined by the recurrence relations:

   1. $G_{n+1} = 4 \cdot 8G_n + 0 \cdot 4$ with $G_0 = 80$

   2. $K_{n+1} = 0 \cdot 3K_n + 11$ with $K_0 = 0$

Q95: Which of the above recurrence relations approaches a limit as n tends to infinity?

. . . .

Q96: What is the necessary condition for the recurrence relation $u_{n+1} = au_n + b$ to approach a limit as n tends to infinity.

   a) $-1 < b < 1$
   b) $-1 < a < 1$
   c) $b > 1$
   d) $a > 1$

. . . .

Q97: What is the exact value of the limit?

Biologists calculate that, when the concentration of a particular chemical in a sea loch reaches 5 milligrams per litre (mg/l), the level of pollution endangers the life of the fish.
A factory wishes to release waste containing this chemical into the loch.
It is claimed that the discharge will not endanger the fish.

The Local Authority is supplied with the following information:

1. The loch contains none of this chemical at present.

2. The factory manager has applied to discharge waste once per week which will result in an increase in concentration of 2·8 mg/l of the chemical in the loch.

3. The natural tidal action will remove 42% of the chemical from the loch every week.

Q98: The recurrence relation that describes the amount of chemical in the loch can be written as?

a) $C_{n+1} = 0 \cdot 58C_n - 2 \cdot 8$

b) $C_{n+1} = 0 \cdot 42C_n - 2 \cdot 8$

c) $C_{n+1} = 0 \cdot 42C_n + 2 \cdot 8$

d) $C_{n+1} = 0 \cdot 58C_n + 2 \cdot 8$

. . . .

Q99: Calculate the amount of chemical that would remain in the loch in the long term.
Give your answer in mg/l (to 1 d.p.).

. . . .

Q100: Are the fish endangered?

. . . .

Q101: The company agrees to install a cleaning process that reduces the concentration of chemical released into the loch by 30%.
What is the revised recurrence relation is now?

a) $C_{n+1} = 0 \cdot 28C_n + 2 \cdot 8$

b) $C_{n+1} = 0 \cdot 58C_n + 1 \cdot 96$

c) $C_{n+1} = 0 \cdot 28C_n - 2 \cdot 8$

d) $C_{n+1} = 0 \cdot 42C_n + 1 \cdot 96$

. . . .

Q102: What is the amount of chemical that remains in the loch in the long term with the revised concentration of chemical?
Give your answer to 1 d.p.

. . . .

Q103: Should the Local Authority grant permission?

The level of silt in a harbour just after high tide is 0·3 metres at present.
A dredger manages to clear 80% of the silt in between high tides.
However, each high tide another 1 metre of silt is deposited.

Q104: Using D_n for the level of silt in the harbour after n high tides, what is the recurrence relation for D_{n+1}?

a) $D_{n+1} = 0 \cdot 2D_n + 0 \cdot 3$
b) $D_{n+1} = 0 \cdot 8D_n + 0 \cdot 3$
c) $D_{n+1} = 0 \cdot 8D_n + 1$
d) $D_{n+1} = 0 \cdot 2D_n + 1$

....

Q105: How many metres of silt are there in the harbour after 4 high tides?
Give your answer to 2 d.p.

....

Q106:

To keep the harbour open to fishing boats the level of silt must not exceed 2 metres.

Will the harbour remain open? Explain your answer.

The sand on a beach is combed each night for rubbish which results in $3/4$ of the rubbish being removed.
However, each day sunbathers drop around 60 kg more rubbish in total.
There are u_n kilograms of rubbish on the beach at the start of a particular day.

Q107: What is the recurrence relation for u_{n+1}, the amount of rubbish on the beach at the start of the next day?

a) $u_{n+1} = 3/4u_n - 60$
b) $u_{n+1} = 1/4u_n + 60$
c) $u_{n+1} = 3/4u_n + 60$
d) $u_{n+1} = 1/4u_n - 60$

....

Q108: What is the limit of the sequence generated by this recurrence relation?

....

Q109: Explain what the limit means in the context of this question.

Q110: What is the recurrence relation for u_{n+1}, the amount of screen wash in her car at the start of the next month?

a) $u_{n+1} = \frac{1}{5}u_n - 1$

b) $u_{n+1} = \frac{4}{5}u_n - 1$

c) $u_{n+1} = \frac{4}{5}u_n + 1$

d) $u_{n+1} = \frac{1}{5}u_n + 1$

....

Q111: What is the limit of the sequence generated by this recurrence relation?

....

Q112: Explain what the limit means in the context of this question.

A sequence is defined by the recurrence relation $u_{n+1} = au_n + b$ and $u_0 = 5$.

Q113: What is u_1 in terms of a and b?

....

Q114: What is u_2 in terms of a and b?

A sequence is defined by the recurrence relation $u_{n+1} = 0 \cdot 3u_n + 2$ and $u_0 = 75$.

Q115: What is the smallest value of n for which $u_n < 3$?

Topic 4

Integration

Contents

Learning objective

By the end of this topic, you should be able to:

- integrate:
    - algebraic expressions;
    - trigonometric expressions;
    - composite functions;
- solve differential equations;
- calculate definite integrals;
- find the area between:
    - a curve and the x-axis;
    - two curves;
- determine and use a function from a given rate of change.

4.1   Integrating algebraic expressions

Reversing the process of differentiation is called anti-differentiation or integration.

If we work backwards and ask ourselves which function or functions have the derivative $4x - 5$? One answer could be $2x^2 - 5x$ but there are others e.g. $2x^2 - 5x + 1$, $2x^2 - 5x - 8$, $2x^2 - 5x + 19$, . . .

The reason why all these functions have the same derivative is because the constant on the end disappears when we differentiate. All of the above answers are anti-derivatives of $4x - 5$ along with many more. We take account of the unknown constant by adding C to the anti-derivative or integral.

Examples

1. Problem:

If $f'(x) = 7$, what was $f(x)$?

Solution:

$f(x) = 7x + C$

....

2. Problem:

If $f'(x) = x$, what was $f(x)$?

Solution:

$f(x) = \frac{x^2}{2} + C$

....

3. Problem:

If $f'(x) = 6x^2$, what was $f(x)$?

Solution:

$f(x) = \dfrac{6x^3}{3} + C$

$\quad\ = 2x^3 + C$

....

4. Problem:

If $f'(x) = 4x^3$, what was $f(x)$?

Solution:

$f(x) = \dfrac{4x^4}{4} + C$

$\quad\ = x^4 + C$

Key point

The notation for finding an integral is $\int x^n dx = \frac{x^{n+1}}{n+1} + C$, where $n \neq -1$ and C is the constant of integration.

The German mathematician Gottfried Leibniz devised the notation used for integration.

Top tip

In general terms $\int f(x)\, dx = F(x) + C$ where $F(x)$ is the anti-derivative of $f(x)$. $f(x)$ is called the integrand, $F(x)$ is called the integral and C is the constant of integration. This is an indefinite integral.

Integration example   Go online

$$\int 4\, dx = \int 4x^0\, dx \qquad \text{Remember } x^0 = 1$$

$$= 4 \int x^0\, dx$$

$$= 4\frac{x^1}{1} + C$$

$$= 4x + C$$

Examples

1. Problem:

Find $\int 2x^4\, dx$.

Solution:

$\int 2x^4\, dx = 2 \int x^4\, dx = \frac{2x^5}{5} + C$

. . . .

2. Problem:

Find $\int 4x^{-3}\, dx$, $x \neq 0$.

Solution:

$$\int 4x^{-3}\, dx = 4 \int x^{-3}\, dx = \frac{4x^{-2}}{-2}$$

$$= -2x^{-2} + C$$

$$= -\frac{2}{x^2} + C$$

. . . .

3. Problem:

Find $\int x^{\frac{2}{3}}\, dx$.

Solution:

$$
\begin{aligned}
\int x^{\frac{2}{3}}\, dx &= \frac{x^{\frac{2}{3}+1}}{\frac{2}{3}+1} + C \\
&= \frac{x^{\frac{5}{3}}}{\frac{5}{3}} + C \\
&= x^{\frac{5}{3}} \times \frac{3}{5} + C \\
&= \frac{3\sqrt[3]{x^5}}{5} + C
\end{aligned}
$$

Integration   Go online

$$
\begin{aligned}
\int x^{-3}\, dx &= \frac{x^{-3+1}}{-3+1} + C \\
&= -\frac{x^{-2}}{2} + C \\
&= -\frac{1}{2x^2} + C
\end{aligned}
$$

Key point

$$
\begin{aligned}
\int ax^n\, dx &= a\int x^n dx \\
&= \frac{ax^{n+1}}{n+1} + C
\end{aligned}
$$

where $n \neq -1$, a is a constant and C is the constant of integration.

Top tip

A good way to remember how to integrate is to:

1. write down the term;

2. increase the power by 1;

3. divide by the new power;

4. simplify your answer if you can.

Integrating algebraic expressions exercise   Go online

Q1: Find $\int x^9\, dx$

. . . .

Q2: Find $\int t^{10}\, dt$

....

Q3: Find $\int x^{-3}\, dx$

....

Q4: Find $\int x^{\frac{4}{9}}\, dx$

....

Q5: Find $\int x^{\frac{-2}{7}}\, dx$

....

Q6: Find $\int x^{\frac{-5}{2}}\, dx$

....

Q7: Find $\int 3x^3\, dx$

....

Q8: Find $\int -6\, dx$

....

Q9: Find $\int 3x^{-2}\, dx$

....

Q10: Find $\int 9x^{-3}\, dx$

....

Q11: Find $\int 11x^{\frac{8}{3}}\, dx$

4.2   Integrating algebraic expressions with multiple terms

Key point

To integrate expressions with multiple terms, each term must be expressed in the form ax^n.

Examples

1. Problem:

Find $\int 3x^2 + 2x - 1\, dx$

Solution:

Integrate each term in turn.

$$\int 3x^2 \, dx \; + \; \int 2x \, dx \; - \; \int 1 \, dx \; = \; \frac{3x^3}{3} + \frac{2x^2}{2} - 1x + C$$

$$= \; x^3 + x^2 - x + C$$

. . . .

2. Problem:

Find $\int \frac{1}{x^2} + \sqrt{x} \, dx$, $x \neq 0$

Solution:

Step 1: Separate the terms and express each one in the form ax^n.

$$\int \frac{1}{x^2} + \sqrt{x} \, dx \; = \; \int \frac{1}{x^2} \, dx + \int \sqrt{x} \, dx$$

$$= \; \int x^{-2} \, dx + \int x^{\frac{1}{2}} \, dx$$

Step 2: Integrate each term in turn.

$$= \; \frac{x^{-1}}{-1} + \frac{x^{\frac{1}{2} + 1}}{\frac{1}{2} + 1} + C$$

$$= \; -\frac{1}{x} + \frac{2}{3}x^{\frac{3}{2}} + C$$

Step 3: Simplify the fractional indices.

$$= \; -\frac{1}{x} + \frac{2\sqrt{x^3}}{3} + C$$

. . . .

3. Problem:

Find $\int \frac{9}{\sqrt[8]{t^5}} - \frac{1}{2} \, dt$, $t \neq 0$

Solution:

Step 1: Separate the terms and express each one in the form ax^n.

$$\int \frac{9}{\sqrt[8]{t^5}} - \frac{1}{2} \, dt \; = \; \int \frac{9}{\sqrt[8]{t^5}} \, dt - \int \frac{1}{2} \, dt$$

$$= \; \int 9t^{-\frac{5}{8}} \, dt - \int \frac{1}{2} \, dt$$

Step 2: Integrate each term in turn.

$$= \; \frac{9t^{\frac{3}{8}}}{\frac{3}{8}} - \frac{1}{2}t + C$$

$$= \; 9t^{\frac{3}{8}} \times \frac{8}{3} - \frac{1}{2}t + C$$

$$= \; 24t^{\frac{3}{8}} - \frac{1}{2}t + C$$

Step 3: Simplify the fractional indices.

$$= \; 24\sqrt[8]{t^3} - \frac{t}{2} + C$$

Integrating algebraic expressions with multiple terms exercise   Go online

Q12: Find $\int 4 - x^{-\frac{3}{2}}\, dx, x \neq 0$

a) $\frac{2}{\sqrt{x}} + C$

b) $4x - 2\sqrt{x^3} + C$

c) $4x + \frac{2}{\sqrt{x}} + C$

d) $4x - 2\sqrt{x} + C$

....

Q13: Find $\int 15x^{-6} + 4x^4 + 12\, dx$

....

Q14: Find $\int 7 - 2x^{\frac{-8}{9}}\, dx$

....

Q15: Find $\int \frac{8}{x^5}\, dx$

....

Q16: Find $\int \left(\sqrt{x}\right)^7\, dx$

....

Q17: Find $\int \frac{1}{7x^{12}}\, dx$

a) $\frac{-7}{11x^{11}}$

b) $\frac{-1}{77x^{11}}$

c) $\frac{-1}{77x^{-11}}$

d) $\frac{-7}{11x^{-11}}$

4.3   Integrating products and quotients

Key point

To integrate more complex functions, the integrand must be expressed as the sum of individual terms each given in the form ax^n.

Integrating products   Go online

Find $\int (2p - 3)^2\, dp$

We need to simplify the expression before we can integrate.

$$\int (2p - 3)^2 \, dp = \int (2p - 3)(2p - 3) \, dp$$
$$= \int 4p^2 - 12p + 9 \, dp$$

Now we can integrate the expression.

$$\int (2p - 3)^2 \, dp = \int (2p - 3)(2p - 3) \, dp$$
$$= \int 4p^2 - 12p + 9 \, dp$$
$$= \frac{4p^3}{3} - 6p^2 + 9p + C$$

Integrating quotients

Go online

Find $\int \frac{u^2 + 2}{\sqrt{u}} \, du$

Simplify the expression before integrating.

$$\int \frac{u^2 + 2}{\sqrt{u}} \, du = \int \frac{u^2}{\sqrt{u}} + \frac{2}{\sqrt{u}} \, du$$
$$= \int \frac{u^2}{u^{\frac{1}{2}}} + \frac{2}{u^{\frac{1}{2}}} \, du$$
$$= \int u^{\frac{3}{2}} + 2u^{-\frac{1}{2}} \, du$$

Now we can integrate the expression.

$$\int \frac{u^2 + 2}{\sqrt{u}} \, du = \int \frac{u^2}{\sqrt{u}} + \frac{2}{\sqrt{u}} \, du$$
$$= \int \frac{u^2}{u^{\frac{1}{2}}} + \frac{2}{u^{\frac{1}{2}}} \, du$$
$$= \int u^{\frac{3}{2}} + 2u^{-\frac{1}{2}} \, du$$
$$= \frac{2u^{\frac{5}{2}}}{5} + 4u^{\frac{1}{2}} + C$$
$$= \frac{2\sqrt{u^5}}{5} + 4\sqrt{u} + C$$

Integrating products and quotients exercise

Go online

Q18: Find $\int (2t + 1)^2 \, dt$

. . . .

Q19: Find $\int \sqrt{u} \left(u^2 + 6 \right) \, du$

. . . .

Q20: Find $\int \frac{x^3 - 6x^8}{x^5} \, dx$, $\quad x \neq 0$

....

Q21: Find $\int \frac{t + \sqrt{t^5}}{\sqrt{t^3}} \, dt$, $\quad t \neq 0$

4.4   Integrating trigonometric and composite functions

We already know how to differentiate trigonometric and composite functions. In the following sections we will learn how to integrate trigonometric and composite functions.

4.4.1   Integration of sin and cos

Try the activity to see if you can find the anti-derivatives or integrals of sin and cos.

Integration of sin x and cos x   Go online

Using the following terms complete the questions below.

$\cos x + c$	$-\sin x + c$	$-\cos x + c$	$\sin x + c$
$-\cos x$	$-\sin x$	$\cos x$	$\sin x$

Q22: We have already seen that:

a) $\frac{d}{dx} (\sin x) = $ _____

b) $\frac{d}{dx} (\cos x) = $ _____

....

Q23: Since integration is the reverse process to differentiation, it therefore follows that:

a) $\int \cos x \, dx = $ _____

b) $\int \sin x \, dx = $ _____

Key point

Remember just as with differentiation x must be measured in radians.

Examples

1. Problem:

Find $\int 8 + 3 \sin x \, dx$

Solution:

$\int 8 + 3 \sin x \, dx = 8x - 3 \cos x + C$

. . . .

2. Problem:

Find $\int 4\sin\theta + 5\cos\theta \, d\theta$

Solution:

$$\int 4\sin\theta + 5\cos\theta \, d\theta = 4\int \sin\theta + 5\int \cos\theta \, d\theta$$
$$= 4 \times (-\cos\theta) + 5 \times \sin\theta + C$$
$$= -4\cos\theta + 5\sin\theta + C$$

Look at the activity on trigonometric integrals to see how to integrate $\sin(ax + b)$ and $\cos(ax + b)$.

Trigonometric integrals Go online

We have seen that:

- $\frac{d}{dx} \sin(ax + b) = a\cos(ax + b)$

- $\frac{d}{dx} \cos(ax + b) = -a\sin(ax + b)$

Since integration is the reverse process to differentiation we can now write:

- $\int \cos(ax + b) \, dx = \frac{1}{a}\sin(ax + b)$

- $\int \sin(ax + b) \, dx = -\frac{1}{a}\cos(ax + b)$

Key point

$$\int \sin ax \, dx = -\frac{1}{a}\cos ax + C$$

$$\int \cos ax \, dx = \frac{1}{a}\sin ax + C$$

Examples

1. Problem:

Find $\int \cos(3x + 5) \, dx$

Solution:

$\int \cos(3x + 5) \, dx = \frac{1}{3}\sin(3x + 5) + C$

. . . .

2. Problem:

Find $\int 2\sin(1 - 6\theta) \, d\theta$

Solution:

$$\int 2\sin(1 - 6\theta) \, d\theta = 2 \int \sin(1 - 6\theta) \, d\theta$$

$$= 2 \times -\frac{1}{-6} \cos(1 - 6\theta) + C$$

$$= -\frac{2}{6} \cos(1 - 6\theta) + C$$

$$= -\frac{1}{3} \cos(1 - 6\theta) + C$$

3. Problem:

Knowing that $\cos^2 x = \frac{1}{2}(1 + \cos 2x)$, find $\int \cos^2 x \, dx$

Solution:

$$\int \cos^2 x \, dx = \int \frac{1}{2}(1 + \cos 2x) \, dx$$

$$= \frac{1}{2} \int (1 + \cos 2x) \, dx$$

$$= \frac{1}{2}\left(x + \frac{1}{2}\sin 2x\right) + C$$

$$= \frac{1}{2}x + \frac{1}{4}\sin 2x + C$$

Key point

$$\int \sin(ax + b) \, dx = -\frac{1}{a}\cos(ax + b)$$

$$\int \cos(ax + b) \, dx = \frac{1}{a}\sin(ax + b)$$

Integration of sin and cos exercise   Go online

Q24: What is $\int 9\cos x \, dx$?

....

Q25: What is $\int \pi \sin t \, dt$?

....

Q26: What is $\int \frac{6}{\sqrt{u}} - \sin u \, du$?

....

Q27: What is $\int \frac{\cos x}{4} + \sqrt{7}\sin x - \pi \, dx$?

....

Q28: What is $\int \sin 2x \, dx$?

....

Q29: What is $\int \cos\left(7x + 6\right) dx$?

....

Q30: What is $\int \sin\left(4x + 5\right) dx$?

....

Q31: What is $\int 6\cos\left(4x + \frac{\pi}{4}\right) dx$?

....

Q32: What is $\int 5\sin\left(\frac{x}{5} - \frac{\pi}{3}\right) dx$?

....

Q33: Use the double angle formula $\cos 2x = 1 - 2sin^2x$ to express $\sin 2x$ in terms of $\cos 2x$.

   a) What is $\sin^2 x$ in terms of $\cos 2x$?

   b) Hence what is $\int \sin^2x \, dx$?

4.4.2 Integrating composite functions

Integration   Go online

We have already seen that:

$$\frac{d}{dx}\left(ax + b\right)^{n+1} = a\left(n + 1\right)\left(ax + b\right)^n$$

Dividing both sides by $a(n + 1)$ we then have:

$$\frac{d}{dx}\frac{\left(ax + b\right)^{n+1}}{a\left(n + 1\right)} = \frac{a\left(n + 1\right)}{a\left(n + 1\right)}\left(ax + b\right)^n$$

$$\frac{d}{dx}\frac{\left(ax + b\right)^{n+1}}{a\left(n + 1\right)} = \left(ax + b\right)^n$$

Since integration is the reverse process to differentiation we can now write:

$$\int \left(ax + b\right)^n dx = \frac{\left(ax + b\right)^{n+1}}{a\left(n + 1\right)} + C \, , \quad n \neq -1$$

Top tip

It is easier to remember how to find $\int (ax + b)^n$ by following a few simple steps:

1. write down the bracket $(ax + b)$

2. increase the power by 1 $(ax + b)^{n+1}$

3. divide by the value of a multiplied by the new power $\frac{(ax + b)^{n+1}}{a(n+1)}$

4. remember to add C $\frac{(ax + b)^{n+1}}{a(n+1)} + C$

Examples

1. Problem:

Find $\int (4x + 3)^4 \, dx$

Solution:

$$\int (4x + 3)^4 \, dx = \frac{(4x + 3)^5}{4 \times 5} + C$$

$$= \frac{(4x + 3)^5}{20} + C$$

....

2. Problem:

Find $\int (2x + 5)^{\frac{3}{4}} \, dx$

Solution:

$$\int (2x + 5)^{\frac{3}{4}} \, dx = \frac{(2x + 5)^{\frac{7}{4}}}{2 \times \frac{7}{4}}$$

$$= \frac{(2x + 5)^{\frac{7}{4}}}{\frac{14}{4}} + C$$

$$= \frac{4}{14}(2x + 5)^{\frac{7}{4}} + C$$

$$= \frac{2}{7}(2x + 5)^{\frac{7}{4}} + C$$

....

3. Problem:

Find $\int \frac{1}{\sqrt{8t - 3}} \, dt$

Solution:

$$\int \frac{1}{\sqrt{8t - 3}} \, dt = \int (8t - 3)^{-\frac{1}{2}} \, dt$$

$$= \frac{(8t - 3)^{\frac{1}{2}}}{8 \times \frac{1}{2}} + C$$

$$= \frac{\sqrt{8t - 3}}{4} + C$$

Key point

Remember your expression must be in the form $(ax + b)^n$ before you can use this method of integration:

$$\int (ax + b)^n \, dx = \frac{(ax + b)^{n+1}}{a(n+1)} + C$$

Integrating composite functions exercise Go online

Q34: What is $\int (7x + 2)^3 \, dx$?

....

Q35: What is $\int (4x + 9)^{-2} \, dx$?

....

Q36: What is $\int (8x + 7)^{\frac{1}{4}} \, dx$?

....

Q37: What is $\int (8 - 3x)^{-\frac{2}{3}} \, dx$?

....

Q38: What is $\int \sqrt{2x + 7} \, dx$?

....

Q39: What is $\int \frac{1}{(4x + 1)^2} \, dx$?

....

Q40: What is $\int \frac{1}{\left(\sqrt{4x + 5}\right)^3} \, dx$?

....

Q41: When $\frac{ds}{dt} = (1 - 8t)^{-7}$, what is s?

4.5 Solving differential equations

$\frac{dy}{dx} = 2x^2 + 5$ and $\frac{ds}{dt} = 3t - 1$ are examples of differential equations.
This type of equation can usually be solved by integration.

Additional information is usually needed to find the constant of integration (i.e. the value of C).

Equation of a curve   Go online

Example

Problem:

The gradient of the tangent to a curve is given by the **differential equation** $dy/dx = 3x$
Find the equation of the curve.

Solution:

Solve this equation by integrating

$$y = \int \frac{dy}{dx}\, dx = \int 2x\, dx$$
$$y = x^2 + C$$

$y = x^2 + C$ gives a family of curves each of which satisfies the differential equation.

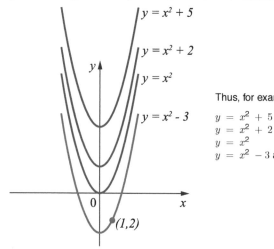

Thus, for example, the curves:

$$y = x^2 + 5$$
$$y = x^2 + 2$$
$$y = x^2$$
$$y = x^2 - 3 \text{ all satisfy } dy/dx = 2x$$

With more information one curve in particular can be identified. For example, given the initial condition that the curve passes through the point (1, -2) means that C can be identified and thus a particular curve.

Since the curve passes through the point (1, -2) then,

$$y = x^2 + C$$
$$-2 = 1^2 + C$$
$$\Rightarrow C = -3$$

Thus the curve that passes through the point (1, -2) has equation $y = x^2 - 3$

For a differential equation an initial condition is additional information required to determine a particular solution. This could be a coordinate on a curve, a velocity at $t = 0$, the amount of money in a bank account on 1st January, etc.

Examples

1. Problem:

Solve the differential equation $f'(x) = 3$, if $x = 0$ and $y = 4$.

Solution:

$$f(x) = \int 3 \, dx$$

$f(x) = 3x + C$ this is the general solution

Let $x = 0$ and $y = 4$.

$4 = 3 \times 0 + C$

$4 = C$

So the particular solution is $f(x) = 3x + 4$.

....

2. Problem:

The curve $y = f(x)$ is such that $\frac{dy}{dx} = 9x^2 - 2x$. The curve passes through the point (1,8).

Express y in terms of x.

Solution:

$$y = \int 9x^2 - 2x \, dx$$

$$y = \frac{9x^3}{3} - \frac{2x^2}{2} + C$$

$y = 3x^3 - x^2 + C$ this is the general solution

Let $x = 1$ and $y = 8$.

$8 = 3 \times 1^3 - 1^2 + C$

$8 = 2 + C$

$6 = C$

So the particular solution is $y = 3x^3 - x^2 + 6$.

....

3. Problem:

At the start of a race a cyclist accelerates so that his speed after t seconds is given by $v = t^2$ How far will he have travelled in the first 6 seconds?

Solution:

Remember velocity (or speed) is a rate of change of distance (or displacement) s at time t so the velocity, $v = \frac{ds}{dt}$ or $s'(t)$.

Let s represent the distance that the cyclist travels after t seconds then $v = \frac{ds}{dt} = t^2$.

The formula for the distance(s) is found by integrating

$$s = \int \frac{ds}{dt}\, dt = \int t^2\, dt$$

$$s = \frac{t^3}{3} + C$$

Since the cyclist has not moved at the start of the race then the initial condition is $s = 0$ when $t = 0$.

This gives $0 = \frac{0^3}{3} + C$ so $C = 0$ and the particular solution is $s = \frac{t^3}{3}$.

Also when $t = 6$, $s = \frac{6^3}{3} = 72\ metres$.

Thus the cyclist travels 72 metres in the first 6 seconds.

Solving differential equations exercise   Go online

Q42: Find the general solutions for each of these differential equations.

a) $\frac{dy}{dx} = 4x$

b) $\frac{ds}{dt} = 6t^2 - 5$

c) $\frac{dy}{dx} = 3 - x$

d) $\frac{ds}{dt} = \frac{t}{2} + 3t^2$

. . . .

Q43: Find the particular solutions for each of these differential equations.

a) $\frac{ds}{dt} = 5t$ and $s = 0$ when $t = 0$

b) $\frac{dy}{dx} = 3x^2 + x - 5$ and $y = 4$ when $x = 0$

c) $\frac{ds}{dt} = -3t^2 + t$ and $s = 0$ when $t = 2$

d) $\frac{dy}{dx} = 9\sqrt{x}$ and $y = 50$ when $x = 4$

. . . .

Q44: The gradient of the tangent to a curve is given by the differential equation: $\frac{dy}{dx} = 2x + 4$. The curve passes through the point (2, 9). Find the equation of the curve.

. . . .

Q45: Find the equation of the function $y = f(x)$ for which $\frac{dy}{dx} = \frac{x}{2} - 2$ and $f(2) = 0$

4.6 Calculating definite integrals

Many practical problems require the evaluation of an area.

Example

Problem:

A cyclist is travelling along a path at a steady speed of 8 metres/second. How far has she travelled after 5 seconds?

Solution:

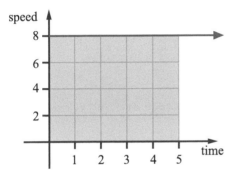

Distance = Speed × Time = 8 ms⁻¹ × 5 s = 40 metres

Note that the same answer can be obtained by calculating the area under the speed-time graph.

The cyclist will travel 40 metres in 5 seconds.

In general, it is true that the area under a speed-time graph represents distance travelled. This is easy to calculate when speed remains constant but is more complicated when speed varies.

Area under a curve   Go online

Example

Problem:

The speed of an aircraft accelerating along a straight stretch of runway is given by the formula $f(t) = 3t^2$.
How far has the aircraft travelled during the first four seconds?

Solution:

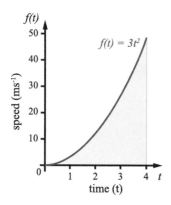

The shaded area in the graph shown here represents the distance travelled by the aircraft in the first 4 seconds. An estimate for this area can be obtained by dividing the shaded area into rectangles as follows.

This first estimate for the area under the curve gives:

$1 \times 3 = 3$
$1 \times 12 = 12 \times 1 \times 27 = 27$
Total area = 42

Clearly this answer is too small as there are large gaps under the curve that have not been included.

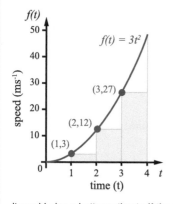

It would give a better estimate if the rectangles were half as wide and so fill up more of the space below the curve.

Note that the height of each rectangle is equal to the y-coordinate of a point on the curve. Thus when $x = 2 \cdot 5$ the height of the corresponding rectangle is $y = 3 \times (2 \cdot 5)^2 = 18 \cdot 375$

Adding up areas of rectangles of $width\ 0 \cdot 5 \times height$ gives **total area = 52·5**

Check this answer. It is more accurate but still too small.

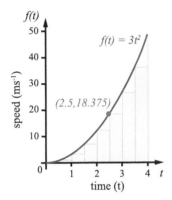

An even better estimate is obtained by making the rectangles even narrower. This time the base of the rectangle is 0·25 units wide.

Total area = 58·125

Again check this. This answer is the most accurate estimate so far. However, it will still be too small as there are uncounted gaps beneath the curve.

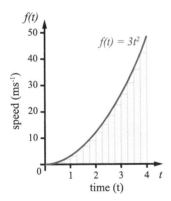

By increasing the number of rectangles the area can be found more accurately. The total area of the rectangles when there are 100 rectangles is 63·0432 square units. In fact the more rectangles that are used the nearer the total area approaches a limit of 64 square units. Thus the conclusion is that the aircraft travels a distance of 64 metres in the first 4 seconds of taking off.

Obviously it would be better if there was a quicker method for determining the area under the curve and thus the distance travelled. The questions in the next exercise will clarify this.

Area between a curve and the x-axis   Go online

The area between the graph of $y = f(x)$ and the x-axis from $x = a$ to $x = b$ can be calculated as the area from $x = 0$ to $x = b$ minus the area from $x = 0$ to $x = a$

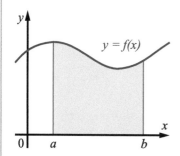

Thus if $F(x)$ is an anti-derivative of $f(x)$ then,

$$\int_a^b f(x)\ dx = (F(b) + C) - (F(a) + C)$$

$$= F(b) - F(a) \qquad (a \leqslant x \leqslant b)$$

This result is known as the **fundamental theorem of calculus**.

Note that C is cancelled out when calculating a definite integral.

Example

Problem:

What is the value of $\int_1^4 2x^2\ dx$?

Solution:

$$\int_1^4 2x^2\ dx = \left[\frac{2x^3}{3}\right]_1^4$$

$$= \left(\frac{2 \times 4^3}{3}\right) - \left(\frac{2 \times 1^3}{3}\right)$$

$$= \frac{128}{3} - \frac{2}{3}$$

$$= \frac{126}{3}$$

$$= 42$$

Top tip

Try entering $\left(\frac{2 \times 4^3}{3}\right) - \left(\frac{2 \times 1^3}{3}\right)$ in your calculator, using brackets and the fraction button, you should get 42.

Practice entering definite integrals into your calculator.

This can save you time in the exam.

Examples

1. Problem:

What is the value of $\int_1^2 (2x + 3)^2 \, dx$?

Solution:

$$\int_1^2 (2x + 3)^2 \, dx = \left[\frac{(2x + 3)^3}{2 \times 3}\right]_1^2$$

$$= \left(\frac{(2 \times 2 + 3)^3}{6}\right) - \left(\frac{(2 \times 1 + 3)^3}{6}\right)$$

$$= \frac{343}{6} - \frac{125}{6}$$

$$= \frac{218}{6}$$

$$= \frac{109}{3}$$

$$= 36\frac{1}{3}$$

Remember if you can enter $\left(\frac{(2 \times 2 + 3)^3}{6}\right) - \left(\frac{(2 \times 1 + 3)^3}{6}\right)$ in your calculator and get $\frac{109}{3}$ you can miss out some of the working.

. . . .

2. Problem:

What is the value of $\int_0^{\frac{\pi}{6}} 5\cos 2x \, dx$?

Solution:

$$\int_0^{\frac{\pi}{6}} 5\cos 2x \, dx = \left[5 \times \frac{1}{2}\sin 2x\right]_0^{\frac{\pi}{6}}$$

$$= \left(\frac{5}{2}\sin 2 \times \frac{\pi}{6}\right) - \left(\frac{5}{2}\sin 2 \times 0\right)$$

$$= \left(\frac{5}{2}\sin \frac{\pi}{3}\right) - \left(\frac{5}{2}\sin 0\right)$$

$$= \frac{5}{2} \times \frac{\sqrt{3}}{2} - 0$$

$$= \frac{5\sqrt{3}}{4}$$

Notice that the integral is in radians, this is essential.

. . . .

---

3. Problem:

What is the value of a when $\int_{-1}^{a} 3x^2 \, dx = 9$?

Solution:

$$\int_{-1}^{a} 3x^2 \, dx = \left[\frac{3x^3}{3}\right]_{-1}^{a} \quad \text{or} \quad \left[x^3\right]_{-1}^{a}$$

$$= a^3 - (-1)^3$$

$$= a^3 + 1$$

We know that $\int_{-1}^{a} 3x^2 \, dx = 9$ so,

$$a^3 + 1 = 9$$

$$a^3 = 8$$

$$a = 2$$

. . . .

4. Problem:

Evaluate $\int_{1/2}^{3/2} 3 + 2x - 3x^2 \, dx$.

Solution:

$$\int_{1/2}^{3/2} 3 + 2x - 3x^2 \, dx = \left[3x + \frac{2x^2}{2} - \frac{3x^3}{3}\right]_{1/2}^{3/2}$$

$$= \left[3x + x^2 - x^3\right]_{1/2}^{3/2}$$

$$= \left(3 \times \frac{3}{2} + \left(\frac{3}{2}\right)^2 - \left(\frac{3}{2}\right)^3\right) - \left(3 \times \frac{1}{2} + \left(\frac{1}{2}\right)^2 - \left(\frac{1}{2}\right)^3\right)$$

$$= \left(\frac{9}{2} + \frac{9}{4} - \frac{27}{8}\right) - \left(\frac{3}{2} + \frac{1}{4} - \frac{1}{8}\right)$$

$$= \frac{6}{2} + \frac{8}{4} - \frac{26}{8}$$

$$= 3 + 2 - \frac{13}{4}$$

$$= 5 - 3\frac{1}{4}$$

$$= 1\frac{3}{4}$$

. . . .

5. Problem:

Evaluate $\int_{-1}^{\sqrt{3}} x^3 + 4x \, dx$.

Solution:

$$\int_{-1}^{\sqrt{3}} x^3 + 4x \; dx = \left[\frac{x^4}{4} + \frac{4x^2}{2} \right]_{-1}^{\sqrt{3}}$$

$$= \left[\frac{x^4}{4} + 2x^2 \right]_{-1}^{\sqrt{3}}$$

$$= \left(\frac{(\sqrt{3})^4}{4} + 2\left(\sqrt{3}\right)^2 \right) - \left(\frac{(-1)^4}{4} + 2(-1)^2 \right)$$

$$= \left(\frac{9}{4} + 6 \right) - \left(\frac{1}{4} + 2 \right)$$

$$= \frac{8}{4} + 4$$

$$= 6$$

Remember it is essential that you can evaluate definite integrals with and without a calculator.

Key point

The area between the graph of $f(x)$ and the x-axis from $x = a$ to $x = b$ can be calculated using the fundamental theorem of calculus,

$$\int_{b}^{a} f(x) \; dx = F(b) - F(a) \quad \text{where} \quad a \leqslant x \leqslant b$$

Calculating definite integrals exercise   Go online

Q46: What is the value of each of these definite integrals?

a) $\int_{4}^{7} 2 \; dx$

b) $\int_{3}^{4} 6t \; + \; 4 \; dt$

c) $\int_{4}^{25} 9\sqrt{x} \; dx$

d) $\int_{2}^{5} \frac{4}{x^3} \; dx$

e) $\int_{1}^{2} 4x^3 \; + \; 5 \; dx$

f) $\int_{1}^{5} 3x^2 \; + \; 2x \; - \; 1 \; dx$

. . . .

Q47: What is the value of each of these definite integrals?

a) $\int_{3}^{4} (x \; - \; 2)^2 \; dx$

b) $\int_{-1}^{2} (2x \; - \; 1)^2 \; dx$

c) $\int_{0}^{9} \frac{1}{(v - 3)^2} \; dv$

d) $\int_{0}^{9} \frac{10x^2 \; + \; 6x \; - \; 1}{\sqrt{x}} \; dx$

. . . .

Q48: Evaluate the following definite integrals.

a) $\int_{-1/2}^{1/2} x^2 - 5x + 1 \, dx$

b) $\int_{\sqrt{2}}^{1} 2 - x^2 \, dx$

....

Q49: Evaluate the following definite integrals.

a) $\int_{\frac{\pi}{2}}^{\pi} 2 \sin\left(x - \frac{\pi}{2}\right) dx$

b) $\int_{\pi}^{2\pi} 1 + \cos x \, dx$

c) $\int_{0}^{\pi} -5 \cos(2x) + 2 \, dx$

Finding a Value

Q50: What is the positive value of a when $\int_{a}^{3} 5x \, dx = 20$?

....

Q51: What is the positive value of u when $\int_{u}^{2u} 4x + 1 \, dx = 5$?

....

Q52: What is the negative value of t when $\int_{-t}^{t} 6x^2 + 1 \, dx = 0$?

4.7 Finding the area under a curve

You may already have spotted that we can calculate the area under a curve by finding a definite integral.

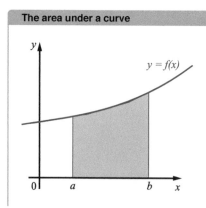

The area under a curve   Go online

The area between the graph $y = f(x)$ and the x-axis from $x = a$ to $x = b$ is,

$$\int_a^b f(x)\, dx$$

This is called a **definite integral**, a is the **lower limit of integration** and b is the **upper limit of integration**.

Key point

To calculate the area under a curve we evaluate the definite integral $\int_a^b f(x)\, dx$ ($a \leq x \leq b$), where a is the lower limit of integration and b is the upper limit of integration.

Examples

1. Problem:

Find the area under the straight line $y = 2x$ between $x = 0$ and $x = 4$

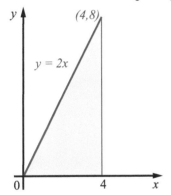

Solution:

Since the area is a triangle it can be calculated as $Area = {}^1\!/_2\, b\, h$.

$Area = {}^1\!/_2 \times 4 \times 8 = 16 = units^2$

Compare this with the integral,

$$\int_0^4 2x\, dx = \left[\frac{2x^2}{2}\right]_0^4 \quad or \quad \left[x^2\right]_0^4$$
$$= 4^2 - 0^2$$
$$= 16\ units^2$$

Thus the definite integral gives the area under the line which is consistent with the formula for the area of a triangle.

. . . .

---

2. Problem:

Part of the graph of the function $y = x^2 - 7x + 10$ is shown below.
Calculate the shaded are bounded by the curve and the x and y axes.

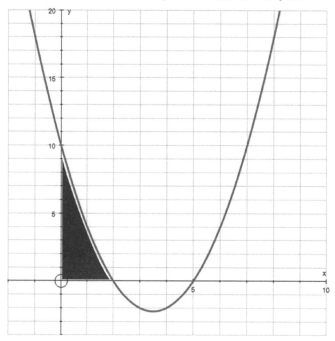

Solution:

The area looks like a triangle but it is not since the parabola is a curve.

$$
\begin{aligned}
Area &= \int_0^2 x^2 - 7x + 10 \, dx \\
&= \left[\frac{x^3}{3} - \frac{7x^2}{2} + 10x \right]_0^2 \\
&= \left(\frac{2^3}{3} - \frac{7 \times 2^2}{2} + 10 \times 2 \right) - \left(\frac{0^3}{3} - \frac{7 \times 0^2}{2} + 10 \times 0 \right) \\
&= \frac{26}{3} \\
&= 8\frac{2}{3} \ units^2
\end{aligned}
$$

....

3. Problem:

Calculate the shaded are bounded by the curve $y = 4x^3 + 12x^2 + 12x + 8$, the x-axis and the line $x = -1$.

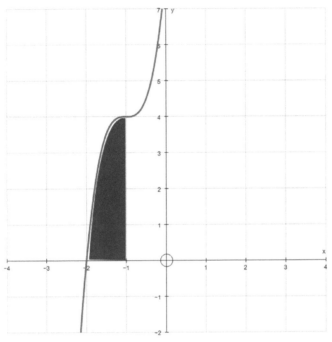

Solution:

$$Area = \int_{-2}^{-1} 4x^3 + 12x^2 + 12x + 8 \, dx$$

$$= \left[\frac{4x^4}{4} + \frac{12x^3}{3} + \frac{12x^2}{2} + 8x \right]_{-2}^{-1}$$

$$= \left[x^4 + 4x^3 + 6x^2 + 8x \right]_{-2}^{-1}$$

$$= \left((-1)^4 + 4 \times (-1)^3 + 6 \times (-1)^2 + 8 \times (-1) \right)$$

$$\qquad - \left((-2)^4 + 4 \times (-2)^3 + 6 \times (-2)^2 + 8 \times (-2) \right)$$

$$= 3 \; units^2$$

. . . .

4. Problem:

Calculate the shaded area under the curve $y = x^3 - 7x + 6$.

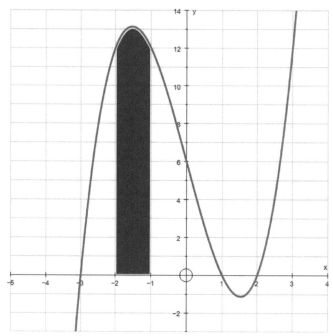

Solution:

$$\text{Area} = \int_{-2}^{-1} x^3 - 7x + 6 \, dx$$

$$= \left[\frac{x^4}{4} - \frac{7x^2}{2} + 6x \right]_{-2}^{-1}$$

$$= \left(\frac{(-1)^4}{4} - \frac{7 \times (-1)^2}{2} + 6 \times (-1) \right) - \left(\frac{(-2)^4}{4} - \frac{7 \times (-2)^2}{2} + 6 \times (-2) \right)$$

$$= \frac{51}{4} \quad or \quad 12 \cdot 75 \ units^2$$

Key point

Note that the value of the integral is

- **positive** when the area is **above** the x-axis
- **negative** when the area is **below** the x-axis

Key point

To calculate an area between a curve and the x-axis:

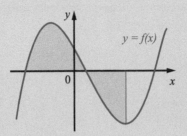

1. make a sketch, noting where the curve crosses the x -axis;

2. calculate the areas above and below the axis separately;

3. ignore the negative sign for areas below the axis because an area cannot be negative;

4. add the areas together.

The area between a curve and the x-axis   Go online

Example

Problem:

Calculate the total shaded area in the graph shown here.

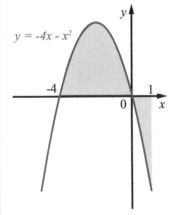

Solution:

Note from the graph that the area is in two sections, one part above the x-axis and the other part below the x-axis. These areas should be calculated separately as follows.

The area above the x-axis is given by the integral,

$$\int_{-4}^{0} \left(-4x - x^2 \right) dx = \left[-2x^2 - \frac{x^3}{3} \right]_{-4}^{0}$$

$$= [0] - \left[-32 + \frac{64}{3} \right]$$

$$= 32 - 21\tfrac{1}{3}$$

$$= 10\tfrac{2}{3}$$

Thus the area above the x-axis is $10\,\tfrac{2}{3}\ units^2$.

The area below the x-axis is given by the integral

$$\int_{0}^{1} \left(-4x - x^2 \right) dx = \left[-2x^2 - \frac{x^3}{3} \right]_{0}^{1}$$

$$= \left[-2 - \frac{1}{3} \right] - [0]$$

$$= -2\tfrac{1}{3}$$

The integral gives a negative answer since the area is below the x-axis thus the area is $2\,\tfrac{1}{3}\ units^2$.

Hence,

Total shaded area $= \ 10\,\tfrac{2}{3}\ +\ 2\,\tfrac{1}{3}\ =\ 13\ units^2$

Finding the area under a curve exercise   Go online

Q53: Find $\int \frac{9}{x^4}\, dx$

....

Q54: Evaluate $\int_{-1}^{1} 10\ -\ 6x^2\, dx$.

....

Q55: Which of these illustrates the area represented by the integral?

a)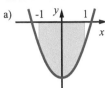

b)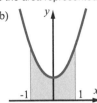

c)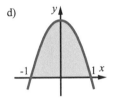

d)

The concrete on the 20 feet by 28 feet rectangular facing of the entrance to an underground cavern is to be repainted.

Coordinate axes are chosen as shown in the diagram with a scale of 1 unit equal to 1 foot. The roof is in the form of a parabola with equation $y = 18 - \frac{x^2}{8}$.

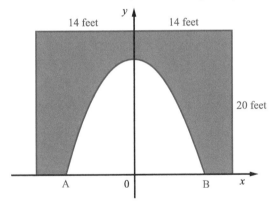

Q56: What are the coordinates of points A and B?

. . . .

Q57: Calculate the total cost of repainting the facing at £5 per square foot.

The diagram shows the area between the curve $y = x(x - 4)^2$ and the x-axis between $x = 0$ and $x = 4$.

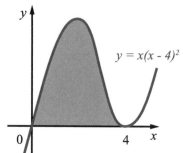

Q58: What is the integral needed to find the shaded area?

....

Q59: Calculate the shaded area.

....

Q60: Calculate the shaded area given in the diagram.

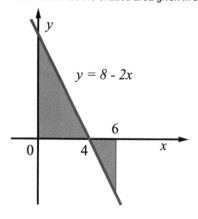

....

Q61: Calculate the total shaded area in the diagram shown here.
Notice that the curve cuts the x-axis in two places at $x = A$ and at $x = B$.

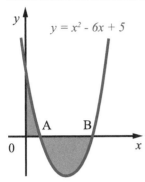

Q62: Calculate the total area between the curve $y = 15 + 2x - x^2$, the x-axis and the lines $x = 6$ and $x = 0$.

Q63: Calculate the area enclosed by the graph of $y = 4x - x^2$ and the x-axis.

Q64: Calculate the area enclosed by the graph of $y = x^3 - 6x^2 + 9x - 4$ and the x-axis.

Q65: The graph for $f(x) = \frac{1}{(2x - 7)^2}$ is shown in the diagram.
Calculate the shaded area.

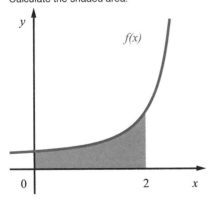

Q66: Calculate the shaded area in the diagram shown here.

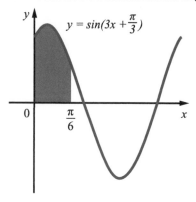

. . . .

Q67: An artist has designed a "bow" shape which he finds can be modelled by the shaded area here,

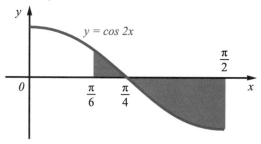

Calculate the area of this shape.

4.8   Finding the area between two curves

The shaded area in the diagram below is between the curves $y = f(x)$ and $y = g(x)$ from $x = a$ to $x = b$.

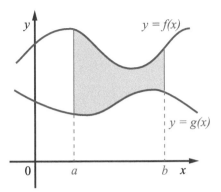

Notice that the graph of $y = f(x)$ is above the graph of $y = g(x)$.

Key point

The shaded area = the area from the x-axis to $y = f(x)$ minus the area from the x-axis to $y = g(x)$.

$$= \int_a^b f(x)\, dx \;-\; \int_a^b g(x)\, dx$$

$$= \int_a^b (f(x) - g(x))\, dx$$

Example

Problem:

Find the area enclosed between the line $y = x + 6$ and the curve $y = 8 + 2x - x^2$

Solution:

First find the points of intersection between the line and the curve.
The graphs intersect where,

$$
\begin{aligned}
x + 6 &= 8 + 2x - x^2 \\
x^2 - x - 2 &= 0 \\
(x - 2)(x + 1) &= 0 \\
x = 2 \text{ or } x &= -1
\end{aligned}
$$

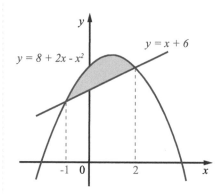

Notice that between $x = -1$ and $x = 2$ the graph for $y = 8 + 2x - x^2$ is above that for $y = x + 6$ so the enclosed area is given by,

$$Area = \int_{-1}^{2} (8 + 2x - x^2) - (x + 6)\, dx$$

$$= \int_{-1}^{2} 2 + x - x^2\, dx$$

$$= \left[2x + \frac{x^2}{2} - \frac{x^3}{3} \right]_{-1}^{2}$$

$$= \left(2 \times 2 + \frac{2^2}{2} - \frac{2^3}{3} \right) - \left(2 \times (-1) + \frac{(-1)^2}{2} - \frac{(-1)^3}{3} \right)$$

$$= \frac{9}{2} \ or \ 4 \cdot 5 \ units^2$$

To calculate an area between two graphs:

- calculate the points of intersection where $f(x) = g(x)$;

- note which graph is above the other between the points of intersection;

- evaluate $\int_a^b f(x) - g(x)\, dx$ for $f(x)$ above $g(x)$ and $a \leq x \leq b$.

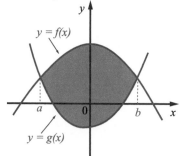

Example

Problem:

The parabolas shown in the diagram have equations $y = 22 - x^2$ and $y = x^2 + 4$.
Calculate the shaded areas between the two curves.

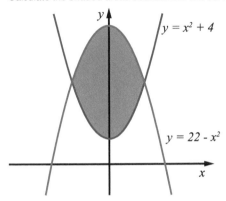

Solution:

Step 1: Find the points of intersection of the parabolas.

$$x^2 + 4 = 22 - x^2$$
$$2x^2 - 18 = 0$$
$$2(x^2 - 9) = 0$$
$$2(x - 3)(x + 3) = 0$$
$$x = 3 \; or \; x = -3$$

Step 2: Determine which curve is above the other.

$y = 22 - x^2$ is above $y = x^2 + 4$ when $-3 \leq x \leq 3$

Step 3: Calculate the area.

$$\int_{-3}^{3} (22 - x^2) - (x^2 + 4) \, dx = \int_{-3}^{3} 18 - 2x^2 \, dx$$
$$= \left[18x - \frac{2x^3}{3} \right]_{-3}^{3}$$
$$= \left(18 \times 3 - \frac{2 \times 3^3}{3} \right) - \left(18 \times (-3) - \frac{2 \times (-3)^3}{3} \right)$$
$$= 72 \; units^2$$

Q68: Calculate the shaded area in the diagram shown here.

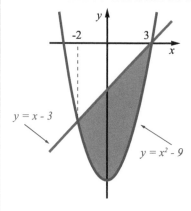

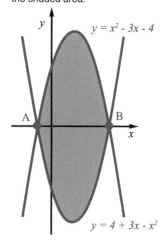

....

Q69: Find the points of intersection between the two graphs shown here and hence calculate the shaded area.

....

Q70: Calculate the area enclosed by the graphs $y = x - 4$ and $y = x^2 - 5x + 4$.

....

Q71: Calculate the area enclosed by the graphs $y = x^2 - 20x + 17$ and $y = -1 - x^2$

....

Q72: The graphs $y = x^3 - 3x - 2$ and $y = x - 2$ intersect in three places as shown in the diagram.

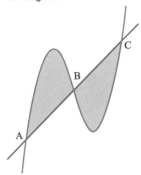

Find the x-coordinates of the three points of intersection and hence calculate the total area enclosed between these two graphs.

....

Q73: The diagram shows the curve with equation $y = 2x^2 - 7x + 7$ and the line with equation $y = x + 7$.

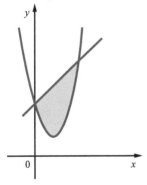

Find the integral which represents the shaded area.

The concrete on the 20 feet by 28 feet rectangular facing of the entrance to an underground cavern is to be repainted.

Coordinate axes are chosen as shown in the diagram with a scale of 1 unit equal to 1 foot.

The roof is in the form of a parabola with equation $y = 16 - \frac{x^2}{4}$.

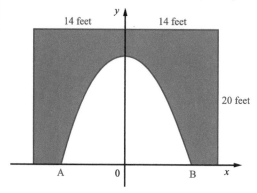

Q74: What are the coordinates of points A and B?

....

Q75: Calculate the total cost of repainting the facing at £5 per square foot.

In the diagram, a winding river has been modelled by the curve $y = x^3 - x^2 - 6x - 2$ and a road has been modelled by the straight line AB. The road is a tangent to the river at the point A(1,-8).

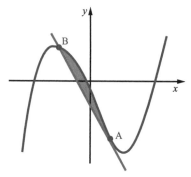

Q76: Find the equation of the tangent at A and hence find the coordinates of B.

....

Q77: Find the area of the shaded part which represents the land bounded by the river and the road.

The diagram shows the line with equation $y = x + 4$ and the curve with equation $y = x^2 - 3x + 4$.

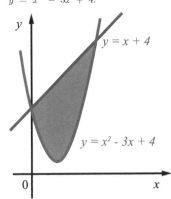

What is the integral which represents the shaded area?

Q78: The line and the curve intersect in two places at x = 0 and x = ?

. . . .

Q79: Calculate the total area between the curve $y = 16 - x^2$, the x-axis and the lines $x = 5$ and $x = -1$.

4.9   Learning points

Integration
Indefinite integrals

- $\int a\,dx = ax + C$, where a is a constant and C is the constant of integration.

- $\int x^n\,dx = \frac{x^{n+1}}{n+1} + C$, where $n \neq -1$.

- $\int ax^n\,dx = a\int x^n\,dx = \frac{ax^{n+1}}{n+1} + C$, where $n \neq -1$ and a is a constant.

- To integrate expressions with multiple terms, each term must first be expressed in the form ax^n.

- Products and quotients must first be expressed as the sum of terms given in the form ax^n.

- $\int \sin x\,dx = -\cos x + C$

- $\int \cos x\,dx = \sin x + C$

- $\int \sin(ax + b)\,dx = -\frac{1}{a}\cos(ax + b) + C$

- $\int \cos(ax + b)\,dx = \frac{1}{a}\sin(ax + b) + C$

- $\int (ax + b)^n\,dx = \frac{(ax + b)^{n+1}}{a(n+1)} + C$, where $n \neq -1$.

Definite integrals

- If $F(x)$ is an anti-derivative or integral of $f(x)$ then $\int_a^b f(x)\,dx = F(b) - F(a)$, where $a \leq x \leq b$.

The area under a curve

- The area between the graph $y = f(x)$ and the x-axis from $x = a$ to $x = b$ is given by the definite integral, $\int_a^b f(x)\,dx$

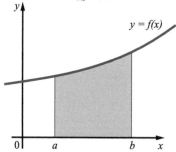

- An area above the x-axis will give a positive value for the integral.

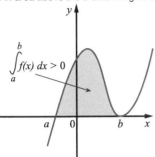

- An area below the x-axis will give a negative value for the integral.

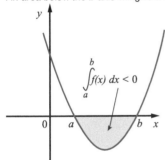

Area above and below the x-axis

- To calculate an area between a curve and the x-axis:
  - calculate the areas above and below the axis separately;
  - ignore the negative sign for areas below the axis;
  - add the areas together.

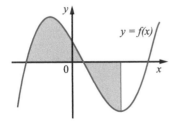

The area between two curves

- To calculate an area between two graphs:
  - calculate points of intersection;
  - note which graph is above the other between the points of intersection.

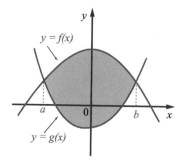

- For the diagram shown here $g(x) \geq f(x)$ for $a \leq x \leq b$ and thus the area enclosed by the curves is given by $\int_a^b (f(x) - g(x))\, dx$

- When calculating definite integrals of trigonometric functions, the limits must be in radians.

4.10 End of topic test

Go online

Q80: What is $\int 1 + x^{-\frac{4}{3}} \, dx$, leave any negative indices in your answer?

....

Q81: What is $\int x^5 - \frac{1}{x^5} \, dx$, giving your answer with positive indices?

....

Q82: What is $\int \frac{2}{\sqrt[4]{x^3}} \, dx$, leave any fractional indices in your answer?

....

Q83: What is $\int (6x - 1)^3 \, dx$?

Q84: Find $\int \frac{6}{7} \sin x \, dx$.

....

Q85: Integrate $4 \cos x$ with respect to x.

....

Q86: Knowing that $\sin^2 x = \frac{1}{2}(1 - \cos 2x)$, find $\int \sin^2 x \, dx$.

Q87: Using the addition formula expand $\cos(2x + x)$.

....

Q88: $\cos 3x = \cos(2x + x)$ rewrite in terms of $\cos^3 x$ and $\cos x$.

....

Q89: Rewrite $\cos^3 x$ in terms of $\cos 3x$ and $\cos x$.

....

Q90: What is the indefinite integral of $\cos^3 x$?

Q91: Evaluate $\int_0^2 x^2 - 7x + 10 \, dx$.

....

Q92: What is the value of $\int_2^4 \frac{2}{\sqrt{t}} \, dt$?

The diagram shows the area between the curve $y = x^2(x + 8)$ and the x -axis between $x = -8$ and $x = 0$.

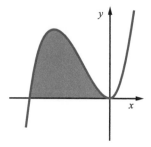

Q93: Calculate the shaded area.

Q94: An artist has designed a "bow" shape which he finds can be modelled by the shaded area here,

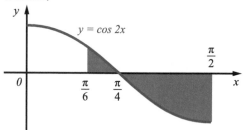

Calculate the area of this shape.

Q95: The diagram shows the curve with equation $y = 2x^2 - 3x + 4$ and the line with equation $y = x + 4$.

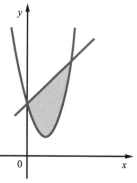

Calculate the shaded area.

Q96: The graphs $y = x^3 - 8x - 4$ and $y = x - 4$ intersect in three places as shown in the diagram.

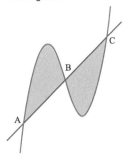

Find the x-coordinates of the three points of intersection and hence calculate the total area enclosed between these two graphs.

Q97: The gradient of a tangent to a curve is given by $\frac{dy}{dx} = 6x^2 + \frac{10}{x^3}$. The curve passes through the point (1,1).

What is the equation of the curve?

Topic 5

Circles

Contents

Learning objective

By the end of this topic, you should be able to:

- determine and use the:
    - equation of a circle with centre the origin;
    - equation of a circle with centre (a,b);
    - general equation of a circle;
    - equation of a tangent to a circle;
- use the properties of tangency;
- determine the point(s) of intersection of:
    - a circle and a line;
    - two circles.

5.1   Looking back at National 5

Summary
Arcs and sectors

- Circumference $= \pi D$

- Diameter $= 2r$

- Circumference $= 2\pi r$

- Area $= \pi r^2$

- $Length\ of\ an\ Arc\quad=\quad\frac{angle}{360°}\ \times\ \pi\ \times\ Diameter$

- $Area\ of\ a\ Sector\quad=\quad\frac{angle}{360°}\ \times\ \pi\ \times\ radius^2$

Angles in polygons and circles: Angle properties in circles

- A triangle formed by 2 radii and a chord is an isosceles triangle.

- The angle in a semi-circle is a right angle.

- A tangent is at right angles to the radius at the point of contact.

- A radius bisects a chord at right angles.

5.1.1   Angles and angle properties in circles

Angle properties   Go online

When two parallel lines are cut by a transversal, the patterns of angles around each point are the same.

We are particularly interested in this pair of equal angles $(x°)$ and this pair $(y°)$. These are alternate angles. . . the ones that form 'Z-bends'.

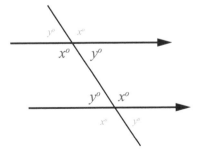

Given any triangle we can always extend the sides and draw a line through the vertex parallel to the opposite side.

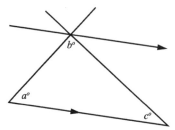

We have formed two pairs of useful alternate angles. Notice in the following diagram that the three angles of the triangle come together to form a straight line. The sum of the angles in any triangle equal $180°$. The angles which form a straight angle are called supplementary angles and equal $180°$.

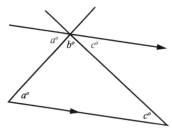

Properties of a circle (1)   Go online

All radii of a circle are equal. If radii are drawn to the end of a chord then the triangle formed will be isosceles.

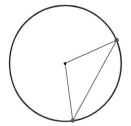

Properties of a circle (2)

Go online

A circle with its centre is drawn and a diameter drawn through the centre. A point is chosen on the circumference of the circle. . . not the end point of the existing diameter. A diameter can always be drawn from this point.

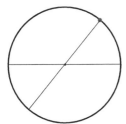

These two diameters are equal and bisect each other. . . the configuration of the diagonals is a rectangle. So given any diameter, any point on the circumference is a corner of a rectangle using the diameter as a diagonal.

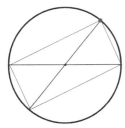

The diameter subtends an angle of 90° at any point on the circumference. The right angle is always on the circumference of the circle opposite the diameter and we call this property "The angle in a semi-circle is a right angle".

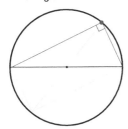

Properties of a circle (3)   Go online

A circle with its centre is drawn and a diameter drawn through the centre. A chord that cuts the circle in two places is drawn at right angles to the diameter. The diameter is an axis of symmetry. . . the chord is bisected.

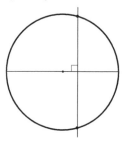

A second chord parallel to the first is drawn to the right. . . the two points of intersection are closer together and the chord is at right angles to the diameter. A third chord parallel to the first two is drawn further to the right. . . the two points of intersection are even closer together and the chord is at right angles to the diameter.

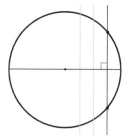

At some point the two points of intersection will become one. . .   the chord will become a tangent and the tangent is at right angles to the diameter. A tangent will be at right angles to a radius drawn to the point of contact.

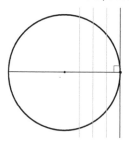

Key point

- Look for isosceles triangles formed with two radii and a chord.

- The right angle is always on the circumference of the circle opposite the diameter and we call this property 'The angle in a semi-circle is a right angle'.

- The diameter and tangent are perpendicular and we call this property 'A tangent is at right angles to the radius at the point of contact'.

Properties of a circle exercise   Go online

Q1:

AB is a diameter and C is a point
on the circumference of the circle.

∠BAC = 42°.

Calculate the size of ∠ACB and ∠CBA.

Write down your working.

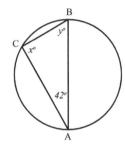

....

Q2:

Find the values of x and y in the diagram
below.

BT and AT are tangents, AC and BC are radii.

Write down your working.

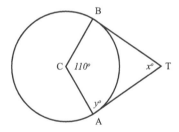

....

Q3:

Find the values of x, y and z in the diagram
below.

BT and AT are tangents, AC and BC are radii.

Write down your working.

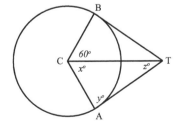

5.2   The equation of a circle

The study of the circle goes back beyond the recorded history. Euclid's Elements Book III, deals with the properties of circles.

A circle is the set of all points (or locus) in a plane that are equidistant from a central point. In this topic we will look at different way of describing the equations of circles.

5.2.1   The equation of a circle with centre the origin

Circle radius   Go online

The easiest circle to construct is a circle with centre O, the origin. Here are some examples.

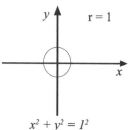

$r = 1$

$x^2 + y^2 = 1^2$

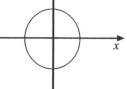

$r = 2$

$x^2 + y^2 = 2^2$

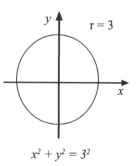

$r = 3$

$x^2 + y^2 = 3^2$

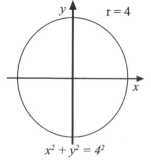

$r = 4$

$x^2 + y^2 = 4^2$

Key point

The equation of a circle with centre (0,0) and radius r is
$x^2 + y^2 = r^2$.

Q4:   What is the equation of the circle with centre (0,0) and radius 9?

Examples

1. Problem:

What is the radius of a circle with equation $x^2 + y^2 = 9$?

Solution:

Since $x^2 + y^2 = r^2$ it follows that $r^2 = 9$

$r = \sqrt{9} = 3$

....

2. Problem:

$x^2 + y^2 = 25$ is the equation of the circle C and the points P and Q lie on the circumference. The x-coordinate of the points P and Q is 4.

What are the y-coordinates of P and Q?

Solution:

$x^2 + y^2 = 25$

Since both points lie on the circle, substitute $x = 4$ into the equation.

$4^2 + y^2 = 25$

$\qquad y^2 = 9$

$\qquad y = 3 \quad and \quad y = -3$

....

3. Problem:

What is the radius and centre of the circle with equation $4x^2 + 4y^2 - 36 = 0$?

Solution:

$4x^2 + 4y^2 = 36$

$x^2 + y^2 = 9$

The equation is now in the form $x^2 + y^2 = r^2$ so the radius is 3 units and the centre is the origin.

....

4. Problem:

Find the equation of a circle passing through the point (5, 12) with centre at the origin.

Solution:

Since the equation is in the form $x^2 + y^2 = r^2$.

Substitute $x = 5$ and $y = 12$ into the equation to find r.

$5^2 + 12^2 = r^2$

$\qquad 169 = r^2$

$\qquad r = 13$

The equation is $x^2 + y^2 = 169$

....

5. Problem:

Does the point (4,-7) lie inside, outside or on the circumference of the circle $x^2 + y^2 = 64$?

Solution:

Substitute $x = 4$ and $y = -7$ into the equation.

$4^2 + (-7)^2 = 65$

Since $65 > 64$ the point (4,-7) lies outside the circumference of the circle.

Note that if $x^2 + y^2 < 64$ the point would have lain inside the circle and if $x^2 + y^2 = 64$ the point would have lain on the circumference of the circle.

. . . .

6. Problem:

A circle passes through the vertices of a rectangle whose sides have equations $x = 4$, $x = -4$, $y = 3$ and $y = -3$.

What is the equation of the circle in the diagram?

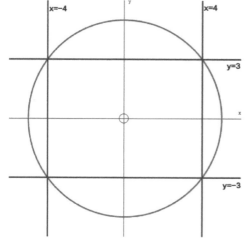

Solution:

The equation takes the form $x^2 + y^2 = r^2$ since the centre of the circle is the origin.

The point (4,3) lies on the circumference of the circle so let $x = 4$ and $y = 3$ in the equation.

$4^2 + 3^2 = r^2$

$\qquad r^2 = 25$

So the equation of the circle is $x^2 + y^2 = 25$

The equation of a circle with centre the origin exercise   Go online

Q5: Find the radius of the circle with equation $x^2 + y^2 = 121$.

....

Q6: Find the radius of the circle with centre the origin which passes through the point (9,2).

....

Q7: Find the radius of the circle with equation $-3x^2 - 3y^2 + 12 = 0$.

....

Q8: Find the radius of the circle with equation $16 - x^2 = y^2$.

....

Q9: Find the radius of the circle with centre the origin which passes through the point (-5,3).

....

Q10: What is the radius of the circle with equation $x^2 + y^2 = 100$.

....

Q11: What is the radius of the circle with centre the origin which passes through the point (8,8).

....

Q12: What is the radius of the circle with equation $2x^2 + 2y^2 - 8 = 0$.

....

Q13: What is the radius of the circle with equation $36 - x^2 = y^2$.

....

Q14: What is the radius of the circle with centre the origin which passes through the point (-9,-2).

....

Q15: Does the point (-2,-8) lie inside, outside or on the circumference of the circle with equation $x^2 + y^2 = 64$?

....

Q16: Does the point (-6,5) lie inside, outside or on the circumference of the circle with equation $x^2 + y^2 = 63$?

....

Q17: Does the point $\left(\frac{1}{2}, \frac{1}{4}\right)$ lie inside, outside or on the circumference of the circle with equation $x^2 + y^2 = \frac{5}{16}$?

....

Q18: Which of these are equations of a circle with centre at the origin?

a) $ax^2 + by^2 = r^2$ where a and b are different.

b) $x^2 + y^2 = r^2$

c) $ax^2 + by^2 = r^2$ where $a = b$

d) $ax^2 - by^2 + r^2 = 0$ where $a = -b$

. . . .

Q19: If the circle C has centre the origin and diameter 16, name a point on the negative x-axis which lies on its circumference.

. . . .

Q20: A circle passes through the vertices of a rectangle whose sides have equations $x = 5$, $x = -5, y = 8$ and $y = -8$.

What is the equation of the circle?

5.2.2   The equation of a circle with centre (a,b)

┌─ **Key point** ─────────────────────────────

The equation of a circle with centre (a,b) and radius r is:

$(x - a)^2 + (y - b)^2 = r^2$

Examples

1. Problem:

What is the radius and the centre of a circle with equation $(x - 2)^2 + (y - 5)^2 = 9$?

Solution:

The radius is 3 and the centre is (2,5).

. . . .

2. Problem:

What is the radius and centre of the circle with equation:

$3(x + 2)^2 + 3(y - 1)^2 - 15 = 0$?

Solution:

Rearrange into the correct form.

$3(x + 2)^2 + 3(y - 1)^2 = 15$

$(x + 2)^2 + (y - 1)^2 = 5$

This is in the correct form for a circle with centre (-2, 1) and radius $\sqrt{5}$.

. . . .

3. Problem:

$(x - 1)^2 + (y + 3)^2 = 36$ is the equation of the circle and the points P and Q lie on the circumference.

If the line through P, Q and the centre of the circle is parallel to the y-axis, find the coordinates of P and Q.

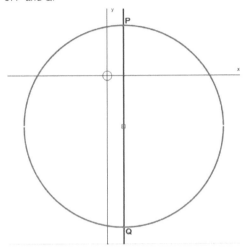

Solution:

If the line is parallel to the y-axis then it is vertical and the x-coordinates of P, Q and the centre will all be the same.

Since the centre of the circle is (1,-3), the x-coordinate of the points P and Q will also be 1.

We know that PQ is a diameter to the circle and that the radius is 6.

So P has y-coordinate of $-3 + 6 = 3$ and Q has a y-coordinate of $-3 - 6 = -9$.

The coordinates of P are (1,3) and Q are (1,-9).

. . . .

4. Problem:

Find the equation of a circle passing through the point P(6,4) with centre at C(-3,2).

Solution:

The general equation is $(x - a)^2 + (y - b)^2 = r^2$

The distance between the points P and C is the radius so we can use the distance formula.

$$\text{Distance} = \sqrt{(x_2 - x_1)^2 + (y_2 - y_1)^2}$$
$$r = \sqrt{((-3) - 6)^2 + (2 - 4)^2}$$
$$= \sqrt{85}$$

The equation is $(x + 3)^2 + (y - 2)^2 = 85$

. . . .

5. Problem:

Does the point (6,-5) lie inside, outside or on the circumference of the circle $(x - 1)^2 + (y + 1)^2 = 42$?

Solution:

Substitute x = 6 and y = -5 into the equation.

$(6 - 1)^2 + ((-5) + 1)^2 = 5^2 + (-4)^2 = 41$

Since 41 < 42 the point (6,-5) lies inside the circumference of the circle.

....

6. Problem:

Find the equation of the circle through the three points:
A (-2,1), B (1,4) and D (-2,7).

Solution:

You may remember from Topic 1: The straight line, that the circumcentre is the point of intersection of the perpendicular bisectors of a triangle.

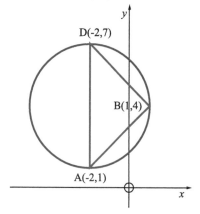

A(-2,1), B(1,4)

$m_{AB} = \frac{4 - 1}{1 - (-2)} = \frac{3}{3} = 1$ so $m_{perp} = -1$ and the mid-point of $AB = \left(\frac{-2 + 1}{2} , \frac{1 + 4}{2}\right) = \left(\frac{-1}{2} , \frac{5}{2}\right).$

$y - \frac{5}{2} = -1\left(x + \frac{1}{2}\right)$

$y = -x + 2$

A(-2,1), D(-2,7)

$m_{AD} = \frac{7 - 1}{(-2) - (-2)} = \frac{6}{0} =$ undefined (a vertical line) so $m_{perp} = 0$ (a horizontal line)

and the mid-point of $AD = \left(\frac{-2 + (-2)}{2} , \frac{1 + 7}{2}\right) = (-2, 4)$

$\underline{\underline{y = 4}}$

B(1,4) and D(-2,7)

$m_{BD} \;=\; \frac{7-4}{(-2)-1} \;=\; \frac{3}{-3} \;=\; -1$ so $m_{perp} \;=\; 1$ and the mid-point of $BD \;=$

$\left(\frac{1+(-2)}{2}, \frac{4+7}{2}\right) \;=\; \left(\frac{-1}{2}, \frac{11}{2}\right)$

$y - \frac{11}{2} \;=\; 1\left(x + \frac{1}{2}\right)$

$y \;=\; x + 6$

To find the coordinates of the circumcentre we can use simultaneous equations.

Let $y = 4$ in $y = -x + 2$

$4 \;=\; -x + 2$

$x \;=\; -2$

The circumcentre is (-2,4) but we must check this with the equation of the third perpendicular bisector $y = x + 6$.

$4 \;=\; -2 + 6$ ✓

The centre of the circle is (-2,4).

The radius is the distance from A, B or D to the centre.
From A(-2,1) to the centre (-2,4) is 3 units.

The equation of the circle is $(x + 2)^2 + (y - 4)^2 \;=\; 9$.

The equation of a circle with centre (a,b) exercise   Go online

Q21: Find the radii and centres of the following circles:

a) $(x + 2)^2 + (y - 1)^2 = 49$

b) $x^2 + (y - 2)^2 - 9 = 0$

c) $3(x + 1)^2 + 3(y + 1)^2 - 2 = 1$

d) $(x + 6)^2 = -y^2 + 12$

e) $-6 = -x^2 - (y - 1)^2 - 3$

f) $-2(x - 1)^2 = 2(y + 4)^2 - 72$

. . . .

Q22:

a) What is the equation of the circle with radius 4 and centre (-3, 4) in the form $(x - a)^2 + (y - b)^2 = r^2$.

b) The circle passing through the point (4, -5) with centre (2, 2).
What is the radius?

c) What is the equation of the circle with radius $4\sqrt{2}$ and centre on the positive x-axis such that the origin is on the circumference in the form $(x - a)^2 + (y - b)^2 = r^2$.

d) What is the equation of the circle passing through the point (4, 0) and with centre (-3, -1) in the form $(x - a)^2 + (y - b)^2 = r^2$.

e) What is the equation of the circle with diameter 6 and centre midway between the points A (2, 4) and B (-6, 2).

f) What is the equation of the circle with diameter PQ where P is the point (8, -4) and Q is the point (2, -12) in the form $(x - a)^2 + (y - b)^2 = r^2$.

....

Q23: A gearing system has two wheels, one large and one small.
The line of centres of the two wheels is parallel to the x-axis and the equation of the larger wheel is $(x - 2)^2 + (y + 4)^2 = 64$.
Find the equation of the smaller wheel which lies to the right of the larger wheel and has a radius of half of that of the larger wheel.

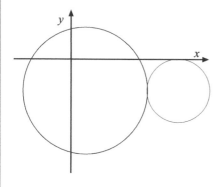

....

Q24: A child's bicycle has two identical wheels with a clearance between them of 15 cm. The bike measures 165 cm long when held against a wall (with the ground as the x-axis). Find the equations of the two circles which represent the wheels. Give your answer in the form $(x - a)^2 + (y - b)^2 = r^2$.

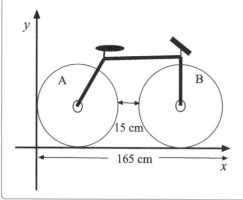

5.3   The general equation of a circle

The general form of the equation of a circle can be obtained by expanding the equation of a circle with centre (a, b) and radius r.

$$(x - a)^2 + (y - b)^2 = r^2$$
$$x^2 - 2ax + a^2 + y^2 - 2by + b^2 - r^2 = 0$$

To avoid confusion with a and b we use the formula $x^2 + y^2 + 2gx + 2fy + c = 0$,

where g replaces $-a$, f replaces $-b$ and c replaces $a^2 + b^2 - r^2$

Key point

The general equation of the circle is $x^2 + y^2 + 2gx + 2fy + c = 0$, with centre (-g,-f) and radius $\sqrt{g^2 + f^2 - c}$, provided $g^2 + f^2 - c > 0$.

Examples

1. Problem:

Find the centre and radius of the circle represented by the equation $x^2 + y^2 + 10x + 6y - 2 = 0$

Solution:

The equation is given in the general form $x^2 + y^2 + 2gx + 2fy + c = 0$
where $2g = 10$ and $2f = 6$ so $g = 5$, $f = 3$ and $c = -2$.

Hence the centre of the circle is (-5,-3).

$$r = \sqrt{5^2 + 3^2 - (-2)} = \sqrt{36}$$

So the radius is 6

. . . .

2. Problem:

Give the equation of the circle with radius 4 and centre (-6, 2) in the general form.

Solution:

The centre is represented by (-g,-f) so $g = 6$ and $f = -2$.

$$r^2 = g^2 + f^2 - c$$
$$4^2 = 6^2 + (-2)^2 - c$$
$$16 = 36 + 4 - c$$
$$c = 24$$

The general form is $x^2 + y^2 + 2gx + 2fy + c = 0$.

So the equation is $x^2 + y^2 + 12x - 4y + 24 = 0$.

. . . .

3. Problem:

PQ is the diameter of the circle with coordinates P(6,7) and Q(-4,-5).
What is the general equation of the circle?

Solution:

The centre of the circle is the midpoint of PQ

$$centre = \left(\frac{x_1 + x_2}{2}, \frac{y_1 + y_2}{2} \right)$$

$$= \left(\frac{6 + (-4)}{2}, \frac{7 + (-5)}{2} \right)$$

$$= (1, 1)$$

The radius is the distance between (1,1) and P or Q

$$Distance = \sqrt{(x_2 - x_1)^2 + (y_2 - y_1)^2}$$

$$r = \sqrt{(1 - 6)^2 + (1 - 7)^2}$$

$$= \sqrt{61}$$

The centre is represented by (-g,-f) so $g = -1$ and $f = -1$

$$r^2 = g^2 + f^2 - c$$

$$\sqrt{61}^2 = (-1)^2 + (-1)^2 - c$$

$$61 = 1 + 1 - c$$

$$c = -59$$

The general form is $x^2 + y^2 + 2gx + 2fy + c = 0$.

So the equation is $x^2 + y^2 - 2x - 2y - 59 = 0$.

. . . .

4. Problem:

The centres of two grinding wheels have to be 18 cm apart for safety.
The equation of one of the wheels is $x^2 + y^2 + 4x + 2y - 4 = 0$.

a) If the clearance between the wheels must be at least 1 cm find the range of values which the radius of the second wheel can take.

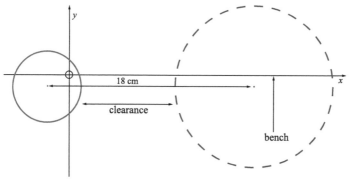

b) If the clearance is set at 11 cm find the equation of the second wheel given that the centres of the two wheels lie on a horizontal bench.

Solution:

a)

From the equation $g = 2$, $f = 1$ and $c = -4$.

$$r = \sqrt{g^2 + f^2 - c}$$
$$= \sqrt{2^2 + 1^2 - (-4)}$$
$$= 3 \ cm$$

With a clearance of at least 1 cm the edge of the second wheel is at least 4 cm away; but the centres are 18 cm apart so the radius of the second wheel must be at the most 14 cm.

The second wheel radius has a range of $0 < r \leq 14$.

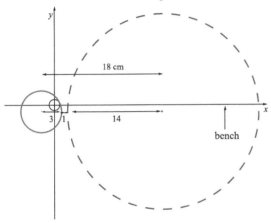

b)

If the clearance is then set at 11 cm, the second wheel has a radius of 4 cm.

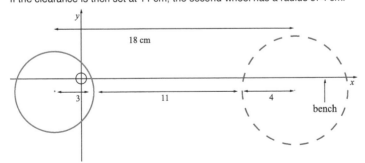

The centre of the first wheel is (-2,-1).

The x-coordinate of the centre of the second wheel will be $-2 + 18 = 16$.

The y-coordinate is the same for both wheels at $y = -1$.

The centre of the second wheel is (16,-1) with radius 4.

The equation for the second wheel is $(x - 16)^2 + (y + 1)^2 = 16$.

. . . .

5. Problem:

The circles with equations $x^2 + y^2 - kx - 6y - 4k = 0$ and $(x - 2)^2 + (y - 3)^2 = 36$ have the same centre.
What is the radius of the larger circle?

Solution:

The centre of the second circle is (2,3) and the radius is 6.

The equation of the first circle is given in the general form $x^2 + y^2 + 2gx + 2fy + c = 0$ where $2g = -k$ and $2f = -6$ so $g = -\frac{k}{2}$, $f = -3$ and $c = -4k$.

Hence the centre of the circle is $\left(\frac{k}{2}, 3\right)$.

If the circles have the same centre then $\frac{k}{2} = 2$ and $k = 4$.

$$
\begin{aligned}
r^2 &= g^2 + f^2 - c \\
&= \left(-\frac{k}{2}\right)^2 + (-3)^2 + 4k \\
&= \left(-\frac{4}{2}\right)^2 + (-3)^2 + 4 \times 4 \\
&= 4 + 9 + 16 \\
&= 29 \\
r &= \sqrt{29}
\end{aligned}
$$

So the radius of the first circle is $\sqrt{29}$ or 5·4.

Hence the radius of the larger circle is 6.

Key point

Circles with the same centre are concentric.

The general equation of a circle exercise   Go online

Q25: Find the centre and radii of the circles with the following equations:

a) $x^2 + y^2 - 4x - 2y - 4 = 0$
b) $x^2 + 6x - 1 = -y^2 + 4y + 2$
c) $x^2 + y^2 + 8y - 9 = 0$
d) $x^2 + y^2 - 10x + 21 = 0$

. . . .

Q26: Find the centre and radii of the circles with the following equations:

a) $x^2 + y^2 + 18x - 115 = 0$
b) $x^2 + y^2 - 12y = -11$
c) $x^2 + y^2 + 12x - 18y + 53 = 0$
d) $x^2 + y^2 + 16x - 6y = -9$

....

Q27: Find the y-coordinate of the point P which lies on the circle C with equation $x^2 + y^2 + 8x + 10y + 37 = 0$ where P has x-coordinate = -2.

....

Q28: The two points P and Q lie on the circle C with equation $x^2 + y^2 - 2x - 2y - 23 = 0$. P and Q have an x-coordinate = 4.

a) What is the y-coordinate of P?
b) What is the y-coordinate of Q?

....

Q29: For what range of values of c does the equation $x^2 + y^2 - 6x + 4y + c = 0$ represent a circle?

5.4   Relationships between a line and a circle

Geometrically, a circle and line can:

- intersect at two distinct points;
- touch at one point (in effect they intersect at two equal points);
- not intersect at all.

Line and circle   Go online

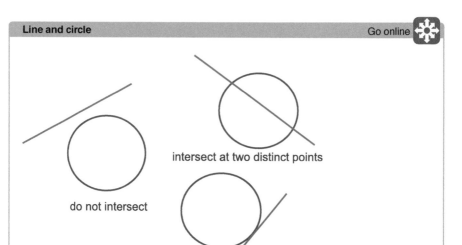

intersect at two distinct points

do not intersect

touch at one point

Key point

When a line meets a circle at one point, it is called a tangent to the circle.

Example : Intersection of a line and a circle

Problem:

Find where the line $y = -2x - 3$ meets the circle with equation $x^2 + y^2 - 4x + 2y - 4 = 0$.

Solution:

Let $y = -2x - 3$ in the equation of the circle giving,

$$x^2 + (-2x - 3)^2 - 4x + 2(-2x - 3) - 4 = 0$$
$$x^2 + (4x^2 + 12x + 9) - 4x + (-4x - 6) - 4 = 0$$
$$5x^2 + 4x - 1 = 0$$
$$(5x - 1)(x + 1) = 0$$
$$x = \frac{1}{5} \quad or \quad x = -1$$

Use the equation of the straight line to find the y-coordinates of the points of intersection.

When $x = \frac{1}{5}$, $y = -2 \times \frac{1}{5} - 3 = -\frac{17}{5}$
When $x = -1$, $y = -2 \times -1 - 3 = -1$

The two points of intersection are $\left(\frac{1}{5}, -\frac{17}{5}\right)$ and $(-1, -1)$.

Key point

Evaluating and interpreting the **discriminant**:

- if $b^2 - 4ac = 0$ then the line is a **tangent** to the circle;
- if $b^2 - 4ac > 0$ then there are **2** points of intersection;
- if $b^2 - 4ac < 0$ then the line **does not** meet the circle at all.

Key point

A radius and tangent are perpendicular at the point of contact.

To find the gradient of the tangent we can therefore use the relationship $m_{tangent} \times m_{radius} = -1$.

Examples

1. Tangent to a circle

Problem:

Find the equation of the tangent to the circle $x^2 + y^2 = 25$ at the point P (3, 4).

Solution:

The centre of the circle is (0,0), the origin.

$m_{OP} = \frac{4}{3}$

The tangent is perpendicular to the radius at the point of contact P(3,4)

so $m_{tangent} = -3/4$ and the equation of the tangent is,

$$y - 4 = -\frac{3}{4}(x - 3)$$
$$4y - 16 = -3x + 9$$
$$3x + 4y - 25 = 0$$

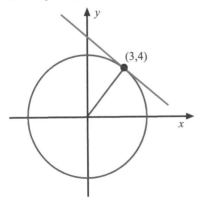

....

2. Line and circle do not touch

Problem:

Does the line $y = 2x + 5$ intersect the circle with equation $(x - 2)^2 + (y + 1)^2 = 4$?

Solution:

Let $y = 2x + 5$ in the equation of the circle.

$$(x - 2)^2 + (2x + 5 + 1)^2 = 4$$
$$x^2 - 4x + 4 + (2x + 6)^2 = 4$$
$$x^2 - 4x + 4 + 4x^2 + 24x + 36 - 4 = 0$$
$$5x^2 + 20x + 36 = 0$$

We can use the discriminant $(b^2 - 4ac)$ to find the nature of the solution.

$b^2 - 4ac = 20^2 - 4 \times 5 \times 36 = -320$

Since the discriminant is negative the line and circle do not meet.

. . . .

3. Intersection of circle and tangent

Problem:

Find the coordinates of the point at which the circle with equation $x^2 + y^2 + 6x - 8y - 7 = 0$ and the tangent $y = x - 1$ meet.

Solution:

Let $y = x - 1$ in the equation of the circle.

$$x^2 + (x - 1)^2 + 6x - 8(x - 1) - 7 = 0$$
$$x^2 + x^2 - 2x + 1 + 6x - 8x + 8 - 7 = 0$$
$$2x^2 - 4x + 2 = 0$$
$$2(x^2 - 2x + 1) = 0$$
$$2(x - 1)(x - 1) = 0$$

and $x = 1$ twice so the line is a tangent.

Using the equation of the tangent, when $x = 1$, $y = 1 - 1 = 0$

The point of contact of the circle and tangent is (1, 0).

. . . .

4. Problem:

Find the two values of k such that the line $y = -2x + k$ is a tangent to the circle $x^2 + y^2 - 8x - 2y + 12 = 0$.

Solution:

Let $y = -2x + k$ in the equation of the circle

$$x^2 + (-2x + k)^2 - 8x - 2(-2x + k) + 12 = 0$$
$$x^2 + 4x^2 - 4kx + k^2 - 8x + 4x - 2k + 12 = 0$$
$$5x^2 - 4kx - 4x + k^2 - 2k + 12 = 0$$
$$5x^2 + x(-4k - 4) + k^2 - 2k + 12 = 0$$

If the line is a tangent then the discriminant will be equal to zero.

Notice that $a = 5$, $b = -4k - 4$ and $c = k^2 - 2k + 12$

b^2 - 4ac = 0

$$(-4k - 4)^2 - 4 \times 5 \times (k^2 - 2k + 12) = 0$$
$$16k^2 + 32k + 16 - 20k^2 + 40k - 240 = 0$$
$$-4k^2 + 72k - 224 = 0$$
$$-4(k^2 - 18k + 56) = 0$$
$$-4(k - 4)(k - 14) = 0$$
$$k = 4 \quad or \quad k = 14$$

. . . .

5. Problem:

Find the equation of the tangent to the circle $x^2 + y^2 - 4x - 10y - 12 = 0$ at the point Q(7,9).

Solution:

First we must check that the point lies on the circumference of the circle by substituting $x = 7$ and $y = 9$ in the equation of the circle

$7^2 + 9^2 - 4 \times 7 - 10 \times 9 - 12 = 0$ hence (7,9) lies on the circle.

$2g = -4$ so $g = -2$ and $2f = -10$ so $f = -5$.

The centre of the circle is $(-g, -f)$ which in this case is (2,5).

To find the gradient of the tangent we must first find the gradient of the radius.

$m_{radius} = \frac{9 - 5}{7 - 2} = \frac{4}{5}$

The radius is perpendicular to the tangent so $m_{\text{tangent}} = -\frac{5}{4}$.

Hence the equation of the tangent at Q(7,9) is,

$$y - 9 = -\frac{5}{4}(x - 7)$$
$$4y - 36 = -5x + 35$$
$$5x + 4y - 71 = 0$$

Relationships between a line and a circle exercise   Go online

Q30: A tangent T touches the circle C with equation $x^2 + y^2 - 6x - 6y - 7 = 0$ at the point (6,7).
What is the equation of tangent T?

. . . .

Q31: A tangent T with equation $y = -x + 8$ touches the circle C with equation $x^2 + y^2 - 4x - 4y = 0$ at the point P.
What are the coordinates of point P?

. . . .

Q32: A line L with equation $y = 3x - 18$ intersects the circle C with equation $x^2 + y^2 - 6x - 2y - 10 = 0$ at points Q and R. Where Q has the larger x-coordinate.

What are the coordinates of point Q?

....

Q33: A line with equation $y = -x + k$ is a tangent to the circle C with equation $x^2 + y^2 - 4x - 4y = 0$.

Find the two possible values of k.

5.5   Relationships between circles

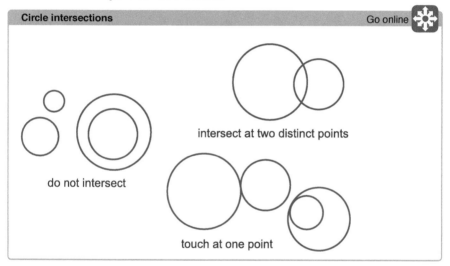

Circle intersections   Go online

do not intersect

intersect at two distinct points

touch at one point

Examples

1. Problem:

Determine whether the circle A with equation $(x + 3)^2 + (y - 1)^2 = 9$ touches the circle B with equation $(x - 5)^2 + (y + 4)^2 = 25$.

Solution:

Circle A has centre (-3,1) and radius 3.

Circle B has centre (5,-4) and radius 5.

The distance between the two centres is
$$\sqrt{(-3 - 5)^2 + (1 - (-4))^2} = \sqrt{89} \ or \ 9 \cdot 43.$$

The sum of the radii is $3 + 5 = 8$.

Since the sum of the radii is less than the distance between the two centres the circles do not touch.

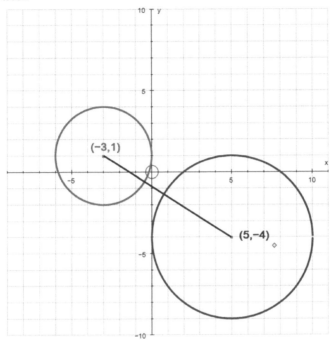

2. Problem:

Determine if the two circles with equations $(x - 2)^2 + (y - 3)^2 = 16$ and $(x + 1)^2 + (y - 2)^2 = 25$ intersect each other.

Solution:

Let C be the circle with:

- equation $(x - 2)^2 + (y - 3)^2 = 16$;
- centre (2,3);
- and radius 4.

Let D be the circle with:

- equation $(x + 1)^2 + (y - 2)^2 = 25$;
- centre (-1, 2);
- and radius 5.

The distance between the centres is $\sqrt{(2 - (-1))^2 + (3 - 2)^2} = \sqrt{10}$ *or* $3 \cdot 16$

The two radii are both greater than this distance and so the circles intersect.

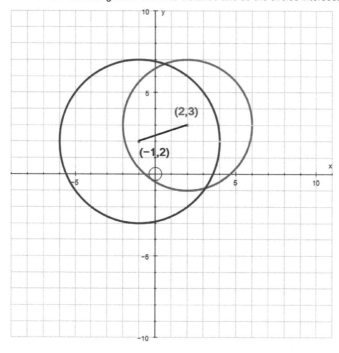

3. Problem:

Determine whether the circle A with equation $x^2 + y^2 = 4$ touches circle B with equation $x^2 + y^2 + 8x - 6y + 16 = 0$.

Solution:

Let A be the circle with:

- equation $x^2 + y^2 = 4$;
- centre (0,0);
- and radius 2.

Let B be the circle with:

- equation $x^2 + y^2 + 8x - 6y + 16 = 0$
- centre (-4, 3)
- and radius 3.

The distance between the centres is $\sqrt{(-4 - 0)^2 + (3 - 0)^2} = 5$

The sum of the radii is $2 + 3 = 5$.

Since the sum of the radii is equal to the distance between the two centres the circles touch at one point.

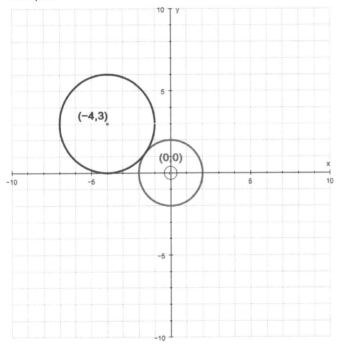

Beware: There are times where one circle could lie completely within another circle and so do not intersect.

Using the approach shown in the last example works in some cases *only*. It will not work when the sum of the distance between the centres and the radius of the smaller circle is less than the radius of the larger circle.

In the next diagram the radius of the larger circle is 5, the radius of the smaller circle is 1 and the distance between the centres is 3.

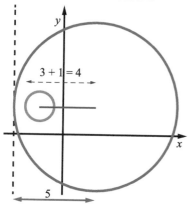

The distance between the two centres plus the radius of the smaller circle is 4 and this is less than the radius of the larger circle. Therefore the small circle is completely inside the large circle and they do not intersect.

> **Top tip**
>
> Always make a sketch to help visualize the problem.

Examples

1. Problem:

Show that the circle P with equation $(x - 4)^2 + (y - 2)^2 = 36$ touches the circle Q with equation $(x - 7)^2 + (y - 2)^2 = 9$ and find the point of contact.

Solution:

Circle P has centre (4,2) and radius 6.

Circle Q has centre (7,2) and radius 3.

The distance between the two centres is $\sqrt{(7 - 4)^2 + (2 - 2)^2} = \sqrt{9} = 3$

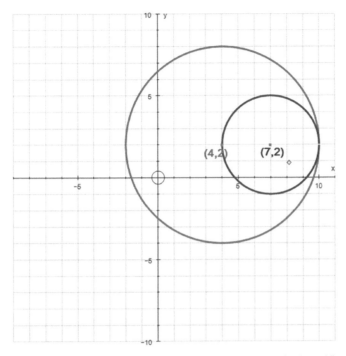

Also notice that the centres of the circles both lie on the same horizontal line.

The centre of P is (4,2) so the circumference must lie 6 units from this point i.e. (10,2). The centre of Q is (7,2) and the circumference must lie 3 units to the right of it i.e. (10,2). Hence the point of contact of circles P and Q is (10,2) and the circles touch internally.

....

2. Problem:

Find the coordinates of the points of intersection of circle V with equation $(x - 2)^2 + (y - 3)^2 = 16$ and circle W with equation $(x + 1)^2 + (y - 3)^2 = 25$.

Solution:

The points of intersection can be found by solving the two equations simultaneously.

This is only done easily because both equations contain $(y - 3)^2$.

$$(x - 2)^2 + (y - 3)^2 = 16 \quad (1)$$
$$(x + 1)^2 + (y - 3)^2 = 25 \quad (2)$$

Subtract equation 2 from equation 1.

$$(x - 2)^2 - (x + 1)^2 = 16 - 25$$
$$x^x - 4x + 4 - \left(x^2 + 2x + 1\right) = -9$$
$$-6x + 3 = -9$$
$$-6x = -12$$
$$x = 2$$

Let $x = 2$ in equation 1.

$$(2 - 2)^2 + (y - 3)^2 = 16$$
$$(y - 3)^2 - 16 = 0$$
$$y^2 - 6y - 7 = 0$$
$$(y - 7)(y + 1) = 0$$
$$y = 7 \text{ or } y = -1$$

The two points of intersection are (2, 7) and (2, -1)

If the two circles touch instead of intersecting then the quadratic equation will give two equal values on substitution.

Key point

Identical or congruent circles are exactly the same size. Size can be radius, diameter or circumference.

Relationships between circles exercise   Go online

Q34: Two congruent small circles c_1 and c_2 are drawn inside a large circle with the equation $x^2 + y^2 - 12x - 8y + 43 = 0$.

All centres lie on a line parallel to the x-axis.

If the pattern is continued, what are the coordinates of the centre of circle c_3?

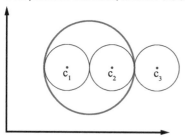

. . . .

Q35: Determine whether circle A with equation $(x - 3)^2 + (y - 2)^2 = 4$ touches or intersects circle B with equation $(x + 5)^2 + (y + 6)^2 = 24$.

. . . .

Q36: Determine whether circle P with equation $(x - 2)^2 + (y - 3)^2 = 16$ and circle Q with equation $(x + 1)^2 + (y - 2)^2 = 25$ intersect each other.

. . . .

Q37: Find the coordinates of the points of intersection of circle C with equation $(x - 3)^2 + (y + 1)^2 = 16$ and circle D with equation $(x - 3)^2 + (y - 2)^2 = 25$.

5.6   Learning points

Circles
The equation of a circle

- The equation of a circle with centre (0,0) and radius r is $x^2 + y^2 = r^2$.

- The equation of a circle with centre (a, b) and radius r is $(x - a)^2 + (y - b)^2 = r^2$.

- The general equation of the circle is $x^2 + y^2 + 2gx + 2fy + c = 0$, with centre (-g,-f) and radius $\sqrt{g^2 + f^2 - c}$, provided $g^2 + f^2 - c > 0$.

Lines and circles

- The relationship between a line and a circle can be found by:

  1. **substituting** the equation of the line into the equation of the circle;
  2. **collecting like terms** to obtain a quadratic equation;
  3. evaluating and interpreting the **discriminant:**
     - if $b^2 - 4ac = 0$ then the line is a **tangent** to the circle;
     - if $b^2 - 4ac > 0$ then there are **2** points of intersection;
     - if $b^2 - 4ac < 0$ then the line **does not** meet the circle at all.

- The coordinates of any points of intersection can be found by **solving** the quadratic.

- A radius and tangent are perpendicular at the point of contact.

- The equation of a tangent to a circle at the point (a, b) can be found by:

  1. finding the gradient of the radius;
  2. using $m_{\text{tangent}} \times m_{radius} = -1$ to find the gradient of the tangent;
  3. substituting the gradient of the tangent and the coordinates of the point of contact into $y - b = m(x - a)$.

- It is useful to remember that the angle in a semi-circle is a right angle.

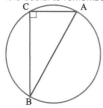

- It is useful to remember that a radius bisects a chord at right angles.

Intersecting circles

- Circles which do not touch can be one inside the other or completely apart.

- Circles can touch internally or externally.

- Circles may intersect.

- The distance between the centres can help to determine the relationship between two circles.

- The journey between the coordinates of centres or points of contact can help in problem solving situations.

The circumcentre

- The centre of the circle which passes through the vertices of a triangle is the point of intersection of the perpendicular bisectors of the triangle.

Concentric and Congruent circles

- Concentric circles have the same centre.

- Congruent circles have the same size. Size can be radius, diameter or circumference.

5.7   End of topic test

End of topic 9 test   Go online

Q38: What are the coordinates of the centre of the circle with equation $4x^2 + 4y^2 = 36$?

Q39: A circle has radius 7 units and centre (-8,7). What is the equation of the circle?

....

Q40: A circle has equation $x^2 + y^2 + 2x - 8y - 13 = 0$. What are the coordinates of its centre?

....

Q41: What is the length of the radius of the circle with equation $x^2 + y^2 + 2x - 8y - 13 = 0$?

Q42: What are the coordinates of the centre and the radius of the circle with the equation $x^2 + y^2 + 18x - 115 = 0$?

....

Q43: What are the coordinates of the centre and the radius of the circle with the equation $x^2 + y^2 - 12y = -20$?

A circle has diameter AB where A(-3,-4) and B(5,8).

Q44: What are the coordinates of the centre of this circle?

....

Q45: What is the radius of this circle?

Q46: Determine whether the line with equation $y = 2x + 6$ is a tangent to the circle with equation $x^2 + y^2 - 4x - 16 = 0$.

Q47: The point P(0,1) lies on the circle with centre C(-5,5) as shown in the diagram. Find the equation of the tangent at P.

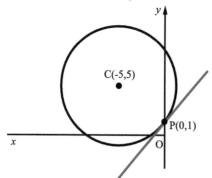

Q48: Find the equation of the tangent T touches the circle C with equation $x^2 + y^2 + 6x - 6y - 7 = 0$ at the point (-7,0).

Q49: Find the coordinates of Point P where the tangent T with equation $y = -2x + 9$ touches the circle C with equation $x^2 + y^2 - 2x - 4y = 0$.

Q50: Determine whether circle A with equation $(x + 4)^2 + (y - 3)^2 = 8$ touches or intersects circle B with equation $(x - 2)^2 + (y + 1)^2 = 3$.

Q51: Determine whether circle P with equation $(x + 5)^2 + (y - 2)^2 = 16$ and circle Q with equation $(x + 4)^2 + (y - 3)^2 = 4$ intersect each other.

Topic 6

Logs and exponentials

Contents

Learning objective

By the end of this topic, you should be able to:

- solve problems involving exponential equations;
- use the laws of logarithms to simplify log expressions;
- solve problems using logarithmic equations;
- use a straight line graph to determine relationships of the form:
  - $y = kx^n$ from experimental data;
  - $y = ab^x$ from experimental data.

6.1 Logarithmic and exponential functions

We already know what the equations and graphs of logs and exponentials look like.

Logarithms are the "opposite" of exponentials, just as subtraction is the opposite of addition and division is the opposite of multiplication. Logarithms can be used to "undo" exponentials and exponentials can be used to "undo" logarithms.

Logarithms are the inverses of exponentials and their graphs are a reflection of the other in the line $y = x$.

6.1.1 Growth and decay functions

Exponential functions take the form $y = a^x$.

If $a > 1$ the graph is increasing.

Notice that the curve gets very close to the x-axis as x approaches negative infinity $(-\infty)$ and it passes through the points (0,1) and (1,a).

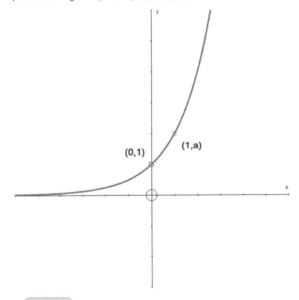

Key point

This type of function is called a growth function.

Examples of growth functions are compound interest, nuclear chain reaction, bacteria, viruses and population.

If $0 < a < 1$ the graph is decreasing.

Notice that the curve gets very close to the x-axis as x approaches positive infinity (∞) and it also passes through the points (0,1) and (1,a).

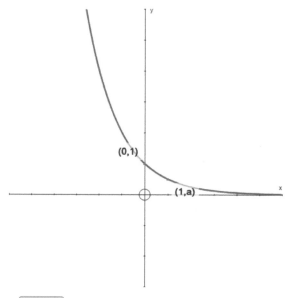

Examples of decay functions are depreciation, heat transfer, vibration and radioactivity.

Examples

1. Exponential growth

Problem:

A lump sum of £25000 is invested at a fixed rate of 6·5% per annum.

a) How much interest will be accrued in 5 years?
b) How long will it take to double the investment?

Solution:

a)
After 5 years the investment will be worth $25000 \times 1 \cdot 065^5 = £34252 \cdot 17$

So the interest accrued will be $34252 \cdot 17 - 25000 = £9252 \cdot 17$

b)
This part is trickier!

Double £25000 is £50000.

What we want to know is when $25000 \times 1 \cdot 065^n \geq 50000$.
This can be simplified to $1 \cdot 065^n \geq 2$.

Trial and error will help here...
...after 10 years $1 \cdot 065^{10} = 1 \cdot 877$
...after 11 years $1 \cdot 065^{11} = 1 \cdot 999$

This answer is close to 2 but not ≥ 2...
...after 12 years $1 \cdot 065^{12} = 2 \cdot 129$

Hence the sum invested will double after 12 years.

. . . .

2. Exponential decay

Problem:

A 50 ml bottle of perfume will evaporate at a rate of 2·25% per day if the top is left open.

a) What volume of perfume will be in the bottle after 2 weeks?
b) How long will it take for half of the perfume to evaporate?

Solution:

a)
If 2·25% of the perfume evaporates then 97·75% will remain.
After 14 days the volume of perfume will be $50 \times 0 \cdot 9775^{14} = 36 \cdot 358\ ml$.

b)
Half of 50ml is 25 ml.

What we want to know is when $50 \times 0 \cdot 9775^n \leq 25$.
This can be simplified to $0 \cdot 9775^n \leq 0 \cdot 5$.

Trial and error will help here...
...after 28 days $0 \cdot 9775^{28} = 0 \cdot 528$
...after 29 days $0 \cdot 9775^{29} = 0 \cdot 517$
...after 30 days $0 \cdot 9775^{30} = 0 \cdot 505$

This is close to 0·5 but not $\leq 0·5$
...after 31 days $0 \cdot 9775^{31} = 0 \cdot 493$

Hence after 31 days the volume of perfume will have halved.

Key point

The term **half-life** is the time required for any specified property to decrease by half.

Growth and decay functions data exercise   Go online

The population of a designated new town is 2450 and is estimated to increase at a rate of 9·25% per annum.

Q1: What will the population be after 5 years?

. . . .

Q2: How long will it take for the population to double?

A new car worth £17995 depreciates in value by 18·5% each year.

Q3: What is the half-life of the car?

....

Q4: If the car is to be scrapped when it's value falls below £1000, after how many years will the car be scrapped?

6.1.2 The exponential function

We already know how to find the values of exponential expressions on our calculator. There are several buttons that we already regularly use e.g. x^3, x^2 and x^n but there are two other buttons which can be useful too.

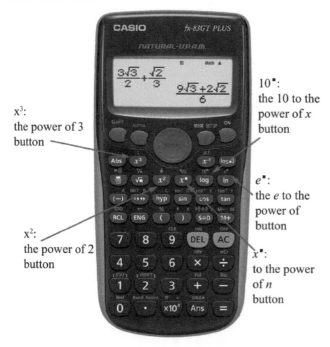

x^3:
the power of 3 button

x^2:
the power of 2 button

$10^{\bullet}$:
the 10 to the power of x button

$e^{\bullet}$:
the e to the power of button

$x^{\bullet}$:
to the power of n button

A special exponential function e^x is usually found by pressing $shift$ and ln.

The value of e is 2·718281828... where e is sometimes called Euler's number. e is a special number like pi and you will find that,
If $f(x) = e^x$ then $f'(x) = e^x$ (i.e. the exponential function e is its own derivative.

Example

Problem:

A population, P, is modelled using the equation $P = P_0 e^{0.0039t}$ where P_0 is the population in 2014 and t is the time in years since 2014.

In 2014 the population was approximately 9·5 million what will the population be in 2020?

Solution:

$P_0 = 9 \cdot 5$ and $t = 6$

$P = 9 \cdot 5 \times e^{0.0039 \times 6} = 9 \cdot 72$ million

Note that $e^{0.0039}$ *represents the annual rate of increase in the population.*

The exponential function exercise   Go online

Use your calculator to evaluate the following exponentials.

Q5: e^5?

....

Q6: $e^{3.75}$?

....

Q7: e^{-4}?

....

Q8: $e^{\frac{2}{7}}$?

....

Q9: The mass, $\mathbf{m}$, of an amount of radioactive material after a period of time, $\mathbf{t}$, in days is given by $m = 75e^{-0.7t}$.
How much material will there be after 9 days?

6.1.3   Logarithmic functions

A function of the form $f(x) = \log_a x$ where $a \neq 1$ and $x > 0$ is called a Logarithmic function, $\log_a x$ reads "log to the base a of x".

Notice $y = \log_a x$ is only defined when $x > 0$.

If $a > 1$ the graph is increasing.

Notice that the curve gets very close to the y-axis (i.e. y approaches negative infinity as x approaches 0) and the graph passes through the points (1,0) and (a,1).

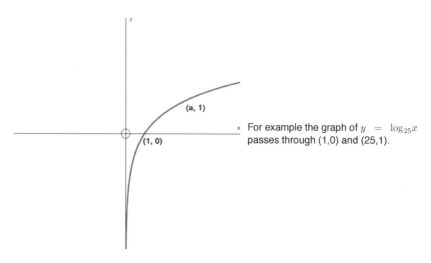

For example the graph of $y = \log_{25} x$
passes through (1,0) and (25,1).

If $0 < a < 1$ the graph is decreasing.

Notice that the curve gets very close to the y-axis (i.e. y approaches infinity as x approaches 0) and the graph passes through the points (1,0) and (a,1).

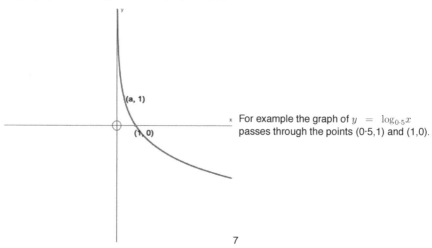

For example the graph of $y = \log_{0.5} x$
passes through the points (0·5,1) and (1,0).

7

Remember the inverse of an exponential function is a logarithmic function and vice versa.

Key point

If $f(x) = a^x$ then $f^{-1}(x) = \log_a x$.

Notice the base is the same in the exponential function and the logarithmic function.

Logs and exponentials relationships Go online

Examples

1. We know that $3^4 = 81$

... but it can be written as $\log_3 81 = 4$

....

2. We know that $2^{-3} = \frac{1}{2^3} = \frac{1}{8}$

... but it can be written as $\log_2 \frac{1}{8} = -3$

....

3. We know that $8^{\frac{2}{3}} = \sqrt[3]{8^2} = 4$

... but it can be written as $\log_8 4 = \frac{2}{3}$

....

4. We know that $e^0 = 1$

... but it can be written as $\log_e 1 = 0$

Key point

$$\text{If } y = a^x \text{ then } \log_a y = x.$$

There are some more useful buttons on your calculator.

$\log_{\blacksquare}\square$ button
means $\log_a x$

log button
means $\log_{10} x$

In button
means $\log_e x$

$y = \log_e x$ is called the natural logarithm.

Logarithms and calculator buttons practice exercise   Go online

Evaluate the following exponential expressions, correct to 2 d.p. using a calculator.

Q10: $e^{1\cdot8}$

....

Q11: $10^{2\cdot9}$

....

Q12: $2e^{1\cdot83}$

....

Q13: 3^e

Evaluate the following logarithmic expressions, correct to 2 d.p. using a calculator.

Q14: $\ln 2 \cdot 5$

....

Q15: $\log_e 3 \cdot 79$

....

Q16: $\log_{10} 3$

....

Q17: $\ln 3^e$

Evaluate the following logarithmic expressions, correct to 2 d.p. using a calculator.

Q18: $\log_{10} 2 \cdot 9$

....

Q19: $\log_e 2 \cdot 769$

....

Q20: $6\log_e 2 \cdot 698$

....

Q21: $8\log_e 7 \cdot 8$

Evaluate the following log expressions, correct to 2 d.p. using a calculator.

Q22: $\log_4 5$

....

Q23: $\log_3 0 \cdot 143$

....

Q24: $2\log_{0.275} 8 \cdot 2$

....

Q25: $7\log_{0.85} e^1$

Rather than trial and error we can now use logarithms to solve problems where the unknown value is the power.

Examples

1. Problem:

If $\log_5 x \;=\; 2$, find x.

Solution:

$\log_5 x \;=\; 2$ can be written as the exponential equation.

$5^2 \;=\; x$

So $x \;=\; 25$

....

2. Problem:

If $5^y \;=\; 2 \cdot 3$, find y.

Solution:

$5^y \;=\; 2 \cdot 3$ can be written as the logarithmic equation.

$\log_5 2 \cdot 3 \;=\; y$

Put this in your calculator using the $\log$ button to find y.

$y \;=\; 0 \cdot 5175$

....

3. Problem:

If $\log_e p \;=\; 20$, find p.

Solution:

$\log_e p \;=\; 20$ can be written as the exponential equation.

$e^{20} \;=\; p$

$p \;=\; 485165195 \cdot 4$

Remember to use the shift ln buttons to find e^x.

Logarithmic functions exercise   Go online

Q26: Solve $6^x = 40$.

....

Q27: Give $a^y = x$ in log form.

....

Q28: Give $a^7 = p$ in log form.

....

Q29: Give $3^a = b$ in log form.

....

Q30: Give $2^x = y$ in log form.

....

Q31: Write $\log_a x = b$ in exponential form.

....

Q32: Write $\log_4 x = y$ in exponential form.

....

Q33: Write $\log_r s = 2$ in exponential form.

....

Q34: Find the value for x if $10^x = 5$ correct to two decimal places.

....

Q35: What is the value of c if $\log_2 c = 7$?

....

Q36: Find b if $\log_b 2^4 = 4$.

....

Q37: What is x if $\log_{10} x = 2$?

....

Q38: Find n if $e^n = 1 \cdot 284$.

6.2 Laws of logarithms

You already know the laws of indices from the National 5 course:

1. $a^m \times a^n = a^{m+n}$

2. $\frac{a^m}{a^n} = a^{m-n}$

3. $(a^m)^n = a^{m \times n}$

4. $a^0 = 1$

5. $a^{-m} = \frac{1}{a^m}$

6. $a^{\frac{m}{n}} = \sqrt[n]{a^m}$

The first few laws will help us to understand the associated laws of logarithms. Remember that logs are the inverse of exponentials so the laws of logs should be just as easy.

> **Key point**
>
> The first law of indices states that $a^m \times a^n = a^{m+n}$ and leads us to the first law of logarithms.
>
> $$\log_a m + \log_a n = \log_a(m \times n)$$

Examples

1. Problem:

Evaluate $\log_6 4 + \log_6 9$

Solution:

$$\log_6 4 + \log_6 9 = \log_6(4 \times 9)$$
$$= \log_6 36$$

....

2. Problem:

What is $\log_2 32 + \log_2 64$?

Solution:

$$\log_2 32 + \log_2 64 = \log_2(32 \times 64)$$
$$= \log_2 2048$$

We can simplify this further with a calculator but we must also be able to evaluate it without a calculator..

Let $y = \log_2 2048$ turn this into an exponential

$$2^y = 2048$$

2 to the power is easy to find by repeated doubling (use your fingers to keep track of the power).

2	4	8	16	32	64	128	256	512	1024	2048
2^1	2^2	2^3	2^4	2^5	2^6	2^7	2^8	2^9	2^{10}	2^{11}

and $\log_2 2048 = 11$

Hence $\log_2 32 + \log_2 64 = 11$

Key point

The second law of indices states that $\frac{a^m}{a^n} = a^{m-n}$ and leads us to the second law of logarithms.

$$\log_a m - \log_a n = \log_a \frac{m}{n}$$

Example

Problem:

What is $\log_3 81 - \log_3 9$?

Solution:

$$\log_3 81 - \log_3 9 = \log_3 \frac{81}{9}$$
$$= \log_3 9$$

We can evaluate this with a calculator but again we must be able to work out the answer without a calculator.

Let $y = \log_3 9$
$3^y = 9$

we know that $y = 2$ because $3^2 = 9$

so $\log_3 9 = 2$

Hence $\log_3 81 - \log_3 9 = 2$.

Key point

The third law of logarithms is:

$$\log_a x^n = n\log_a x$$

Notice that the power becomes a scalar.

Example

Problem:

What is $\log_5 125^4$?

Solution:

$$\log_5 125^4 = 4 \log_5 125$$

We can simplify this further with a calculator but we must also be able to evaluate it without a calculator.

Let $y = \log_5 125$
$5^y = 125$

we know that $y = 3$ because $5^3 = 125$

so $4\log_5 125 = 4 \times 3 = 12$

Hence $\log_5 125^4 = 12$.

Key point

The fourth law of indices states that $a^0 = 1$ and leads us to the fourth law of logarithms.

$$\log_a 1 = 0$$

Key point

We also know that $a^1 = a$ and that leads us to the fifth law of logarithms.

$$\log_a a = 1$$

Example

Problem:

What is $\log_8 4 + \log_8 6 - \log_8 3$?

Solution:

$$\log_8 4 + \log_8 6 - \log_8 3 = \log_8 \left(\frac{4 \times 6}{3} \right)$$
$$= \log_8 8$$
$$= 1$$

Log laws and relationships   Go online

Examples

1. Problem:

Find x when $\log_x 36 = 2$.

Solution:

$\log_x 36 = 2 \Rightarrow 36 = x^2$

This is because $\log_a y = x \Rightarrow y = a^x$

Therefore, $x = 6$

....

2. Problem:

Simplify $\log_4 28 - 2\log_4 2$.

Solution:

$$\log_4 28 - 2\log_4 2 = \log_4(7 \times 4) - \log_4 2^2$$
$$= \log_4 7 + \log_4 4 - \log_4 4$$

Why?

Firstly $n\log_a b = \log_a b^n$
then $\log_a bc = \log_a b + \log_a c$

$$\log_4 28 - 2\log_4 2 = \log_4(7 \times 4) - \log_4 2^2$$
$$= \log_4 7 + \log_4 4 - \log_4 4$$
$$= \log_4 7$$

. . . .

3. Problem:

Evaluate $\log_5 40 - \log_5 8$.

Solution:

$$\log_5 40 - \log_5 8 = \log_5\left(\frac{40}{8}\right)$$

Why?

... because $\log_a\left(\frac{b}{c}\right) = \log_a b - \log_a c$

$$\log_5 40 - \log_5 8 = \log_5\left(\frac{40}{8}\right)$$
$$= \log_5 5$$
$$= 1$$

Why?

... because $\log_a a = 1$

A word of warning $\log_a m - \log_a n = \log_a \frac{m}{n}$ and should not be confused with $\frac{\log_a m}{\log_a n}$ which can only be evaluated as it stands.

> **Key point**
>
> The laws of logarithms only apply when the bases of the logs are equal.

These laws are required for manipulation of expressions involving logs and exponentials. Although it is important to learn these laws, familiarity with them will increase with practice.

> **Key point**
>
> The laws of logarithms are:
>
> 1. $\log_a m + \log_a n = \log_a(m \times n)$
>
> 2. $\log_a m - \log_a n = \log_a \frac{m}{n}$
>
> 3. $\log_a x^n = n\log_a x$
>
> 4. $\log_a 1 = 0$
>
> 5. $\log_a a = 1$

Examples

1. Problem:

Simplify $\log_3(p + 2) - 4\log_3 2$.

Solution:

$$\begin{aligned}
\log_3(p + 2) - 4\log_3 2 &= \log_3(p + 2) - \log_3 2^4 \\
&= \log_3(p + 2) - \log_3 16 \\
&= \log_3 \frac{p + 2}{16}
\end{aligned}$$

....

2. Problem:

What is the value of $\frac{\log_2 16}{\log_2 2}$?

Solution:

$$\begin{aligned}
\frac{\log_2 16}{\log_2 2} &= \frac{\log_2 2^4}{\log_2 2} \\
&= \frac{4\log_2 2}{\log_2 2} \\
&= 4
\end{aligned}$$

because $\dfrac{\log_2 2}{\log_2 2} = 1$ and $4 \times 1 = 4$

....

3. Problem:

If $\log_8 r = \frac{1}{3}$, what is the value of r?

Solution:

$\log_8 r = \frac{1}{3}$ can be simplified to,

$$r = 8^{\frac{1}{3}}$$
$$r = \sqrt[3]{8}$$
$$r = 2$$

....

4. Problem:

What is the exact value of $\log_4 64$?

Solution:

$$\begin{aligned}
\log_4 64 &= \log_4 4^3 \\
&= 3\log_4 4 \\
&= 3 \times 1 \\
&= 3
\end{aligned}$$

Laws of logarithms exercise Go online

Without using a calculator answer these questions.

Q39: Simplify $\log_a 3 \;+\; \log_a 8 \;-\; 2\log_a 2$

....

Q40: What is $\log_6 18 \;+\; \log_6 2$?

....

Q41: What is $\log_4 128 \;-\; \log_4 2$?

....

Q42: What is $5\log_5 25$?

....

Q43: What is $2\log_e 4 \;-\; \log_e 16$?

....

Q44: What is $\frac{1}{4}\log_2 16$?

....

Q45: What is $5\log_{10}\left(\frac{1}{100}\right)$?

Without using a calculator, simplify these expressions.

Q46: $\log_{10} 5 \;+\; \log_{10} 2$

....

Q47: $3\log_{10} 4 \;-\; \log_{10} 8$ giving your answer as a log.

....

Q48: $8\log_{10} 10$

....

Q49: $\log_{10}\left(5 \;\times\; 10^{1000}\right) \;-\; \log_{10} 5$

Find the value of x in the following by using the log laws.

Q50: $2\log_3 12 \;-\; \log_3 16 \;=\; x$

....

Q51: $\ln x^2 \;-\; \ln 36 \;=\; \ln e$

....

Q52: $3\log_5 x \;-\; \log_5 6^3 \;=\; 0$

6.3 Problem solving

The laws of logs can be used to solve problems involving more complex equations.

Examples

1. Problem:

Solve $\log_{30}(x - 2) + \log_{30}(x - 1) = 1$

Solution:

$$\log_{30}(x - 2) + \log_{30}(x - 1) = 1$$
$$\log_{30}(x - 2)(x - 1) = 1$$
$$30^1 = (x - 2)(x - 1)$$
$$x^2 - 3x + 2 = 30$$
$$x^2 - 3x - 28 = 0$$
$$(x - 7)(x + 4) = 0$$
$$x = 7 \quad or \quad x = -4$$

-4 is a solution to the quadratic but is not a solution to the original $\log$ equation. Since for $x = -4$, $\log_{30}(x - 1)$ is undefined so that solution must be rejected.

Hence $x = 7$ is the only solution.

. . . .

2. Problem:

Solve $3^x = 4$

Solution:

It may seem obvious to start with the relationship $a^y = x \iff \log_a x = y$.

This would give x in $\log$ terms but there is no easy way of finding x.

The solution lies in applying logs to each side of the equation.

You can choose logs to any base which can be entered in your calculator e.g.

$$\log_{10} 3^x = \log_{10} 4$$
$$x \log_{10} 3 = \log_{10} 4$$
$$x = \log_{10} 4 \div \log_{10} 3$$
$$= 1 \cdot 2619$$

. . . .

3. Problem:

Solve $\log_6(x^2 - 9) - \log_6(x - 3) - 2 = 0$

Solution:

$$\log_6\left(x^2 - 9\right) - \log_6\left(x - 3\right) - 2 = 0$$
$$\log_6\left(x^2 - 9\right) - \log_6\left(x - 3\right) = 2$$
$$\log_6\frac{x^2 - 9}{x - 3} = 2$$
$$\log_6\frac{(x - 3)(x + 3)}{x - 3} = 2$$
$$\log_6\left(x + 3\right) = 2$$
$$6^2 = x + 3$$
$$33 = x$$

....

4. Problem:

If $\log_5 y = 3\log_5 x + \log_5 4$, express y in terms of x.

Solution:

$$\log_5 y = 3\log_5 x + \log_5 4$$
$$\log_5 y = \log_5 x^3 + \log_5 4$$
$$\log_5 y = \log_5 4x^3$$

Now remove the logs from both sides of the equation to give,

$$y = 4x^3$$

....

5. Problem:

What are the coordinates of the point where the graph with the equation $y = \log_4(x + 2) - 1 \cdot 6$ crosses the x-axis?

Solution:

$y = 0$ at the point where the graph crosses the x-axis so we have to solve,

$$\log_4\left(x + 2\right) - 1 \cdot 6 = 0$$
$$\log_4\left(x + 2\right) = 1 \cdot 6$$
$$4^{1 \cdot 6} = x + 2$$
$$x = 4^{1 \cdot 6} - 2$$
$$x = 7 \cdot 19 \quad \text{(to 2 d.p.)}$$

Hence the graph of the equation $y = \log_4(x + 2) - 1 \cdot 6$ crosses the x-axis at $(7 \cdot 19, 0)$.

....

6. Problem:

Functions f, g and h are defined on suitable domains where $f(x) = \log_3 x$, $g(x) = x^2 + 3x - 4$ and $h(x) = x - 1$.

Solve $f(g(x)) - f(h(x)) = 2$

Solution:

$$f(g(x)) = \log_3(x^2 + 3x - 4)$$

$$f(h(x)) = \log_3(x - 1)$$

You will need to use the laws of logs to subtract,

$$
\begin{aligned}
f(g(x)) - f(h(x)) &= \log_3\left(x^2 + 3x - 4\right) - \log_3\left(x - 1\right) \\
&= \log_3\left(\frac{x^2 + 3x - 4}{x - 1}\right) \\
&= \log_3\left(\frac{(x + 4)(x - 1)}{x - 1}\right) \\
&= \log_3(x + 4)
\end{aligned}
$$

Now $f(g(x)) - f(h(x)) = 2$ gives $\log_3(x + 4) = 2$

Turn this log equation into an exponential equation,

$$3^2 = x + 4$$
$$9 = x + 4$$
$$x = 5$$

The previous examples and exercises dealt with solutions to equations with an unknown variable. However, there are many real life situations which can be modelled and solved using logarithmic and exponential functions.

We have already met examples of exponential growth and exponential decay but there are times when we will have to use logs to find the solutions to problems.

Examples

1. Exponential decay problem

Problem:

The mass M_t of a radioactive substance at time t years is given by the equation $M_t = M_0\,e^{-kt}$ where M_0 is the initial mass and k is a constant.

a) 90 grams of this substance decays to leave 30 grams over 4 years. Find k to 3 d.p.

b) If another sample is found weighing 500 grams, how much, to the nearest gram, will remain in 20 years?

c) What is the half life of this substance?

d) Illustrate this information on a graph.

Solution:

a)

$$M_t = M_0 e^{-kt}$$

$$30 = 90 \times e^{-k \times 4}$$

$$\frac{30}{90} = e^{-4k}$$

$$\frac{3}{9} = e^{-4k}$$

$$\log_e\left(\frac{1}{3}\right) = -4k$$

$$\frac{\log_e\left(\frac{1}{3}\right)}{-4} = k$$

$$k = 0 \cdot 275$$

b)

$$M_t = 500e^{-20(0 \cdot 275)} = 2 \text{ grams.}$$

c)

$$M_t = M_0 e^{-0 \cdot 275t}$$

At the half life $M_t = 0 \cdot 5M_0$ so we get

$$0 \cdot 5M_0 = M_0 e^{-0 \cdot 275t}$$

$$0 \cdot 5 = e^{-0 \cdot 275t}$$

$$\log_e 0 \cdot 5 = -0 \cdot 275t$$

$$\frac{\log_e 0 \cdot 5}{-0 \cdot 275} = t$$

$$t = 2 \cdot 52 \text{ years}$$

d)

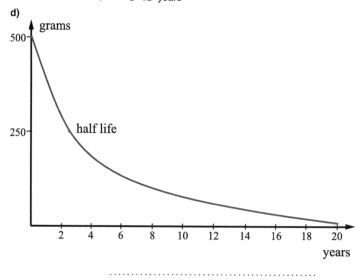

2. Exponential growth

Problem:

A sample of bacteria multiplies at a rate according to the formula $B = 25\,e^{kt}$ where k is a constant, B is the number of bacteria in thousands present after t minutes.

a) How many bacteria are assumed to be taken initially for the sample?

b) If after 18 minutes there are 35000 bacteria, what is the value of k (to 5 d.p.)?

c) How long to the nearest second will it take for the bacteria to double?

d) How many whole bacteria are present after one hour.

Solution:

a)
Since $t = 0$ at the start
$B = 25 \times e^{k \times 0}$
$B = 25$ but since B is the number of bacteria in thousands the initial sample is 25000.

b)
$$35 = 25e^{18k}$$
$$\frac{35}{25} = e^{18k}$$
$$18k = \log_e\left(\frac{35}{25}\right)$$
$$k = \log_e\left(\frac{35}{25}\right) \div 18$$
$$k = 0 \cdot 01869$$

c)
$B = 25$ initially, so double would be 50.
$$50 = 25e^{0 \cdot 01869t}$$
$$2 = e^{0 \cdot 01869t}$$
$$0 \cdot 01869t = \log_e 2$$
$$t = \log_e 2 \div 0 \cdot 01869$$
$$t = 37 \cdot 09 \text{ minutes}$$

0·09 minutes $\times$ 60 = 5·4 seconds.

The bacteria double after 37 minutes and 5 seconds.

d)
$$B = 25\,e^{0 \cdot 01869 \times 60}$$
$$B = 76 \cdot 7287$$

There will be 76728 whole bacteria present after one hour.

Problem solving exercise   Go online

Q53: Solve for x: $\log_2(x - 3) + \log_2(x - 1) = 3$

....

Q54: Solve for a: $8^a = 4$.

....

Q55: Solve for x: $\log_4(x^2 - 81) - \log_4(x - 9) - 2 = 0$

....

Q56: Solve $\log_{20}(x - 6) + \log_{20}(x + 2) = 1$

....

Q57: Solve $\log_6(x + 1) + \log_6(x + 2) = 1$

....

Q58: Solve $\log_{14}(x + 1) + \log_{14}(x - 4) = 1$

....

Q59: Solve $5^x = 4$, correct to 3 decimal places.

....

Q60: Solve $\log_x 81 = 4$

....

Q61: Solve $3\log_e(2a - 1) = 0$.

....

Q62: Solve $4\log_e(2k - 3) = 0$.

....

Q63: Solve $7^{2p + 5} = 2$, correct to 2 decimal places.

....

Q64: Solve $5^{3q - 1} = 12$, correct to 2 decimal places.

....

Q65: Bacteria increase according to the formula $B = 2e^{0.6t}$ where t is the time in hours and B is the number of bacteria in thousands.

  a) How many bacteria are present at the start of the experiment?

  b) How long does it take, in minutes, for the bacteria to double?

  c) A sample of 2 bacteria are placed in a dish. After 12 hours the thermostat breaks. How many bacteria are present when this happens?

....

Q66: A chemical evaporates according to the formula $C = C_0 e^{-kt}$ where t is the time in hours, k is a constant and C_0 is the initial volume of the chemical.

  a) If 130 ccs evaporates to leave 70 ccs after 5 hours, find k.

  b) How long does it take, in minutes, for the volume of the chemical to reach 35 ccs if the initial volume is 210 ccs?

....

Q67: A faulty high pressure container is filled to a pressure of 140 psi. The pressure in the container after t hours is given by the formula $P_1 = P_0 e^{-kt}$ where P_0 is the initial pressure.

  a) After 9 hours the pressure drops to 50 psi. Find the value of k.

  b) To avoid damage, the contents in the container must be kept at a pressure of at least 60 psi. If the container is pressurised to 190 psi, how long, in minutes, will the contents be safe?

....

Q68: The half life of radium is 11·4 days.

If R_0 represents the amount of radium in a sample at the start and R_t represents the amount remaining after t days, then $R_t = R_0 e^{-at}$

What is the value of a, correct to 3 significant figures?

6.4 Formulae from experimental data

Scientists undertaking experiments are normally interested in finding a relationship between the variables which they are investigating. In some cases, where two variables are involved, the data may suggest exponential formulae.

Not only can the graphs of the variables be plotted against each other, but in particular instances, if an exponential relationship is suspected, then it is easier to plot the logs of the variables against each other. In this way, if the resulting graph is a straight line, then the variables are connected by an exponential formula.

The reasoning behind this follows. Suppose that results suggest that two variables x and y are connected according to the formula $y = kx^n$.

$$y = kx^n \qquad \text{apply } \log_{10} \text{ to both sides of the equation}$$
$$\log_{10}y = \log_{10}kx^n$$
$$\log_{10}y = \log_{10}k + \log_{10}x^n$$
$$\log_{10}y = \log_{10}k + n\log_{10}x$$
$$\log_{10}y = n\log_{10}x + \log_{10}k$$

Now this equation looks a bit like $y = mx + c$ but is written as,
$Y = mX + c$ where $Y = \log_{10}y$, $X = \log_{10}x$, $m = n$ and $c = \log_{10}k$.

$Y = mX + c$ is indeed the formula for a straight line.

By evaluating m and c in the normal way to give the equation of a straight line, the resulting information is enough to find the constants k and n and hence the exponential equation required.

Key point

If $y = kx^n$ then $\log y = n \log x + \log k$

(which is in the form $Y = mX + c$)

Examples

1.

A scientist obtained the following data:

x	13	28	63	126
y	14	6	3	1·5

If we graph the data we get,

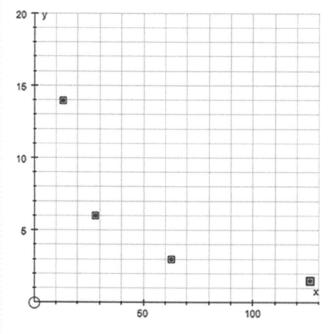

The data indicates exponential decay and it is thought that x and y are related by the equation $y = ax^n$ so we apply logs to all x and y values to see if the resulting graph is linear (a straight line).

$\log_{10} x$ has been chosen here but it would be possible to apply logs of any base.

$\log_{10}x$	1·11	1·45	1·8	2·1
$\log_{10}y$	1·15	0·78	0·48	0·18

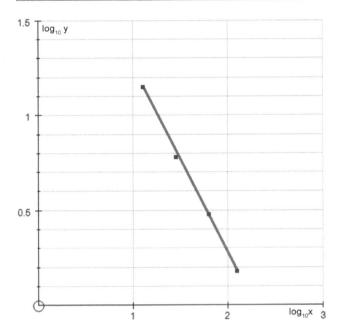

The graph looks approximately linear so the original variables look to be connected exponentially in the form $y = ax^n$.

We can find the equation of the straight line above in the form $y = mx + c$ by using the points (1·11,1·15) and (2·1,0·18).

$$m = \frac{0 \cdot 18 - 1 \cdot 15}{2 \cdot 1 - 1 \cdot 11}$$
$$= \frac{-0 \cdot 97}{0 \cdot 99}$$
$$= -0 \cdot 98$$

Now find the equation using the point (2·1,0·18) and $m = -0 \cdot 98$

$Y - b = m(X - a)$ where $Y = \log_{10}y$ and $X = \log_{10}x$

$Y - 0 \cdot 18 = -0 \cdot 98(X - 2 \cdot 1)$

$Y - 0 \cdot 18 = -0 \cdot 98X + 2 \cdot 058$

$\qquad Y = -0 \cdot 98X + 2 \cdot 238$

Now remember if $y = ax^n$ then
$\log_{10}y = n\log_{10}x + \log_{10}a$
$\qquad Y = -0 \cdot 98X + 2 \cdot 238$

Hopefully you can see that $n = -0 \cdot 98$ and $\log_{10} a = 2 \cdot 238$.

To find the value of "a" we change the equation into the exponential $10^{2 \cdot 238} = a$ so $a = 172 \cdot 98$

and the formula connecting the data is $y = 172 \cdot 98 x^{-0 \cdot 98}$.

. . . .

2. Problem:

The variables y and x are related by the equation $y = ax^n$.

The graph of $\log_4 x$ against $\log_4 y$ gives the straight line shown below.

What are the values of a and n?

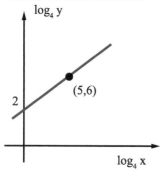

Solution:

We can find the equation of the straight line above in the form $Y = mX + c$ by using the points (0,2) and (5,6).

$$m = \frac{6 - 2}{5 - 0}$$
$$= \frac{4}{5}$$
$$= 0 \cdot 8$$

We can find the equation using the point (0,2) and $m = 0 \cdot 8$ in
$Y = 0 \cdot 8X + 2$ where $Y = \log_4 y$ and $X = \log_4 x$

We know that if $y = ax^n$ then $\log_4 y = n\log_4 x + \log_4 a$

so from $Y = 0 \cdot 8X + 2$

we can see that $n = 0 \cdot 8$

and $\log_4 a = 2 \Rightarrow 4^2 = a$ so $a = 16$

and the formula connecting x and y is $y = 16x^{0 \cdot 8}$

Key point

To find the equation $y = ax^n$ from experimental data:

1. identify 2 points from the line of best fit on the $\log y$ against $\log x$ graph;

2. find the equation of the line;

3. remember or derive $y = ax^n \rightarrow \log y = n \log x + \log a$;

4. identify the value of n and evaluate the value of a;

5. write down the exponential equation.

Formulae from experimental data practice   Go online

The variables y and x are related by the equation $y = ax^n$.

The graph of $\log_3 y$ against $\log_3 x$ gives the straight line shown.

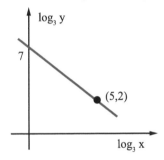

Q69: What is the value of n, in its simplest form?

....

Q70: What is the value of a, in its simplest form?

The variables y and x are related by the equation $y = ax^n$.

The graph of $\log_5 y$ against $\log_3 x$ gives the straight line shown.

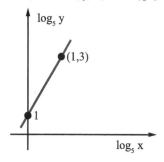

Q71: What is the value of n, in its simplest form?

....

Q72: What is the value of a, in its simplest form?

However, suppose that results suggest that two variables x and y are connected according to the formula $y = ab^x$.

$$y = ab^x \qquad \text{apply } \log_e \text{ to both sides of the equation}$$
$$\log_e y = \log_e ab^x$$
$$\log_e y = \log_e a + \log_e b^x$$
$$\log_e y = \log_e a + x\log_e b$$
$$\log_e y = x\log_e b + \log_e a$$

Now this equation looks a bit like $y = mx + c$ but is written as,
$Y = mx + c$ where $Y = \log_e y$, $m = \log_e b$ and $c = \log_e a$.

By evaluating m and c in the normal way to give the equation of a straight line, the resulting information is enough to find the constants a and b and hence the exponential equation required.

Notice that in this form only the y coordinates have logs applied to them.

Key point

If $y = ab^x$ then
$\log y = x \log b + \log a$
(which is in the form $Y = mx + c$).

Examples

1.

Scientists think that the data below suggests that the formula connecting x and y is of the form $y = ab^x$.

x	5	10	36	40
y	8	7·5	4·5	4

Now we know that if $y = ab^x$ then $\log y = x \log b + \log a$.

So we apply $\log_e$ to all the y coordinates then plot the points.

x	5	10	36	40
$\log_e y$	2·1	2	1·5	1·4

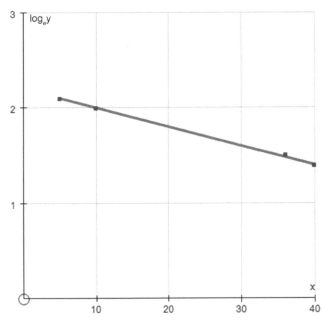

The graph looks approximately linear so the original variables look to be connected exponentially in the form $y = ab^x$.

We can find the equation of the straight line above in the form $Y = mx + c$ by using the points (5,2·1) and (36,1·5).

$$m = \frac{1 \cdot 5 - 2 \cdot 1}{36 - 5}$$
$$= \frac{-0 \cdot 6}{31}$$
$$= -0 \cdot 019$$

Now find the equation using the point (5,2·1) and $m = -0 \cdot 019$

$Y - b = m(x - a)$ where $Y = \log_e y$

$Y - 2 \cdot 1 = -0 \cdot 019(x - 5)$

$Y - 2 \cdot 1 = -0 \cdot 019x + 0 \cdot 095$

$\quad\quad Y = -0 \cdot 019x + 2 \cdot 195$

Now remember if $y = ab^x$ then

$\log_e y = x\log_e b + \log_e a$

$\quad Y = -0 \cdot 019x + 2 \cdot 195$

Hopefully you can see that $\log_e b = -0 \cdot 019$ and $\log_e a = 2 \cdot 195$

To find a and b we change the equations into exponentials giving

$e^{2 \cdot 195} = a$ and $e^{-0 \cdot 019} = b$

so $a = 8 \cdot 98$ and $b = 0 \cdot 98$

and the formula connecting the data is $y = 8 \cdot 98 \times 0 \cdot 98^x$

. . . .

2. Problem:

The variables y and x are related by the equation $y = ab^x$.

The graph of $\log_2 y$ against x gives the straight line shown below.

What are the values of a and b?

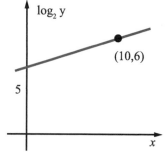

Solution:

We can find the equation of the straight line above in the form $Y = mx + c$ by using the points (0,5) and (10,6).

We can find the equation using the point (0,5) and $m = 0.1$

$Y = 0 \cdot 1x + 5$

Now remember if $y = ab^x$ then

$\log_e y = x\log_e b + \log_e a$

$\quad Y = 0 \cdot 1x + 5$

Hopefully you can see that $\log_e b = 0 \cdot 1$ and $\log_e a = 5$

To find a and b we change the equations into exponentials giving

$e^5 = a$ and $e^{0 \cdot 1} = b$

so $a = 148 \cdot 4$ and $b = 1 \cdot 1$

and the formula connecting the data is $y = 148 \cdot 4 \times 1 \cdot 1^x$

Key point

To find the equation $y = ab^x$ from experimental data:

1. identify 2 points from the line of best fit on the $\log y$ against x graph;

2. find the equation of the line;

3. remember or derive $y = ab^x \Rightarrow \log y = x\log b + \log a$

4. identify and evaluate the values of a and b;

5. write down the exponential equation.

Formulae from experimental data exercise   Go online

Q73: Given that $y = kx^n$ where k and n are constants, what would you plot to get a straight line graph?

a) x against y
b) x against $\log y$
c) $\log x$ against y
d) $\log x$ against $\log y$

. . . .

Q74: Given that $y = ab^x$ where a and b are constants, what would you plot to get a straight line graph?

a) x against y
b) x against $\log y$
c) $\log x$ against y
d) $\log x$ against $\log y$

. . . .

Q75:

The variables y and x are related by the equation $y = kx^n$ where k and n are constants.
The graph of $\log_6 y$ against $\log_6 x$ gives the straight line shown below.

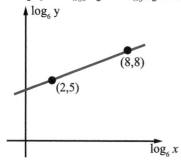

What are the values of n and k?

In a scientific experiment data was recorded and put into logarithmic form.

$\log_2 x$	1·6	1·7	1·8	2·0
$\log_2 y$	12·01	12·92	13·51	15·03

Plot this data.

Q76: Is the data linear?

....

Q77: If so, what is the form of the equation of the original data?

  a) $y = kx^n$

  b) $y = ab^x$

....

Q78: If the points (1·6,12·01) and (2·0,15·03) lie on the line of best fit what is the equation of the original data?

....

Q79:

The diagram below shows part of the graph of x against $\log_3 y$.

The straight line has gradient -2 and y-intercept (0,6).

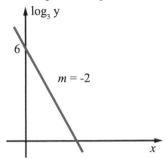

The variables y and x are related by the equation $y = ab^x$ where a and b are constants.

What are a and b?

In a scientific experiment data was recorded and logs applied to the y-values.

The diagram below shows part of the graph of x against $\log_e y$ with the line of best fit added.

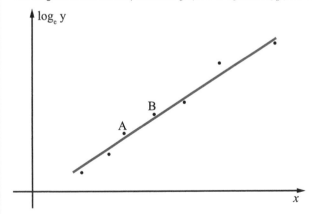

Q80: Why must the original data take the form $y = ab^x$?

....

Q81: The points A and B have coordinates (0·8,1·79) and (1·01,2·39) respectively.

What are the values of a and b in the original equation?

6.5   Learning Points

Logs and exponentials
Exponential functions take the form $y = a^x$

- If $a > 1$ it is a growth function.

- If $0 < a < 1$ it is a decay function.

- A special exponential function is $y = e^x$ where e is 2·718281828...

Logs and exponentials

- Logarithms and exponentials are the inverse of each other.

- If $y = a^x$ then $\log_a y = x$

- If $\log_a x = y$ then $a^y = x$

Laws of exponentials

1. $a^m \times a^n = a^{m+n}$

2. $\frac{a^m}{a^n} = a^{m-n}$

3. $(a^m)^n = a^{m \times n}$

4. $a^0 = 1$

5. $a^{-m} = \frac{1}{a^m}$

6. $a^{\frac{m}{n}} = \sqrt[n]{a^m}$

Laws of logarithms

1. $\log_a m + \log_a n = \log_a(m \times n)$

2. $\log_a m - \log_a n = \log_a \frac{m}{n}$

3. $\log_a x^n = n\log_a x$

4. $\log_a 1 = 0$

5. $\log_a a = 1$

Experimental data

- $y = kx^n$ apply logs to both sides of the equation
  choose a base e.g. 2, 3, 10, e, ...
  $$\log_a y = \log_a kx^n$$
  $$\log_a y = \log_a k + \log_a x^n$$
  $$\log_a y = \log_a k + n\log_a x$$
  $$\log_a y = n\log_a x + \log_a k$$

- ○ This equation looks a bit like $y = mx + c$ but is written as:
  - ▪ $Y = mX + c$ where $Y = \log_a y$, $X = \log_a x$, $m = n$ and $c = \log_a k$
- ○ Find the linear equation from the graph of $\log x$ against $\log y$.
  - ▪ $n = m$ where m is the gradient.
  - ▪ $k = a^c$ where c is the value of the y-intercept.

- $y = ab^x$ apply logs to both sides of the equation

  choose a base e.g. 2, 10, e, ... the example below uses base 10

  $\log_{10} y = \log_{10} ab^x$

  $\log_{10} y = \log_{10} a + \log_{10} b^x$

  $\log_{10} y = \log_{10} a + x \log_{10} b$

  $\log_{10} y = x \log_{10} b + \log_{10} a$

  - ○ This equation looks a bit like $y = mx + c$ but is written as
    - ▪ $Y = mx + c$ where $Y = \log_{10} y$, $m = \log_{10} b$ and $c = \log_{10} a$
  - ○ Find the linear equation from the graph of x against $\log y$
    - ▪ $b = 10^m$ where m is the gradient
    - ▪ $a = 10^c$ where c is the value of the y-intercept

6.6   End of topic test

End of topic 10 test   Go online

Q82: Simplify $\log_{10}4 + \log_{10}3$ and give the answer as a log.

....

Q83: If $3\log_5 4 - \log_5 8 = \log_5 A$, what is A?

....

Q84: Simplify $2\log_7 7$

....

Q85: If $x = \frac{\log_e 7}{\log_e 2}$ find an approximation for x to 1 decimal place.

....

Q86: If $\log_2 y = 3 \cdot 4$, write down an expression for the exact value of y.

....

Q87: If $y = e^{3.4}$ find an approximation for y to 2 decimal places.

....

Q88: Simplify $4\log_3 3$.

....

Q89: Simplify $2\log_2 4 + \log_2 3$.

....

Q90: Simplify $2\log_3 6 - \log_3 3$.

....

Q91: If $a = \log_e 5 \times 2\log_e 3$, find an approximate value for a.

....

Q92: If $\log_e p = 2$, find an approximate value for p.

....

Q93: If $m = e^e$, find an approximate value for m.

....

Q94: Simplify $\log_3 625 - 4\log_3 5$.

....

Q95: Evaluate $\log_e e^{-7}$.

....

Q96: Solve $\log_7(x + 5) + \log_7(x - 1) = 1$ and give the smaller value of x.

....

Q97: If $4 = 10^t$ find the value of t correct to two decimal places.

Bacteria increase according to the formula $B = 8e^{0.6t}$ where t is the time in hours and B is the number of thousands of bacteria.

Q98: How many bacteria are present at the start of the experiment?

....

Q99: How long does it take, in minutes, for the bacteria to double?

....

Q100: A sample of 8000 bacteria are placed in a dish. After 12 hours the thermostat breaks. How many bacteria are present when this happens?

A chemical evaporates according to the formula $P = P_0 e^{-kt}$ where t is the time in hours, k is a constant and P_0 is the initial volume of the chemical.

Q101: If 130 ccs evaporates to leave 90 ccs after 9 hours, find k correct to four decimal places?

....

Q102: How long does it take, in minutes, for the volume of the chemical to reach 30 ccs if the initial volume is 180 ccs?

In an experiment, a gas expands at a rate according to the formula $G = G_0 e^{kt}$ where k is a constant, t is the time in seconds and G_0 is the initial volume of the gas.
In one experiment, the initial volume of the gas is 30 ccs and after 5 seconds this expands to 550 ccs.

Q103: What is the value of k to four decimal places.

....

Q104: How long does it take the gas cloud to double? Give your answer correct to one decimal place.

A radioactive substance decays at a rate given by the formula $M_1 = M_0 e^{-kt}$ where k is a constant, t is the time in years and M_0 is the initial mass of the substance.

Q105: What is the half life of the element when $k = 0 \cdot 055$ correct to one decimal place.

....

Q106: How long does it take the mass to reduce to 25 grams when $M_0 = 100 \ grams$? Give your answer correct to one decimal place.

....

Q107: The variables y and x are related by the equation $y = kx^n$ where k and n are constants.

The graph of $\log_6 y$ against $\log_6 x$ gives the straight line shown below.

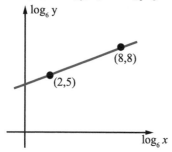

What are the values of n and k?

. . . .

Q108: The diagram below shows part of the graph of x against $\log_3 y$.
The straight line has gradient -2 and y-intercept $(0,6)$.

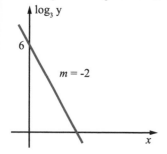

The variables y and x are related by the equation $y = ab^x$ where a and b are constants.
What are a and b?

In an experiment data was recorded and two of the points were $(8, 9 \cdot 8)$ and $(2, 8 \cdot 6)$. From these points and the remaining data it is thought that the relationship between the variables takes the form $y = ax^n$.

Use three decimal places in ALL your working to determine the equation in the form $y = ax^n$.

Q109: What are the values of a and n?

. . . .

Q110: The graph of $y = 9 \log_3 (9x + 2)$ and the line $y = 27$ intersect at the point A. Give the x-coordinate of the point A correct to one decimal place.

. . . .

Q111: Where does the graph of $y = 3\log_e(2x + 3)$ cross the x-axis? Give your answer correct to one decimal place.

In an experiment data was recorded and two of the points were (2,1·9) and (5,2·1). From these points and the remaining data it is thought that the relationship between the variables takes the form $y = ab^x$.

Use three decimal places in ALL your working to determine the equation in the form $y = ab^x$.

Q112: What are the values of a and b?

A faulty high pressure container is filled to a pressure of 120 psi. The pressure in the container after t hours is given by the formula $P_1 = P_0e^{-kt}$ where P_0 is the initial pressure.

Q113: After 5 hours the pressure drops to 90 psi. Find the value of k correct to four decimal places.

. . . .

Q114: To avoid damage, the contents in the container must be kept at a pressure of at least 45 psi. If the container is pressurised to 140 psi, how long, in minutes, will the contents be safe?

Glossary

The chain rule

Function notation: $h'(x) = g'(f(x)) \times f'(x)$

Leibniz notation: $\frac{dy}{dx} = \frac{dy}{du} \times \frac{du}{dx}$

definite integral

A definite integral is one which has a numerical value
thus when F (x) is the anti-derivative of f (x) then

$$\int_a^b f(x)\,dx = F(b) - F(a) \quad (a \leqslant x \leqslant b)$$

derived function

the instantaneous speed, or rate of change of distance with respect to time, can be written as $f'(t)$ and is known as the derived function of $f(t)$

differential equation

a differential equation is an equation involving an unknown function and its derivatives

Fibonacci

Fibonacci was born in 1170 and died in 1250 in Italy. Fibonacci is actually a nickname, his real name being Leonardo Pisano; he also sometimes called himself Bigollo, which may mean either a traveller or a good-for-nothing

fundamental theorem of calculus

the fundamental theorem of calculus states that if $F(x)$ is an anti-derivative of $f(x)$ then

$$\int_a^b f(x)\,dx = (F(b) + C) - (F(a) + C)$$

$$= F(b) - F(a) \quad (a \leqslant x \leqslant b)$$

half-life

the time required for any specified property to decrease by half

lower limit of integration

a is the lower limit of integration in the definite integral $\int_a^b f(x)\,dx$

radian

an angle subtended at the centre of a circle by an arc of length equal to the radius of the circle is called a radian

recurrence relation

a sequence in which each term is a function of the previous term or terms

sequence

a series of terms with a definite pattern; can be defined by a rule or a formula for the nth term

stationary points

stationary points are points on a curve where the gradient of the tangent to the curve is zero; at these points $f'(x) = 0$

upper limit of integration

b is the upper limit of integration in the definite integral $\int_a^b f(x)\,dx$

Answers to questions and activities

Topic 1: Differentiation

Multiplication and division of indices exercise (page 5)

Q1: $x^6 \times x^4 \div x^5 = x^{6+4-5} = x^5$

Q2: $\frac{x^6 \times x^2}{x^3} = x^{6+2-3} = x^5$

Q3:
$$2x^{\frac{1}{4}} \times 5x^{\frac{1}{4}} = 2 \times 5 \times x^{\frac{1}{4}} \times x^{\frac{1}{4}}$$
$$= 2 \times 5 \times x^{\frac{1}{4}+\frac{1}{4}}$$
$$= 10 \times x^{\frac{2}{4}}$$
$$= 10x^{\frac{1}{2}}$$

Raising powers exercise (page 6)

Q4: $\left(a^2\right)^7 = a^{2 \times 7} = a^{14}$

Q5: $\left(3y^4\right)^3 = 3^3 \times y^{4 \times 3} = 27y^{12}$

Q6: $\left(5m^{\frac{3}{2}}\right)^2 = 5^2 \times m^{\frac{3}{2} \times 2} = 25m^{\frac{6}{2}} = 25m^3$

Negative and zero indices exercise (page 7)

Q7: $a^{(-3)+5-2} = a^0 = 1$

Q8: $\left(3m^{-4}\right)^2 = 3^2 \times m^{(-4) \times 2} = 9m^{-8} = \frac{9}{m^8}$

Q9: $y^{(-10)+\frac{3}{2}-\frac{1}{2}} = y^{(-10)+1} = y^{-9} = \frac{1}{y^9}$

Fractional indices exercise (page 9)

Q10: $9^{\frac{1}{2}} = \sqrt{9} = 3$

Q11: $49^{\frac{1}{2}} = \sqrt{49} = 7$

Q12: $27^{\frac{1}{3}} = \sqrt[3]{27} = 3$ because $3^3 = 27$

Q13: $16^{\frac{1}{4}} = \sqrt[4]{16} = 2$ because $2^4 = 16$

Q14: $27^{\frac{2}{3}} = \sqrt[3]{27^2} = 9$ because $\sqrt[3]{27} = 3$ and $3^2 = 9$

Q15: $4^{\frac{3}{2}} = \sqrt{4^3} = 8$ because $\sqrt{4} = 2$ and $2^3 = 8$

Answers from page 10.

Q16: The car is travelling faster at $t = 4$

Q17: At $t = 4$ the gradient of the curve is steeper, therefore the car is travelling faster at this point.

Q18: Since the distance-time graph given is a curve, the speed is not constant and as it is changing continuously we can only give an average.

Rules for differentiation exercise (page 16)

Q19:

a) $9x^8$

b) $-3x^{-4}$

c) $f'(x) = \frac{5}{4}x^{\frac{1}{4}}$

d) 0

e) $f'(x) = \frac{4}{5}x^{-\frac{1}{5}}$

f) $f'(x) = -\frac{9}{2}x^{-\frac{11}{2}}$

Q20:

a) $f'(x) = x^{-7} = -7x^{-8} = -\frac{7}{x^8}$

b) $f'(x) = x^{-\frac{9}{8}} = -\frac{9}{8}x^{-\frac{17}{8}} = -\frac{9}{8x^{\frac{17}{8}}}$

c) $f'(x) = x^{-\frac{3}{5}} = -\frac{3}{5}x^{-\frac{8}{5}} = -\frac{3}{5x^{\frac{8}{5}}}$

d) $f'(x) = x^{\frac{7}{2}} = \frac{7}{2}x^{\frac{5}{2}} = \frac{7}{2}\sqrt{x^5}$

e) $f'(x) = x^{-\frac{5}{2}} = -\frac{5}{2}x^{-\frac{7}{2}} = -\frac{5}{2\sqrt{x^7}}$

Q21:

a) $f'(x) = 4 \times -2x^3 = -8x^3$

b) $f'(x) = 4 \times \frac{3}{5}x^3 = \frac{12}{5}x^3$

c) $f'(x) = 4x^{-3} = -12x^{-4} = -\frac{12}{x^4}$

d) $f'(x) = \frac{1}{9}x^{-4} = -\frac{4}{9}x^{-5} = -\frac{4}{9x^5}$

e) $f'(x) = \frac{9}{4}x^{-1} = -\frac{9}{4}x^{-2} = -\frac{9}{4x^2}$

f) $f'(x) = -x^{\frac{1}{2}} = -\frac{1}{2}x^{-\frac{1}{2}} = -\frac{1}{2\sqrt{x}}$

Q22:

a) $f'(x) = 2x^{-\frac{1}{2}} = -1x^{-\frac{3}{2}} = -\frac{1}{\sqrt{x^3}}$

b) $f'(x) = -10x^{\frac{1}{4}}$

c) $f'(x) = -2x + 4$

d)

$$f'(x) = 5x^5 + \frac{1}{3}x^{-6}$$

$$= 25x^4 - \frac{6}{3}x^{-7}$$

$$= 25x^4 - 2x^{-7}$$

$$= 25x^4 - \frac{2}{x^7}$$

e)

$$f'(x) = \frac{1}{2}x^{-1} + 4x^{-\frac{1}{2}}$$

$$= -\frac{1}{2}x^{-2} - 2x^{-\frac{3}{2}}$$

$$= -\frac{1}{2x^2} - \frac{2}{\sqrt{x^3}}$$

f)

$$f'(x) = 1 - 9x^{\frac{1}{2}} + 4x^5$$

$$= -\frac{9}{2}x^{-\frac{1}{2}} + 20x^4$$

$$= -\frac{9}{2\sqrt{x}} + 20x^4$$

Differentiating products and quotients exercise (page 19)

Q23:

Steps:

- Simplify $(4x + 7)(x - 2)$ and give your answer in the form ax^n. $4x^2 - x - 14$

Answer: $f'(x) = 8x - 1$

Q24:

Steps:

- Simplify $\sqrt{x}(x - \sqrt{x})$ and give your answer in the form ax^n. $x^{\frac{3}{2}} - x$

Answer: $f'(x) = \frac{3\sqrt{x}}{2} - 1$

Q25:

Steps:

- Simplify $\frac{(2x + 6)(4x - 4)}{x}$ and give your answer in the form ax^n. $8x + 16 - 24x^{-1}$

Answer: $8 + \frac{24}{x^2}$

Q26:

Steps:

- Simplify $\left(x - \frac{3}{x}\right)^2$ and give your answer in the form ax^n. $x^2 - 6 + 9x^{-2}$

Answer: $f'(x) = 2x - \frac{18}{x^3}$

Q27:

Steps:

- Simplify and give your answer in the form ax^n. $8x^{\frac{1}{2}} + 2x^{-\frac{1}{2}}$

Answer: $f'(x) = \frac{4}{x^{\frac{1}{2}}} - \frac{1}{x^{\frac{3}{2}}}$

Q28:

Steps:

- $x\sqrt{x} = x^p$ where $p = ?$ $\frac{3}{2}$
- Simplify $\frac{x^3 - 8x^4}{x\sqrt{x}}$ and give your answer in the form ax^n. $x^{\frac{3}{2}} - 8x^{\frac{5}{2}}$

Answer: $f'(x) = \frac{3}{2}x^{\frac{1}{2}} - 20x^{\frac{3}{2}}$

Calculating the value of the derivative exercise (page 22)

Q29:

Steps:

- Find $f'(x)$ giving your answer with a positive power. $f'(x) = \frac{1}{2x^{\frac{1}{2}}}$

Answer: $f'(4) = \frac{1}{2 \times 4^{\frac{1}{2}}} = \frac{1}{4}$

Q30:

Steps:

- What is $\frac{dy}{dx}$? $\frac{4}{3}x^{\frac{1}{3}}$

Answers:

a) $2\frac{2}{3}$

b) $\frac{4}{5}$

c) -4

Q31:

Steps:

- What is $h'(t)$? $-10t + 20$

Answer:

a) 20

b) -10

Q32:

Steps:

- Find $f'(x)$ giving your answer with a positive power. $f'(x) = -\frac{2}{3x^{\frac{5}{3}}}$

Answer: $f'(8) = -\frac{2}{3 \times 8^{\frac{5}{3}}} = -\frac{1}{48}$

Q33:

Steps:

- What is $s'(t)$? $s'(t) = -\frac{3}{t^4}$

Answer: $s'(2) = -\frac{3}{2^4} = -\frac{3}{16}$

Q34:

Steps:

- $\frac{dy}{dx} = 6x^2 - 10x + 1$
- Substitute in the value of x and solve. $3 \times (3)^2 - 6 \times (3) + 1 = 27 - 18 + 1 = ?$

Answer: $m_{\text{tangent}} = 10$

Determining the equation of a tangent to a curve exercise (page 26)

Q35:

Steps:

- What is $\frac{dy}{dx}$? $4x - 9$
- Find the gradient of the tangent. $4 \times 3 - 9 = 3$
- Use $y - b = m(x - a)$ to find the equation.

Answer: $y = 3x - 26$

Q36:

Steps:

- What is $\frac{dy}{dx}$? $-\frac{9}{x^2}$
- Find the gradient of the tangent. $-\frac{9}{-1^2} = -9$
- Use $y - b = m(x - a)$ to find the equation.

Answer: $y = -9x - 18$

Q37:

Steps:

- What is $\frac{dy}{dx}$? $4x + 10$

Answer: (-3,0)

Q38: $y = -2x - 6$

Q39:

Steps:

- What is $\frac{dy}{dx}$? $\frac{3}{2}x^{\frac{1}{2}} = 3$

Answer: (4,8)

Q40: $y = 3x - 4$

Determining stationary points exercise (page 32)

Q41:

$y = x^4 - 4x^3 + 1$
$\frac{dy}{dx} = 4x^3 - 12x^2 = 4x^2(x - 3)$

Stationary points occur when $\frac{dy}{dx} = 0$

$4x^2(x - 3) = 0$
$4x^2 = 0 \quad or \quad x - 3 = 0$
$x = 0 \quad or \quad x = 3$

When $x = 0$ then $y = 1$
When $x = 3$ then $y = -26$

Thus the coordinates of the stationary points are (0,1) and (3,-26).

To determine their nature we draw a nature table.

x	$\begin{array}{c}-1\\ \rightarrow\end{array}$	0	$\begin{array}{c}1\\ \rightarrow\end{array}$	3	$\begin{array}{c}4\\ \rightarrow\end{array}$
$4x^2$	+	0	+	+	+
$(x - 3)$	-	-	-	0	+
$4x^2(x - 3)$	-	0	-	0	+
shape	\	—	\	—	/

This gives us a falling point of inflection at (0,1) and a minimum turning point at (3,-26).

Q42:

When $y = -2x^2 + 20x + 5$ then $\frac{dy}{dx} = -4x + 20$

At a stationary point $\frac{dy}{dx} = 0$ therefore $x = 5$

When $x = 5$ then $y = 55$

The nature of these stationary point

This gives us a maximum turning point at (5,55).

Q43:

When $y = x^3 + 3x^2 + 9$ then $\frac{dy}{dx} = 3x^2 + 6x$

At a stationary point $\frac{dy}{dx} = 0$ therefore $x = 0$ and $x = -2$

When $x = 0$ then $y = 9$

When $x = -2$ then $y = 13$

This gives us a minimum turning point at (0,9) and a maximum turning point at (-2,13).

Q44:

When $y = 8x^3 + x^4$ then $\frac{dy}{dx} = 24x^2 + 4x^3$

At a stationary point $\frac{dy}{dx} = 0$ therefore $x = 0$ and $x = -6$

When $x = 0$ then $y = 0$

When $x = -6$ then $y = -432$

This gives us a rising point of inflection at (0,0) and a minimum turning point at (-6,-432).

Q45:

When $f(x) = x^4 - 8x^2 - 1$ then $f'(x) = 4x^3 - 16x$

At a stationary point $f'(x) = 0$ therefore $x = -2$, $x = 0$ and $x = 2$

When $x = -2$ then $y = -17$

When $x = 0$ then $y = -1$

When $x = 2$ then $y = -17$

x	$\rightarrow$	-2	$\rightarrow$	0	$\rightarrow$	2	
$f'(x)$	-	0	+	0	-	0	+
shape	\	—	/	—	\	—	/

The nature of the stationary points from left to right are a minimum turning point at (-2,-17), a maximum turning point at (0,-1) and a minimum turning point at (2,-17).

Curve sketching exercise (page 36)

Q46:

Steps:

- The curve cuts the x-axis when $y = 0$, therefore solve $x^2 - 5x + 6 = 0$ to find the two places where the curve cuts the x-axis.
- Factorise $x^2 - 5x + 6$. $(x - 3)(x - 2)$

Answer: (3,0) and (2,0)

Q47:

Steps:

- The curve cuts the y-axis when $x = 0$, therefore substitute $x = 0$ into $y = x^2 - 5x + 6$ to find where the curve cuts the y-axis.

Answer: (0,6)

Q48:

Steps:

- If $y = x^2 - 5x + 6$ then $\frac{dy}{dx} = ?\ 2x - 5$
- At a stationary point the value of $\frac{dy}{dx} = ?\ 0$

Answer: $\left(\frac{5}{2},\ -\frac{1}{4}\right)$

Q49:

Steps:

- Remember that to find the nature of a stationary point you will need to calculate the sign of the derivative on either side.

Answer: Minimum

Q50: b) $y \to +\infty$

Q51: b) $y \to +\infty$

Q52:

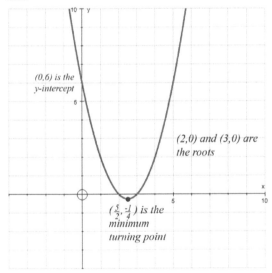

Q53:

Steps:

- The curve cuts the x-axis when $y = 0$, therefore solve $6x^2 - x^3 = 0$.

Answer: (0,0) and (6,0)

Q54:

Steps:

- The curve cuts the y-axis when $x = 0$, therefore substitute $x = 0$ into $y = 6x^2 - x^3$.

Answer: (0,0)

Q55:

Steps:

- If $y = 6x^2 - x^3$ then $\frac{dy}{dx} = ? \, 12x - 3x^2$
- At a stationary point the value of $\frac{dy}{dx} = ? \, 0$

Answer: (0,0) and (4,32)

Q56: Minimum

Q57: Maximum

Q58: a) $y \to -\infty$

Q59: b) $y \to +\infty$

Q60:

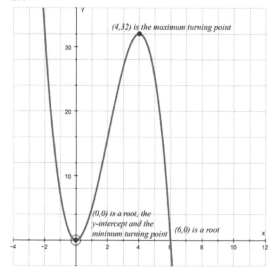

Q61:

Steps:

- The curve cuts the y-axis when $x = 0$, therefore substitute $x = 0$ into $y = x^3 + x^2 - x - 1$.

Answer: (0,-1)

Q62:

Steps:

- The curve cuts the x-axis when $y = 0$, therefore solve $x^3 + x^2 - x - 1 = 0$.

Answer: (-1,0) and (1,0)

Q63: Maximum

Q64:

Steps:

- What is $f(-1)$?

Answer: (-1,0)

Q65: Minimum

Q66:

Steps:

- What is $f(1)$?

Answer: $\left(\frac{1}{3}, -\frac{32}{27}\right)$

Q67: b) $y \to +\infty$

Q68: a) $y \to -\infty$

Q69:

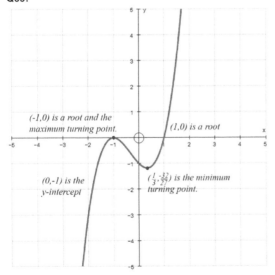

Increasing and decreasing functions exercise (page 40)

Q70:

Steps:

- $\frac{dy}{dx} = ? \ 2x + 6$
- Now find the stationary points and make a nature table to determine where the function is increasing or decreasing.

Answer: b) $x > -3$

Q71:

Steps:

- $\frac{dy}{dx} = ? \ 2x + 3$
- Now find the stationary points and make a nature table to determine where the function is increasing or decreasing.

Answer: b) $(-1{\cdot}5, \infty)$

Q72:

Steps:

- $\frac{dy}{dx} = ? \ 4x^3 + 12x$
- Now find the stationary points and make a nature table to determine where the function is increasing or decreasing.

Answer: d) $x < -3$

Q73:

Steps:

- $\frac{dy}{dx} = ? \ 6x^2 + 6x - 12$
- Now find the stationary points and make a nature table to determine where the function is increasing or decreasing.

Answer: c) $x > 1$

Q74:

Steps:

- $\frac{dy}{dx} = ? \ -3x^2 + 6x$
- Now find the stationary points and make a nature table to determine where the function is increasing or decreasing.

Answer: b) $x > 2$

Derivative puzzle (page 44)

Q75:

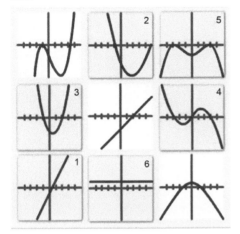

The graph of the derivative exercise (page 44)

Q76: c)

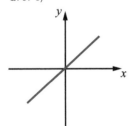

Q77: b)

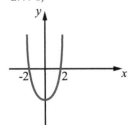

Q78: d)

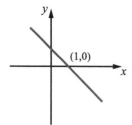

Q79: a)

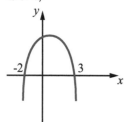

Q80: d)

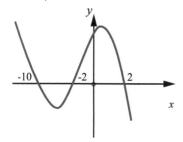

Closed intervals exercise (page 50)

Q81:

Steps:

- Where does the maximum value occur? The stationary point (-2, 5)
- Where does the minimum value occur? The stationary point (4, -3)

Answer:

- Maximum value = 5
- Minimum value = -3

Q82:

Steps:

- Where does the maximum value occur? The end point (0, 5)
- Where does the minimum value occur? The stationary point (6, -3)

Answer:

- Maximum value = 5
- Minimum value = -3

Q83:

Steps:

- When $y = 4x^2 - 16x + 2$ then $\frac{dy}{dx} = ?$ $8x - 16$
- When $\frac{dy}{dx} = 0$ then $x = ?$ 2

Answer: -14

Q84: $y = 2$

Q85: $y = 50$

Q86: c) The function $y = 4x^2 - 16x + 2$ has a minimum at (2, -14) and a maximum at (6, 50).

Q87: 6

Q88: -6

Q89: $y = 6$

Q90: $y = 54$

Q91: a) The function $y = 3x^3 - 9x^2 + 6$ has a maximum at (4, 54) and a minimum at (2, -6).

Rate of change exercise (page 53)

Q92:

Steps:

- $\frac{dV}{dt} = ?$ $12t^2 + 2t + 1$

Answer: 15 cm s^{-3}

Q93:

Steps:

- $v(t) = \frac{ds}{dt} = ?$ $9t^2 - 4t + 4$

Answer: 9 ms^{-1}

Q94:

Steps:

- $a(t) = \frac{dv}{dt} = ? \; 18t - 4$

Answer: 14 ms^{-2}

Q95:

Steps:

- $\frac{dR}{dt} = ? \; \frac{2}{\sqrt{t}}$

Answer: $\frac{2}{3} \; cm \; s^{-1}$

Optimisation exercise (page 57)

Q96:

a) *Steps:*
- $x + y = 20$ Make y the subject of the formula and use it to express P in terms of x alone.

Answer: $2 \times 10x - x^2$

b) *Steps:*
- In terms of x, $\frac{dP}{dx} = ? \; 2 \times 10 - 2x$
- At a turning point the value of $\frac{dP}{dx} = ? \; 0$
- What type of turning point does this give? A maximum turning point.

Answer: $x = 10$

Q97:

a) *Steps:*
- When $v(t) = 6\sqrt{t} - 0 \cdot 6t$ then, in terms of t, $\frac{dv}{dt} = ? \; \frac{3}{\sqrt{t}} - 0 \cdot 6$
- At maximum speed the value of $\frac{dv}{dt} = ? \; 0$

Answer: $t = 25$

b) *Steps:*
- Substitute your answer from part 1 into the given formula for $v(t)$. You will need to convert from ms^{-1} to km h^{-1}.

Answer: 54 km h^{-1}

Q98:

a) *Steps:*
- Let y represent the length of the rectangle then we can write $2x + 2y = 20$. So, $y = ? \; 10 - x$

Answer: $A = 10x - x^2$

b) *Steps:*
- In terms of x, $\frac{dA}{dx} = ? \; 10 - 2x$

- At a turning point the value of $\frac{dA}{dx}$ = ? 0
- What type of turning point have you found? A maximum turning point.

Answer: $x = 5$

Q99:

a) $18 - 2x$

b) $324x - 72x^2 + 4x^3$

c) **Steps:**

- In terms of x, $\frac{dV}{dx}$ = ? $324 - 144x + 12x^2$
- At turning points the value of $\frac{dV}{dx}$ = ? 0
- Only one of the turning points gives a sensible answer for x in the context of this question.

Answer: $x = 3$

Q100:

a) $\frac{4}{x^2}$

b) **Steps:**

- In terms of x and h the surface area of the box is $S = x^2 + 4xh$.

Answer: $x^2 + \frac{16}{x}$

c) **Steps:**

- In terms of x, $\frac{dS}{dx}$ = ? $2x - \frac{16}{x^2}$
- At a turning point the value of $\frac{dS}{dx}$ = ? 0

Answer: $x = 2$

d) $h = 1$

Differentiating sin x and cos x exercise (page 60)

Q101:

x	0	$\frac{\pi}{2}$	π	$\frac{3\pi}{2}$	2π
m_T	0	-1	0	1	0

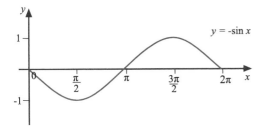

$y = -\sin x$

Q102: c) $-\sin x$

Q103:

Steps:

- Remember that when $f(x) = \sin x$ then $f'(x) = \cos x$

Answer: $f'(x) = 7 \cos x$

Q104:

Steps:

- Remember that when $f(x) = \cos x$ then $f'(x) = -\sin x$

Answer: $f'(x) = 5 \sin x$

Q105: $f'(x) = -\cos x + 8 \sin x$

Q106: $f'(x) = 8x + 2 \sin x$

Q107:

Steps:

- Rewrite $\frac{2 + 8x \sin x}{7x}$ as two separate fractions.

Answer: $f'(x) = \frac{-2}{7x^2} + \frac{8}{7} \cos x$

Differentiation of (x + a)ⁿ (page 62)

Q108:

a) $f'(x) = 4(x + \ )^3$
b) $f'(x) = 5(x + 3)^4$
c) $f'(x) = 6(x + 3)^5$
d) $f'(x) = 4(x - 2)^3$
e) $f'(x) = 5(x - 2)^4$
f) $f'(x) = 6(x - 2)^5$

Differentiating (x + a)ⁿ exercise (page 63)

Q109:

a) $f'(x) = 9(x - 8)^8$
b) $f'(x) = -2(x - 9)^{-3}$
c) *Steps:*
    - $\frac{8}{3} - 1 = ? \frac{5}{3}$

    Answer: $f'(x) = \frac{8}{3}(x - 3)^{\frac{5}{3}}$
d) *Steps:*
    - $f(x) = \frac{1}{(x - 6)^2} = (x - 6)^n$ where $n = ?$ -2

Answer: $f'(x) = \frac{-2}{(x-3)^3}$

e) **Steps:**

- $\left(\sqrt{x+2}\right)^9 = (x+2)^k$ where $k = ?$ $\frac{9}{2}$

Answer: $f'(x) = \frac{9}{2}\left(\sqrt{x+2}\right)^7$

Q110:

Steps:

- When $f(x) = (x+5)^5$ what is $f'(x) = ?$ $5(x+5)^4$

Answer: $f'(0) = 3125$

Q111: $f'(3) = 20480$

Q112:

Steps:

- When $y = \frac{1}{x+1}$ then $\frac{dy}{dx} = ?$ $\frac{-1}{(x+1)^2}$

Answer: -1

Q113: $y = -x + 1$

Answers from page 64.

Q114:

a) $\frac{dy}{dx} = 8(2x+1)^3$

b) $\frac{dy}{dx} = 12(3x+1)^3$

c) $\frac{dy}{dx} = 20(5x+1)^3$

d) $\frac{dy}{dx} = 40(5x-2)^7$

e) $\frac{dy}{dx} = 28(7x+5)^3$

Differentiating (ax + b)^n exercise (page 65)

Q115:

a) $f'(x) = 72(8x+5)^8$

b) $f'(x) = -14(6-7x)$

c) $f'(x) = -16(8x+1)^{-3}$

d) **Steps:**

- $\frac{1}{5x+2} = (5x+2)^n$ $n = ?$ -1

Answer: $f'(x) = \frac{-5}{(5x+2)^2}$

Q116: $f'(x) = 15(6x + 7)^{\frac{3}{2}}$

Q117:

Steps:

- $\left(\sqrt{9x + 8}\right)^3 = (9x + 8)^n \; n = ? \; \frac{3}{2}$

Answer: $f'(x) = \frac{27}{2}\sqrt{9x + 8}$

Q118:

Steps:

- $\frac{1}{\sqrt{8x + 7}} = (8x + 7)^m \; m = ? \; \frac{-1}{2}$

Answer: $f'(x) = \frac{-4}{\left(\sqrt{8x + 7}\right)^3}$

Q119:

Steps:

- $f(x) = \frac{1}{\left(\sqrt{4x + 5}\right)^5} \; k = ? \; \frac{-5}{2}$

Answer: $f'(x) = \frac{-10}{\left(\sqrt{4x + 5}\right)^7}$

Differentiating composite functions exercise (page 68)

Q120:

Step 1:	Turn the square root into a power.	$h(x) = (x^2 + 6x)^{\frac{1}{2}}$
Step 2:	Bring down the power.	$\frac{1}{2}$
Step 3:	Write down the bracket.	$\frac{1}{2}(x^2 + 6x)$
Step 4:	Reduce the power by 1.	$\frac{1}{2}(x^2 + 6x)^{-\frac{1}{2}}$
Step 5:	Differentiate the bracket.	$\frac{1}{2}(x^2 + 6x)^{-\frac{1}{2}} \times (2x + 6)$
Step 6:	Simplify the answer.	$\frac{dy}{dx} = \frac{2x + 6}{2\sqrt{x^2 + 6x}}$
		$= \frac{2(x + 3)}{2\sqrt{x^2 + 6x}}$
		$= \frac{x + 3}{\sqrt{x^2 + 6x}}$

Q121:

Step 1:	Remember:	$\cos^3 x = (\cos x)^3$
Step 2:	Bring down the power.	3
Step 3:	Write down the bracket.	$3(\cos x)$
Step 4:	Reduce the power by 1.	$3(\cos x)^2$
Step 5:	Differentiate the bracket.	$3(\cos x)^2 \times (-\sin x)$
Step 6:	Simplify the answer.	$f'(x) = -3\cos^2 x \sin x$

Q122:

$$h'(x) = 3(x^3 + 9x)^2 \times (3x^2 + 9)$$
$$= 3(3x^2 + 9)(x^3 + 9x)^2$$

Q123:

$$y = \sqrt{4x^2 + 4} = (4x^2 + 4)^{\frac{1}{2}}$$
$$\frac{d}{dx} = \frac{1}{2}(4x^2 + 4)^{-\frac{1}{2}} \times 8x$$
$$= \frac{4x}{\sqrt{4x^2 + 4}}$$

Q124:

$$\frac{dy}{dx} = -\sin\left(8x + \frac{\pi}{6}\right) \times 8$$
$$= -8\sin\left(8x + \frac{\pi}{6}\right)$$

Q125:

$$\frac{dy}{dx} = \cos\left(x^4 + 5\right) \times 4x^3$$
$$= 4x^3 \cos\left(x^4 + 5\right)$$

Q126:

$$h(x) = \sin^2 x = (\sin x)^2$$
$$h'(x) = 2(\sin x) \times \cos x$$
$$= 2\sin x \cos x$$

Q127:

$$y = \frac{1}{\sqrt{\cos x}} = (\cos x)^{-\frac{1}{2}}$$
$$\frac{dy}{dx} = -\frac{1}{2}(\cos x)^{-\frac{3}{2}} \times -\sin x$$
$$= \frac{\sin x}{2\sqrt{\cos^3 x}}$$

End of topic 5 test (page 75)

Q128:

Steps:

- Simplify $(2x + 9)(x - 3)$, give your answer in the form ax^n. $2x^2 + 3x - 27$

Answer: $\frac{dy}{dx} = 4x + 3$

Q129:

Steps:

- Simplify $\frac{4x + 8}{\sqrt{x}}$, give your answer in the form ax^n. $4x^{\frac{1}{2}} + 8x^{\frac{-1}{2}}$

Answer: $\frac{dy}{dx} = \frac{2}{\sqrt{x}} - \frac{4}{x^{\frac{3}{2}}}$

Q130:

Steps:

- Simplify $\frac{x^4 - 2x + 4}{\sqrt{x}}$, give your answer in the form ax^n. $x^{\frac{7}{2}} - 2x^{\frac{1}{2}} + 4x^{\frac{-1}{2}}$

Answer: $\frac{dy}{dx} = \frac{7}{2}x^{\frac{5}{2}} - \frac{1}{\sqrt{x}} - \frac{2}{x^{\frac{3}{2}}}$

Q131:

a) *Steps:*

- Simplify $(x + 5)(4x - 1)$, give your answer in the form ax^n. $4x^2 + 19x - 5$

  Answer: $g'(x) = 8x + 19$

b) $g'(3) = 43$

Q132:

Steps:

- Simplify $\sqrt{x}(x + \sqrt{x})$, give your answer in the form ax^n. $x^{\frac{3}{2}} + x$

Answer: $\frac{dy}{dx} = \frac{3}{2}\sqrt{x} + 1$

Q133:

Steps:

- Simplify $\frac{x^3 - 2}{3x}$, give your answer in the form ax^n. $\frac{x^2}{3} - \frac{2}{3}x^{-1}$

Answer: $\frac{dy}{dx} = \frac{2x}{3} + \frac{2}{3x^2}$

Q134:

Steps:

- When $y = (x - 5)^2$, then $\frac{dy}{dx} = ?$. $2x - 10$
- To find the gradient when $x = 3$ substitute 3 for x in the expression you have found for $\frac{dy}{dx}$.

Answer: $m = -4$

Q135:

Steps:

- When $y = \frac{3}{x}$, then $\frac{dy}{dx} = ?$. $\frac{-3}{x^2}$
- To find the gradient when $x = 2$ substitute 3 for x in the expression you have found for $\frac{dy}{dx}$.

Answer: $m = -\frac{3}{4}$

Q136:

a) $y = -7$

b) $\frac{dy}{dx} = 4 - 9x$

c) $m = -32$

d) $y = -32x + 57$

Q137:

a) $3x^2 + 6x$

b) (0, 7)

c) (-2, 11)

d) There is a minimum stationary point at (0,7) and a maximum stationary point (-2, 11).

Q138:

a) (0,0)

b) $x = 0$ and $x = 0$

c) Falling point of inflection.

d) ***Steps:***
  - What is $f(0)$?

  Answer: (0,0)

e) Minimum

f) ***Steps:***
  - What is $f(6)$?

  Answer: (6,-432)

g)

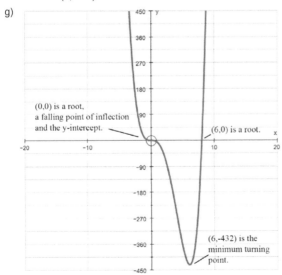

(0,0) is a root, a falling point of inflection and the y-intercept.

(6,0) is a root.

(6,-432) is the minimum turning point.

Q139:

Steps:

- Differentiate and make a nature table.

Answer: b. f is never decreasing

Q140: a)

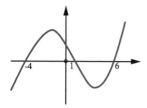

Q141:

a) $g(-1) = -49$

b) $g(8) = 32$

c) *Steps:*

- $g'(x) = ?$ $g'(x) = 3x^2 - 24x + 36$
- When does $g'(x) = 0$? $x = 2$ and $x = 6$

Answer: 32

d) 0

e) Maximum value = 32
Minimum value = -49

Q142:

Steps:

- What is the gradient of line L? $\frac{-3}{2}$
- What is the y-intercept of line L? 30
- What is the equation of a line with gradient, m, that cuts the y-axis at $(0,c)$? $y = mx + c$

Answer: $y = \frac{-3}{2}x + 30$

Q143:

Steps:

- The area of the sheep pen is $A = xy$, rewriting this in terms of x will use the expression that you have already found for y.

Answer: $A = 30x - \frac{3}{2}x^2$

Q144:

Steps:

- What is $\frac{dA}{dx}$? $30 - 3x$

Answer: $x = 10$

Q145: $A = 150 \ m^2$

Q146:

Steps:

- Area of a rectangle = length × breadth, what is an expression for the breadth, b?
  $A = lb \Rightarrow 10 = xb \Rightarrow b = {}^{10}/_x$
- Use this answer to find an expression for the perimeter.

Answer: $P = 2x + 20x^{-1}$

Q147:

Steps:

- $P = 2x + 20x^{-1}$, what is $\frac{dP}{dx}$? $2 - 20x^2$
- For stationary points $\frac{dP}{dx} = ?$ 0
- In this context the value of the stationary point, x (the length of the enclosure) must be positive, what is the value of x?

Answer: $\sqrt{10}$

Q148: $\sqrt{10}$

Q149:

Steps:

- Remember that $\frac{d}{dx} \cos x = -\sin x$

Answer: $-8sin\ x$

Q150:

Steps:

- Remember that $\frac{d}{dx} \sin x = \cos x$

Answer: $6cos\ x$

Q151:

Steps:

- Remember that when $f(x) = (x + a)^n$ then $f\,'(x) = n(x + a)^{n-1}$

Answer: $f\,'(x) = -7(x + 9)^{-8}$

Q152: $f'(x) = \frac{2}{3}(x + 3)^{-1/3}$

Q153:

$$f'(x) = 2 \times 2(7 - 4x)^1 \times (-4)$$
$$= -16(7 - 4x)$$
$$f'(2) = -16(7 - (4 \times 2))$$
$$= 16$$

Q154:

Steps:

- Remember to rewrite the equation giving the square root as a power.
- Differentiate what's inside the brackets and multiply what's in front of the brackets by this.

Answer:

$$y = (3 - 7\sin x)^{\frac{1}{2}}$$
$$\frac{dy}{dx} = \frac{1}{2}(3 - 7\sin x)^{-\frac{1}{2}} \times (-7\cos x)$$
$$= -\frac{7\cos x}{2\sqrt{3 - 7\sin x}}$$

Topic 2: Trigonometry

Answers from page 88.

Q1:

$$4 \sin x° = 1$$
$$\sin x° = \frac{1}{4}$$

$$x° = \sin^{-1}\left(\frac{1}{4}\right) = \underline{14 \cdot 5°}$$
$$x° = 180 - 14 \cdot 5 = \underline{165 \cdot 5°}$$

Solving trigonometric equations exercise (page 90)

Q2: $x = 9 \cdot 6°$ and $x = 170 \cdot 4°$

Q3: $x = 131 \cdot 8°$ and $x = 228 \cdot 2°$

Q4: $x = 116 \cdot 6°$ and $x = 296 \cdot 6°$

Q5:

Steps:

- Re-arrange the equation.
- What is sin x? $3/8$
- Use this answer to find your solution remembering to press the sin^{-1} button.

Answer: $x = 22 \cdot 0°$ and $x = 158 \cdot 0°$

Q6:

Steps:

- Re-arrange the equation.
- What is cos x? $2/9$
- Use this answer to find your solution remembering to press the cos^{-1} button.

Answer: $x = 77 \cdot 2°$ and $x = 282 \cdot 8°$

Q7:

Steps:

- Re-arrange the equation.
- What is tan x? $^8/_7$
- Use this answer to find your solution remembering to press the tan^{-1} button.

Answer: $x = 48 \cdot 8°$ and $x = 228 \cdot 8°$

Q8:

Steps:

- Re-arrange the equation.
- What is sin x? $-^4/_5$
- sin$^{-1}(^4/_5) = ?$ 53·1
- Remember to identify the quadrants where sin x is negative and use this answer to find your solutions.

Answer: $x = 233 \cdot 1°$ and $x = 306 \cdot 8°$

Q9:

Steps:

- Re-arrange the equation.
- What is cos x? $-^2/_3$
- What is cos$^{-1}(^2/_3)$? 48·2
- Remember to identify the quadrants where cos x is negative and use this answer to find your solutions.

Answer: $x = 131 \cdot 8°$ and $x = 228 \cdot 2°$

Q10:

Steps:

- Re-arrange the equation.
- What is tan x? $-^7/_2$
- What is tan$^{-1}(^7/_2)$? 74·1
- Remember to identify the quadrants where tan x is negative and use this answer to find your solutions.

Answer: $x = 105 \cdot 9°$ and $x = 285 \cdot 9°$

Exact trigonometric values exercise (page 97)

Q11: a) Positive

Q12: 30 °

Q13: b) $\frac{1}{2}$

Q14: b) Negative

Q15: 30 $^\circ$

Q16: a) $-\frac{1}{\sqrt{3}}$

Using trigonometric identities exercise (page 99)

Q17:

a) $1 - \cos^2 x$

b) $1 - \sin^2 x$

c) $\cos x \tan x$

d) $\frac{\sin x}{\tan x}$

Q18:

a) 2

b) $3 \tan^2 A$

Q19:

a) $\sin^2 x$

b) $2 \cos^2 A$

Q20:

a)
$$
\begin{aligned}
RHS &= (\sin X + \cos X)^2 \\
&= \sin^2 X + 2 \sin X \cos X + \cos^2 X \\
&= \sin^2 X + \cos^2 X + 2 \sin X \cos X \\
&\qquad\qquad\qquad\quad = 1 + 2 \sin X \cos X \\
&= LHS
\end{aligned}
$$

b)
$$
\begin{aligned}
RHS &= (\sin x - \cos x)^2 + (\sin x + \cos x)^2 \\
&= \sin x^2 - 2 \sin x \cos x + \cos x^2 + \sin x^2 + 2 \sin x \cos x + \cos x^2 \\
&= \sin x^2 + \cos x^2 + \sin x^2 + \cos x^2 - 2 \sin x \cos x + 2 \sin x \cos x \\
&= 1 + 1 \\
&= 2 \\
&= LHS
\end{aligned}
$$

c)
$$
\begin{aligned}
RHS &= \cos^2 A - \sin^2 A \\
&= \cos^2 A - (1 - \cos^2 A) \\
&= \cos^2 A - 1 + \cos^2 A \\
&= 2 \cos^2 A - 1 \\
&= LHS
\end{aligned}
$$

Angles in degrees and radians exercise (page 106)

Q21:

  a) $\frac{\pi}{6}$
  b) $\frac{5\pi}{6}$
  c) $\frac{3\pi}{5}$
  d) $\frac{\pi}{2}$
  e) $\frac{2\pi}{5}$
  f) $\frac{5\pi}{4}$
  g) $\frac{3\pi}{4}$
  h) $\frac{3\pi}{2}$

Q22:

  a) $108°$
  b) $150°$
  c) $60°$
  d) $45°$
  e) $144°$
  f) $90°$
  g) $72°$
  h) $36°$

Q23:

  a) $\frac{\sqrt{3}}{2}$
  b) 0
  c) 1
  d) $-\sqrt{3}$
  e) $-\frac{1}{2}$
  f) -1

Graphs of trigonometric functions practice (page 107)

Q24:

Step 1:

Start by plotting the important points from the sin curve on your graph. It starts at the origin and increases to the maximum value.

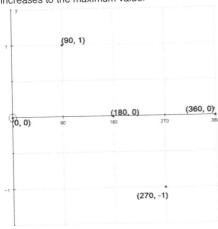

Step 2:

Sketch a smooth curve and label it.

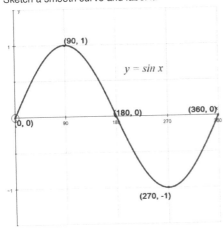

Q25:

Step 1:

Start by plotting the important points from the cos curve on your graph. It starts at the maximum value and decreases.

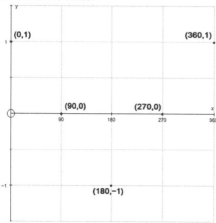

Step 2:

Sketch a smooth curve and label it.

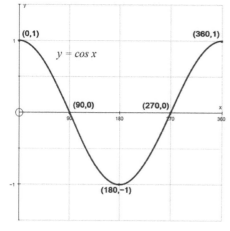

Q26:

Step 1:

Start by plotting the important points on the tan curve and the dotted lines where the graph is undefined. It starts at the origin and increases but remember the tan curve is not continuous.

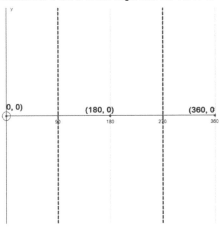

Step 2:

Sketch smooth curves and a label.

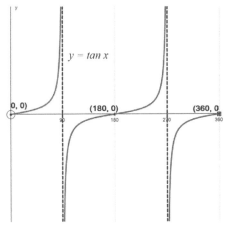

Sketching trigonometric functions exercise 1 (page 114)

Q27:

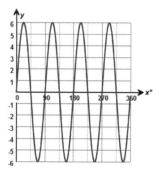

Q28:

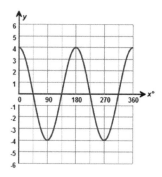

Q29:

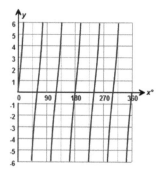

Sketching trigonometric functions exercise 2 (page 119)

Q30:

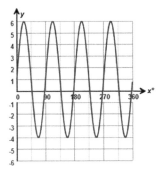

Q31:

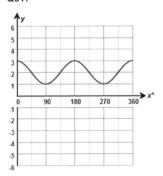

Q32:

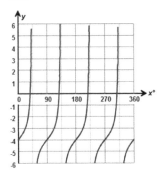

Sketching trigonometric functions exercise 3 (page 125)

Q33:

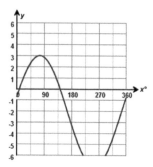

Q34:

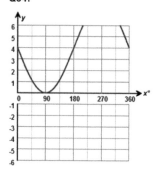

Q35:

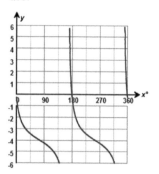

Graphs of trigonometric functions exercise (page 128)

Q36: $\frac{2\pi}{3}$

Q37: 2

Q38: $\frac{\pi}{3}$

Q39: 3

Q40: 6π

Q41: 5

Q42: $4\cos(4x)$

Q43: 4

Q44: $\frac{\pi}{2}$

Q45: $3\sin(2x)$

Q46: 3

Q47: π

Q48: $2\sin\left(\frac{x}{2}\right)$

Q49: 2

Q50: 4π

More complex trigonometric graphs exercise (page 138)

Q51:

Steps:

- What is the period of the graph in degrees? $120°$
- Consider the horizontal shift of the graph. What is the value of b (in degrees)? $20°$

Answer: $y = \sin 3(x + 20)$

Q52:

Steps:

- What is the period of the graph in degrees? $180°$
- Consider the horizontal shift of the graph. What is the value of b (in degrees)? $-45°$

Answer: $y = \cos 2(x - 45)$

Q53: $y = \cos(2x + 60)$

a)

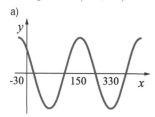

Q54: $y = \sin(4(x - 30))$

d)

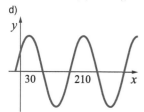

Q55: 3

Q56: $^{360}/_2 = 180°$

Q57: 2

Q58: Right (because of the - 120°)

Q59:

Hints:

- If we factorise the bracket we get $y = 3\sin 2(x - 60)°$

Answer: $^{120}/_2 = 60$

Q60: 5

Q61: $^{360}/_3 = 120 = \frac{2\pi}{3}$

Q62: 3

Q63: Up (because of the +1)

Q64: 1

Q65: Left (because of the $+ \frac{\pi}{4}$)

Q66:

Hints:

- If we factorise the bracket we get $y = 5\cos 3\left(x + \frac{\pi}{12}\right) + 1$
- Remember $\frac{\pi}{4} = 45°$ and $\frac{\pi}{4} \div 3 = \frac{\pi}{12}$ which is the same as 45 ÷ 3 = 15°.

Answer: $\frac{\pi}{4} \div 3 = \frac{\pi}{12}$

Solving trigonometric equations exercise (page 146)

Q67:

Hints:

- $\cos 2x° - 1 = 0$
  $\cos 2x° = 1$

-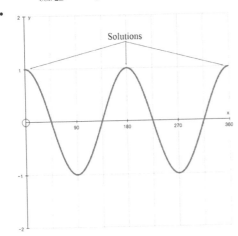

Answer: 3

Q68:

$$2 + 3 \sin(2x - 30) = 4$$
$$3 \sin(2x - 30) = 2$$
$$\sin(2x - 30) = \frac{2}{3}$$

$2x - 30 = 41 \cdot 8°$	$2x - 30 = 138 \cdot 2°$
$2x = 71 \cdot 8°$	$2x = 168 \cdot 2°$
$x = 35 \cdot 9°$	$x = 84 \cdot 1°$

The period for $\sin 2x$ is $180°$ so there are 2 more solutions.

$x = 215 \cdot 9°$ and $x = 264 \cdot 1°$

Which solution lies in the domain?

The solution is $\underline{x = 215 \cdot 9°}$

Q69: $14°$

Q70: S

Q71: 180 - 14 = 166°

Q72: 10·45°

Q73: 34·55°

Q74: 100·45°

Q75: 304·55°

Q76:

Steps:

- We always find the solution in the ALL quadrant first.
- $\cos 5x = -\dfrac{2}{4}$

  $\cos^{-1}\left(\dfrac{2}{4}\right) = 60°$
- $5x = 180 - 60 = 120$ (solution in the sin quadrant).

Answer: $x = 24°$

Q77:

Steps:

- $5x = 180 + 60 = 240$ (solution in the tan quadrant)

Answer: $x = 48°$

Q78:

Steps:

- The period for $\cos 5x$ is $^{360}/_5 = 72°$.
- So the next solution in $24 + 72 = 96°$ and so on.

Answer: 10 solutions in 360°

Q79: $\frac{\pi}{4}$

Q80: $\frac{7\pi}{4}$

Q81:

Steps:

- Factorise $3\sin^2 x° - 7\sin x° - 6 = 0$ then solve the equation.
  The question factorises but only 1 factor has solutions.
  $(3\sin x + 2)(\sin x - 3) = 0$

  $3\sin x + 2 = 0$ $\qquad\qquad\qquad\qquad$ $\sin x - 3 = 0$

  $\qquad\sin x = -\dfrac{2}{3}$ $\qquad\qquad\qquad\qquad$ $\sin x = 3$

  $\qquad\qquad$2 solutions $\qquad\qquad\qquad\qquad\qquad$ 0 solutions

Answer: 2 solutions

Q82: 221·8°

Q83: 318·2°

Q84:

Hints:

- Remember $\tan x = \pm\sqrt{3/4}$

Steps:

- How many solutions lie between π and 2π radians?

Answer: 2 solutions

Q85: 3·999°

Q86: 5·426°

The addition formula exercise (page 152)

Q87: $\sin x \cos 5y - \cos x \sin 5y$

Q88: $-\cos x$

Q89: $\cos 2a \cos 3a - \sin 2a \sin 3a$

Q90: $\dfrac{\sqrt{3}+1}{2\sqrt{2}}$

Q91: $\dfrac{1-\sqrt{3}}{2\sqrt{2}}$

Q92: $\dfrac{\sqrt{3}+1}{2\sqrt{2}}$

Q93: $\dfrac{-1}{\sqrt{2}}$

Q94:

Steps:

- What is the exact value of the hypotenuse on the triangle with angle e? 2
- What is the exact value of the hypotenuse on the triangle with angle f? $\sqrt{5}$
- What is the exact value of $\sin e$? $\frac{\sqrt{3}}{2}$
- What is the exact value of $\sin f$? $\frac{1}{\sqrt{5}}$
- What is the exact value of $\cos e$? $\frac{1}{2}$
- What is the exact value of $\cos f$? $\frac{2}{\sqrt{5}}$

Answer: $\frac{2\sqrt{3}+1}{2\sqrt{5}}$

Q95: $\frac{2-\sqrt{3}}{2\sqrt{5}}$

Q96:

Steps:

- What is the exact value of $\sin A$? $\frac{1}{\sqrt{10}}$
- What is the exact value of $\sin 90°$? 1
- What is the exact value of $\cos A$? $\frac{3}{\sqrt{10}}$
- What is the exact value of $\cos 90°$? 0

Answer: $\frac{1}{\sqrt{10}}$

Q97: $-\frac{3}{\sqrt{10}}$

The double angle formula exercise (page 155)

Q98:

Steps:

- The best formula to use depends on the information given.

Answer: $\frac{7}{25}$

Q99:

Hints: Use $\cos 2x = 1 - 2\sin^2 x$

Answer: $\frac{1}{9}$

Q100:

Hints: $\tan x = \frac{1}{2} = \frac{O}{A}$, use Pythagoras to find the hypotenuse then expand $\sin 2x$.

Answer: $\frac{4}{5}$

Q101:

Steps:

- By Pythagoras, what is the value of $\sin 2A$? $\frac{5}{13}$

Answer: $\frac{120}{169}$

Q102:

Steps:

- What is $\sin 4A$ in terms of $\sin 2A$? $2 \sin(2A) \cos(2A)$
- Express $\cos 4A$ in terms of $\sin 2A$.
- When $\sin x = \frac{3}{5}$ what is the value of $\cos x$? $\frac{4}{5}$

Answer: $\frac{24}{7}$

Q103:

Steps:

- Try Pythagoras to find the cos value.

Answer: $\frac{120}{169}$

Q104: $\frac{1}{2}$

$$2\cos^2 15 - 1 = \cos 2(15) \quad \text{as } \cos 2x - 1 = \cos 2x$$

Q105:
$$= \cos 30$$
$$= \frac{\sqrt{3}}{2}$$

Q106: $\sin(2x) - 1$

Q107:

Hints:

$$\sin 2x = 10 \cos x$$
$$2 \sin x \cos x = 10 \cos x$$
- $2 \sin x \cos x - 10 \cos x = 0$
$$2 \cos x(\sin x - 5) = 0$$
$$2 \cos x = 0 \quad or \quad \sin x - 5 = 0$$
- Find the solution closest to 0 which lies between $0°$ and $180°$.

Answer: 90

Q108:

Hints:

$$
\begin{aligned}
\sin\left(2x \ + \ 90\right)^{\circ} \ &= \ \sin 2x \ \cos 90^{\circ} \ + \ \cos 2x \ \sin 90^{\circ}\\
&= \ \sin 2x \ \times \ 0 \ + \ \cos 2x \ \times \ 1\\
&= \ 0 \ + \ \cos^2 x \ - \ \sin^2 x\\
&= \ \left(\frac{3}{\sqrt{13}}\right)^2 \ - \ \left(\frac{2}{\sqrt{13}}\right)^2\\
&= \ \frac{9}{13} \ - \ \frac{4}{13}\\
&= \ ?
\end{aligned}
$$

Steps:

- What is the length of AC? $\sqrt{13}$
- What is the exact value of $\sin x^{\circ}$? $\frac{2}{\sqrt{13}}$
- What is the exact value of $\cos x^{\circ}$? $\frac{3}{\sqrt{13}}$
- $\sin\left(B\hat{C}D\right) \ = \ \sin\left(2x \ + \ 90\right)^{\circ}$ so use this to find the exact value.

Answer: $\frac{5}{13}$

Q109:

Hints:

$$
\begin{aligned}
\sin 3x \ &= \ \sin\left(2x \ + \ x\right)\\
&= \ \sin 2x \ \cos x \ + \ \cos 2x \ \sin x\\
&= \ \left(2 \sin x \ \cos x\right) \cos x \ + \ \left(2 \cos^2 \ - \ 1\right) \sin x\\
&= \ 2 \sin x \ \cos^2 x \ + \ 2 \cos^2 x \ \sin x \ - \ \sin x
\end{aligned}
$$

- Substitute and simplify.

Steps:

- What is the exact value of $\cos x$?
- $\sin 3x \ = \ \sin\left(2x \ + \ x\right)$, expand the addition formula and substitute for $\sin x$ and $\cos x$.

Answer: $\frac{22}{27}$

Trigonometric identities exercise (page 159)

Q110:

$$
\begin{aligned}
\left(\cos x \ + \ \sin x\right)^2 \ &= \ \left(\cos x \ + \ \sin x\right)\left(\cos x \ + \ \sin x\right)\\
&= \ \cos^2 x \ + \ 2 \sin x \ \cos x \ + \ \sin^2 x\\
&= \ \cos^2 x \ + \ \sin^2 x \ + \ 2 \sin x \ \cos x\\
&= \ 1 \ + \ \sin 2x
\end{aligned}
$$

Q111:

$$\cos 2x = 1 - 2\sin^2 x$$
$$2\sin^2 x = 1 - \cos 2x$$
$$\sin^2 x = \frac{1}{2}(1 - \cos 2x)$$

Q112:

$$\frac{\cos x + \sin x}{\cos 2x} = 1$$
$$\frac{\cos x + \sin x}{\cos^2 x - \sin^2 x} = 1$$
$$\frac{\cos x + \sin x}{(\cos x - \sin x)(\cos x + \sin x)} = 1$$
$$\frac{1}{(\cos x - \sin x)} = 1$$
$$1 = \cos x - \sin x$$
$$1 + \sin x = \cos x$$

Q113:

$$2\cos 2A - \cos^2 A = 2(\cos^2 A - \sin^2 A) - \cos^2 A$$
$$= 2\cos^2 A - 2\sin^2 A - \cos^2 A$$
$$= \cos^2 A - 2\sin^2 A$$
$$= \cos^2 A - \sin^2 A - \sin^2 A$$
$$= 1 - 2\sin^2 A - \sin^2 A$$
$$= 1 - 3\sin^2 A$$

Q114:

Hints:

- Remember $2\cos 2A - \cos^2 A = 1 - 3\sin^2 A$ so
  $2\sin A = 2\cos 2A - \cos^2 A$ gives
  $2\sin A = 1 - 3\sin^2 A$
- Make this equation equal to zero then factorise to solve.

Answer: $a = 19 \cdot 5, b = 90, c = 160 \cdot 5$

The wave function exercise (page 169)

Q115: $\sqrt{29}$

Q116:

Steps:

- What is $k \sin \alpha$ equal to? 2
- What is $k \cos \alpha$ equal to? 5
- Which quadrant is α in (A, S, T or C)? A

Answer: 21·8°

Q117: $\sqrt{25} = 5$

Q118:

Steps:

- What is $k \sin \alpha$ equal to? 4
- What is $k \cos \alpha$ equal to? 3
- Which quadrant is α in (A, S, T or C)? A

Answer: 53·1°

Q119: $\sqrt{45}$

Q120:

Steps:

- What is $k \sin \alpha$ equal to? -3
- What is $k \cos \alpha$ equal to? 6
- Which quadrant is α in (A, S, T or C)? C

Answer: 333°

Q121: $\sqrt{85}$

Q122:

Steps:

- What is $k \sin \alpha$ equal to? -2
- What is $k \cos \alpha$ equal to? 9
- Which quadrant is α in (A, S, T or C)? C

Answer: 347°

Q123: $\sqrt{32}$

Q124:

Steps:

- What is $k \sin \alpha$ equal to? -4
- What is $k \cos \alpha$ equal to? 4
- Which quadrant is α in (A, S, T or C)? C

Answer: $315°$

Q125: $\sqrt{73}$

Q126:

Steps:

- What is $k \sin \alpha$ equal to? -3
- What is $k \cos \alpha$ equal to? -8
- Which quadrant is α in (A, S, T or C)? T

Answer: 3·5 radians

Q127: 2

Q128: $\frac{\pi}{6}$

Q129: $\frac{\pi}{2}$

Q130: $\frac{11\pi}{6}$

Maximum and minimum values of the wave function exercise (page 175)

Q131:

Steps:

- What value of the trig function will generate the maximum of the expression? 1

Answer: $-5 - \sqrt{2}$

Q132:

Steps:

- What value of the trig function will generate the maximum of the expression? 1

Answer: $-8 - \sqrt{4} = -8 - 2 = -10$

Q133:

Steps:

- What value of the trig function will generate the maximum of the expression? 1

Answer: $-7 - \sqrt{7}$

Q134: $5 - \sqrt{3}$

Q135: $8 - \sqrt{5}$

Q136: $7 - \sqrt{5}$

Q137: -4

Q138: -6

Q139: -6

Q140: $-\sqrt{97}$

Q141:

Steps:

- What is $k\sin(x + \alpha)$? 4
- What is $k\cos(x + \alpha)$? 9
- What is k? $\sqrt{97}$
- What is α? 24°

Answer: 246°

Q142: $\sqrt{97}$

Q143: 66°

Q144:

Steps:

- What is the amplitude of the combined trig function? $\sqrt{85}$

Answer: $-6 + \sqrt{85}$

Q145: 282·5°

Q146: $-6 - \sqrt{85}$

Q147: 102·5°

Q148:

Steps:

- What is the amplitude of the combined trig function? $\sqrt{162}$

Answer: $9 + \sqrt{162}$

Q149: 315°

Q150: $9 - \sqrt{162}$

Q151: 135°

End of topic 6 test (page 179)

Q152: 4

Q153: 5

Q154: -3

Q155: 180°

Q156: right

Q157: 25°

Q158: 5

Q159: 2

Q160: $\frac{\pi}{2}$

Q161: $\frac{\pi}{6}$

Q162: $\frac{5\pi}{3}$

Q163: 299·5

Q164: $-\frac{3}{5}$

Q165:
Steps:

- What is sin x? $\frac{2}{\sqrt{5}}$
- Expand sin $2x$ and substitute for cos x and sin x.

Answer: $\frac{4}{5}$

Q166: $\frac{1+\sqrt{3}}{2\sqrt{2}}$

Q167: $\frac{\pi}{4} - \frac{\pi}{6}$

Q168: $\frac{\sqrt{3}-1}{2\sqrt{2}}$

Q169: $\sqrt{34}$

Q170: 59°

Q171:
Steps:

- Replace $3 \sin x° - 5 \cos x°$ with $R \sin(x - \alpha)°$ then solve the equation.

Answer: 248·9°

Q172:

Steps:

- What is the value of k? 17
- What is the value of $a°$? 28·1

Answer: 17

Q173: 331·9

Q174: -17

Q175: 151·9

Q176:

$$\frac{\sin 2x}{\cos 2x + 1} = \frac{2 \sin x \cos x}{(2 \cos^2 - 1) + 1}$$
$$= \frac{2 \sin x \cos x}{2 \cos^2 x}$$
$$= \frac{2 \sin x \cos x}{2 \cos x \cos x}$$
$$= \frac{\sin x}{\cos x}$$
$$= \tan x$$

Q177:

Steps:

- Sketch two separate right-angled triangles.
- What is the length of AD as an exact value? $\sqrt{160}$
- What is the length of BC? 5
- If $\angle BAC = m°$ and $\angle BAD = n°$ what is $x°$ in terms m and n? $m - n$
- Use your answers to find cos $x°$.

Answer: $\frac{41}{13\sqrt{10}}$

Topic 3: Recurrence relations

Solving simultaneous equations by elimination exercise (page 188)

Q1:

a) x = 6
b) y = 9

Q2:

a) a = 7
b) b = 4

Q3:

a) c = 2
b) d = 3

Q4:

a) e = 0
b) f = 1

Q5:

a) g = 4
b) h = 2

Q6:

a) m = 1
b) n= 4

Q7:

a) p = 3
b) q = 4

Solving simultaneous equations by substitution exercise (page 191)

Q8:

a) x = 3
b) y = 3

Q9:

a) x = -2
b) y = 2

Q10:

a) x = 7

b) y = 0

Q11:

a) x = 2

b) y = 4

Q12:

a) x = 1

b) y = 5

Simple recurrence relations exercise (page 199)

Q13: $c_{n+1} = 0 \cdot 6c_n$

Q14: A geometric sequence

Q15:

Steps:

- What is the value of the car after 1 year? £9600

Answer: $£1244 \cdot 16$

Q16: $c_n = 0 \cdot 6^n c_0$

Q17: $T_{n+1} = T_n + 14$ with $T_0 = 20$

Q18:

Steps:

- How many trees does the farmer have in his orchard after 1 day? 34
- How many trees does the farmer have in his orchard after 2 days? 48
- How many trees does the farmer have in his orchard after 3 days? 62

Answer: 104

Q19: $P_{n+1} = P_n + 18$

Q20: An arithmetic sequence

Q21: £226

Q22: $P_n = 10 + 18n$

Q23:

Steps:

- If 7% of the iceberg melts then the next year what percentage of the iceberg will remain? 93

Answer: $V_{n+1} = 0 \cdot 93 V_n$ with $V_0 = 3200$

Q24:

Steps:

- After 1 year the volume of the iceberg = ? 2976 km^3
- After 2 years the volume of the iceberg = ? 2768 km^3

Answer: $2070 \ km^3$

Q25: $V_n = 0 \cdot 93^n V_0$

Q26: 17 years

Q27:

Steps:

- $u_2 = 3u_1 + 1$

Answer: 13

Q28:

Steps:

- $u_3 = 3u_2 + 1$

Answer: 40

Q29:

Steps:

- $u_4 = 3u_3 + 1$

Answer: 121

Q30: 88573

Q31: 64

Q32: 16·8

Q33: 7·36

Q34: 5·472

Q35: 5·00015104

Q36: c. $u_{n+1} = 4u_n$

Q37: 2

Q38: 3

Q39: 5

Q40: 8

Q41: 13

Q42: 21

Q43: 34

Q44: 55

Q45: $u_{n+1} = 1 \cdot 07 u_n + 90$ with $u_o = 90$

Q46:

Steps:

- How much did Ben have in his account on his 16th birthday? £186
- How much did Ben have in his account on his 17th birthday? £289

Answer: £779

Q47:

Steps:

- If 20% of the fish leave the shoal then what percentage of the shoal remain? 80

Answer: $F_{n+1} = 0 \cdot 8 F_n + 20$ with $F_0 = 250$

Q48:

Steps:

- After 1 minute the number of fish in the shoal is? 220
- After 2 minutes the number of fish in the shoal is? 196

Answer: 125

Q49:

Steps:

- If 90% of the chemical is washed away each day then what percentage of chemical remains in the river? 10%

Answer: $u_{n+1} = 0 \cdot 1 u_n + 50$ with $u_0 = 50$

Q50:

Steps:

- How many kg of chemical waste are there in the river after one day? 55·0 kg
- How many kg of chemical waste are there in the river after two days? 55·5 kg

Answer: 55·6 kg

Q51: 55·6 kg

Q52: $u_{n+1} = 0 \cdot 8u_n + 50$ with $u_0 = 50$

Q53:

Steps:

- The drug is injected every 6 hours, so after 36 hours $n = \frac{36}{6} = 6$.

Answer: 197·5712

Q54: 20

Q55: 4

Q56: 438

Q57: 2155·248

Q58: 4

Finding a limit exercise (page 208)

Q59:

a) $u_1 = 50$
b) $u_2 = 15$
c) $u_3 = 39 \cdot 5$
d) $u_4 = 22 \cdot 35$

Q60: c. $-1 < -0 \cdot 7 < 1$

Q61:

Steps:

- Remember that the limit of the recurrence relation $u_{n+1} = au_n + b$ for $-1 < a < 1$ can be calculated from the formula $L = \frac{b}{1-a}$

Answer: 29·4

Q62:

a) $u_1 = 54$
b) $u_2 = -21$
c) $u_3 = 91 \cdot 5$
d) $u_4 = -77 \cdot 25$

Q63: The recurrence relation $u_{n+1} = au_n + b$ has a limit only when $-1 < a < 1$.
When $a = -1 \cdot 5$ this is not true thus the given recurrence relation does not have a limit.

Q64: Yes

Q65:

Steps:

- When $-1 < a < 1$ then the recurrence relation $u_{n+1} = au_n + b$ has a limit given by the formula $L = ? \frac{b}{1-a}$

Answer: $\frac{80}{3}$

Q66:

Steps:

- Using "Killpest" the recurrence relation that describes the number of pests in the trees is $K_{n+1} = aK_n + b$ where $a =$? $0 \cdot 39$
- Using "Killpest" the recurrence relation that describes the number of pests in the trees is $K_{n+1} = aK_n + b$ where $b =$? 600
- When $-1 < a < 1$ then the recurrence relation $u_{n+1} = au_n + b$ has a limit given by the formula $L = ? \frac{b}{1-a}$

Answer: 984

Q67:

Steps:

- Using "Pestkill" the recurrence relation that describes the number of pests in the trees is $P_{n+1} = aP_n + b$ where $a =$? $0 \cdot 21$
- Using "Pestkill" the recurrence relation that describes the number of pests in the trees is $P_{n+1} = aP_n + b$ where $b =$? 720
- When $-1 < a < 1$ then the recurrence relation $u_{n+1} = au_n + b$ has a limit given by the formula $L = ? \frac{b}{1-a}$

Answer: 911

Q68: Pestkill

Q69:

Steps:

- When the office worker manages to file 76% of the folders what percentage remain on his desk? Give the percentage as a decimal. $0 \cdot 24$

Answer: $F_{n+1} = 0 \cdot 24F_n + 40$ with $F_0 = 50$

Q70:

Steps:

- How many folders does he have on his desk after 1 hour? 52
- How many folders does he have on his desk after 3 hours? 53

Answer: 53

Q71: 53

Solving recurrence relations exercise (page 212)

Q72: $-2a + b$

Q73: $-17a + b$

Q74:

$a = 5$
$b = -7$

Q75:

Steps:

- Let $n = 1$ then $u_{n+1} = au_n + b$ becomes $u_2 = au_1 + b$ hence $7400 = ? \, 9200a + b$
- Let $n = 2$ then $u_{n+1} = au_n + b$ becomes $u_3 = au_2 + b$ hence $6050 = ? \, 7400a + b$
- Solve the above simultaneous equations to find a and b.

Answer: $a = 0 \cdot 75$ and $b = 500$

Q76:

Steps:

- Let $n = 0$ then $u_1 = au_0 + b$. Substitute in the values for u_1, a and b.

Answer: $u_0 = 11600$

Q77:

Steps:

- When $-1 < a < 1$ the recurrence relation $u_1 = au_0 + b$ converges to the limit L as n tends to infinity.
- What is the formula for L? $L = \frac{b}{1-a}$

Answer: $L = 2000$

Q78:

Steps:

- What is u_1? Give your answer in terms of b. $2 + b$
- When $n = 1$ then $u_2 = 2u_1 + b$. Hence $58 = ?$ Give your answer in terms of b. $4 + 3b$

Answer: $b = 18$

Q79:

Steps:

- Let $n = 1$ then $u_{n+1} = au_n + b$ becomes $u_2 = au_1 + b$ hence $1600 = ?$ Give your answer in terms of a and b. $6000a + b$
- Let $n = 2$ then $u_{n+1} = au_n + b$ becomes $u_3 = au_2 + b$ hence $720 = ?$ Give your answer in terms of a and b. $1600a + b$

Answer: $a = 0 \cdot 2$ and $b = 400$

Q80: 80

Q81: 400

Q82: $2x$

Q83: $\frac{10y}{9}$

Q84: $x = \frac{5}{9}y$

End of topic 7 test (page 216)

Q85: d. $u_{n+1} = 1 \cdot 15u_n - 2500$

Q86: 5872

Q87: c. $u_{n+1} = 0 \cdot 28u_n + 60$

Q88: 84 kg

Q89:

Steps:

- If each week the amount of plant food in the geraniums drops by about 65% then what percentage remains in the geraniums? 35%

Answer: b. $G_{n+1} = 0 \cdot 35G_n + 4$

Q90:

Steps:

- Remember that the limit of the recurrence relation $u_{n+1} = au_n + b$ for $-1 < a < 1$ can be calculated from the formula $L = \frac{b}{1-a}$

Answer: 6·2

Q91: Over a long period of time the amount of "Growtall" plant food in the geraniums will stabilise around 6·2 grams.

Q92:

Steps:

- If 70% of the queue are served what percentage are left still in the queue? 30%

Answer: a. $S_{n+1} = 0 \cdot 3S_n + 17$

Q93:

Steps:

- Remember that the limit of the recurrence relation $u_{n+1} = au_n + b$ for $-1 < a < 1$ can be calculated from the formula $L = \frac{b}{1-a}$

Answer: 24

Q94: If the situation continues then the number of students in the queue will settle around 24 (to the nearest whole number).

Q95: 2. $K_{n+1} = 0 \cdot 3K_n + 11$

Q96: b. $-1 < a < 1$

Q97: $\frac{110}{7}$

Q98:

Steps:

- If the natural tidal action removes 42% of the chemical from the loch every week what percentage of the chemical will remain in the loch? 58%

Answer: d. $C_{n+1} = 0 \cdot 58C_n + 2 \cdot 8$

Q99: 6·7 mg/l

Q100: Yes

Q101:

Steps:

- After the installation of the cleaning process what percentage will the concentration of the chemical be reduced by? 0·7 × 2·8 = 1·96

Answer: b. $C_{n+1} = 0 \cdot 58C_n + 1 \cdot 96$

Q102: 4·7 mg/l

Q103: Yes

Q104: d. $D_{n+1} = 0 \cdot 2D_n + 1$

Q105: 1·25 m

Q106: Yes
In the long term the amount of silt in the harbour will settle around 1·25 metres (to 2 decimal places). Since 1·25 < 2 metres then the harbour can remain open.

Q107:

Steps:

- If $3/4$ of the rubbish is removed then what fraction remains? $1/4$

Answer: b. $u_{n+1} = 1/4u_n + 60$

Q108:

Steps:

- Remember that the limit of the recurrence relation $u_{n+1} = au_n + b$ for $-1 < a < 1$ can be calculated from the formula $L = \frac{b}{1-a}$

Answer: 80 kg

Q109: In the long term the amount of rubbish on the beach will tend towards 80 kg at the start of each day.

Q110:

Steps:

- If $\frac{4}{5}$ of the rubbish is removed then what fraction remains? $\frac{1}{5}$

Answer: d. $u_{n+1} = \frac{1}{5}u_n + 1$

Q111:

Steps:

- Remember that the limit of the recurrence relation $u_{n+1} = au_n + b$ for $-1 < a < 1$ can be calculated from the formula $L = \frac{b}{1-a}$

Answer: 1·25 pints

Q112: In the long term the amount of screen wash in her car will settle around 1·25 pints at the end of each month.

Q113: $5a + b$

Q114: $5a^2 + ab + b$

Q115:

Steps:

- What is u_2? 9·35
- What is u_3? 4·805
- What is u_4? 3·4415
- Keep going until the first time u_n goes below 3.

Answer: $n = 6$

Topic 4: Integration

Integrating algebraic expressions exercise (page 225)

Q1: $\int x^9 \, dx \;=\; \frac{x^{10}}{10} \,+\, C$

Q2: $\int t^{10} \, dt \;=\; \frac{t^{11}}{11} \,+\, C$

Q3: $\int x^{-3} \, dx \;=\; -\frac{1}{2x^2} \,+\, C$

Q4: $\int x^{\frac{4}{9}} \, dx \;=\; \frac{9x^{\frac{13}{9}}}{13} \,+\, C$

Q5: $\int x^{\frac{-2}{7}} \, dx \;=\; \frac{7x^{\frac{5}{7}}}{5} \,+\, C$

Q6: $\int x^{\frac{-5}{2}} \, dx \;=\; \frac{-2x^{\frac{-3}{2}}}{3} \,+\, C$

Q7: $\int 3x^3 \, dx \;=\; \frac{3x^4}{4} \,+\, C$

Q8: $\int -6 \, dx \;=\; -6x \,+\, C$

Q9: $\int 3x^{-2} \, dx \;=\; -\frac{3}{x} \,+\, C$

Q10: $\int 9x^{-3} \, dx \;=\; -\frac{9}{2x^2} \,+\, C$

Q11: $\int 11x^{\frac{8}{3}} \, dx \;=\; 3x^{\frac{11}{3}} \,+\, C$

Integrating algebraic expressions with multiple terms exercise (page 228)

Q12: c. $4x \,+\, \frac{2}{\sqrt{x}} \,+\, C$

Q13: $\frac{-3}{x^5} \,+\, \frac{4}{5}x^5 \,+\, 12x \,+\, C$

Q14: $7x \,-\, 18x^{\frac{1}{9}} \,+\, C$

Q15: $\frac{-2}{x^4}$

Q16: $\frac{2}{9}x^{\frac{9}{2}}$

Q17: b. $\frac{-1}{77x^{11}}$

Integrating products and quotients exercise (page 229)

Q18: $\frac{4t^3}{3} \,+\, 2t^2 \,+\, t \,+\, C$

Q19: $\frac{2u^{\frac{7}{2}}}{7} \,+\, 4u^{\frac{3}{2}} \,+\, C$

Q20:

Steps:

- $\frac{x^3 - 6x^8}{x^5} = ?\, x^{-2} - 6x^3$

Answer: $\frac{x^{-1}}{-1} - \frac{6x^4}{4}$

Q21: $2t^{\frac{1}{2}} + \frac{t^2}{2}$

Steps:

- $\frac{t + \sqrt{t^5}}{\sqrt{t^3}} = ?\, t^{-\frac{1}{2}} + t$

Integration of sin x and cos x (page 230)

Q22:

a) $\frac{d}{dx}(\sin x) = \cos x$

b) $\frac{d}{dx}(\cos x) = -\sin x$

Q23:

a) $\int \cos x\, dx = \sin x + c$

b) $\int \sin x\, dx = -\cos x + c$

Integration of sin and cos exercise (page 232)

Q24: $9\sin x + C$

Q25: $-\pi \cos t + C$

Q26: $12\sqrt{u} + \cos u + C$

Q27: $\frac{\sin x}{4} - \sqrt{7}\cos x - \pi x + C$

Q28: $-\frac{1}{2}\cos 2 + C$

Q29: $\frac{1}{7}\sin(7x + 6) + C$

Q30: $-\frac{1}{4}\cos(4x + 5) + C$

Q31: $\frac{3}{2}\sin\left(4x + \frac{\pi}{4}\right) + C$

Q32: $-25\cos\left(\frac{x}{5} - \frac{\pi}{3}\right) + C$

Q33:

a) $\frac{1}{2} - \frac{1}{2}\cos 2x + C$

b) $\frac{1}{2}x - \frac{1}{4}\sin 2x + C$

Integrating composite functions exercise (page 235)

Q34: $f(x) = \frac{(7x + 2)^4}{28} + C$

Q35: $f(x) = -\frac{(4x + 9)^{-1}}{4} + C$

Q36: $f(x) = \frac{(8x + 7)^{\frac{5}{4}}}{10} + C$

Q37: $f(x) = -(8 - 3x)^{\frac{1}{3}} + C$

Q38:

Steps:

- $\sqrt{2x + 7} = (2x + 7)^n \; n = ? \; \frac{1}{2}$

Answer: $f(x) = \frac{(2x + 7)^{\frac{3}{2}}}{3} + C$

Q39:

Steps:

- $\frac{1}{(4x + 1)^2} = (4x + 1)^m \; m = ? \; \text{-2}$

Answer: $f(x) = -\frac{1}{4(4x + 1)} + C$

Q40:

Steps:

- $\frac{1}{\left(\sqrt{4x + 5}\right)^3} = (4x + 5)^k \; k = ? \; -\frac{3}{2}$

Answer: $f(x) = -\frac{1}{2\sqrt{4x + 5}} + C$

Q41:

Steps:

- Given that $\frac{ds}{dt} = (1 - 8t)^{-7}$ then $s = \int \frac{ds}{dt} dt = \int (1 - 8t)^{-7} \, dt$

Answer: $s(t) = \frac{1}{48(1 - 8t)^6} + C$

Solving differential equations exercise (page 238)

Q42:

a) $y = 2x^2 + C$

b) $s = 2t^3 - 5t + C$

c) $y = \frac{x^2}{2} + C$

d) $s = \frac{t^2}{4} + t^3 + C$

Q43:

a) $s = \frac{5t^2}{2}$

b) $y = x^3 + \frac{x^2}{2} - 5x + 4$

c) $s = -t^3 + \frac{t^2}{2} + 6$

d) $y = 6x^{\frac{3}{2}} + 2$

Q44: $y = x^2 + 4x - 3$

Q45: $f(x) = \frac{x^2}{4} - 2x + 3$

Calculating definite integrals exercise (page 245)

Q46:

a) 6

b) 25

c) 702

d) $\frac{21}{50}$

e) 20

f) 144

Q47:

a) $\frac{7}{3}$

b) 21

c) $-\frac{4}{3}$

d) 1074

Q48:

a) $\frac{13}{12}$

b) $\frac{5-4\sqrt{2}}{3}$

Q49:

a) 2

b) 0

c) 2π

Q50:

Steps:

- What is $\int 5x\, dx$, giving your answer in the form $F(x) + C$, $F(x) = ?$ $\frac{5x^2}{2}$
- What is an algebraic expression for $\int_a^3 5x\, dx$? $\frac{45}{2} - \frac{5a^2}{2}$
- Make your solution equal to 20 and solve for the positive value of a.

Answer: 1

Q51:

Steps:

- What is $\int 4x + 1\, dx$, giving your answer in the form $F(x) + C$, $F(x) = ?$ $\frac{4x^2}{2} + x$
- What is an algebraic expression for $\int_u^{2u} 4x + 1\, dx$? $6u^2 + u$
- Make your solution equal to 5 and solve for the positive value of u.

Answer: $\frac{5}{6}$

Q52:

Steps:

- What is $\int 6x^2 + 1\, dx$, giving your answer in the form $F(x) + C$, $F(x) = ?$ $\frac{6x^3}{3} + x$
- What is an algebraic expression for $\int_{-t}^t 6x^2 + 1\, dx$? $4t^3 + 2t$
- Make your solution equal to 0 and solve for the positive value of t.

Answer: -1

Finding the area under a curve exercise (page 252)

Q53:

Steps:

- Rewrite $\frac{9}{x^4}$ in the form ax^n. $9x^{-4}$

Answer: $f(x) = -\frac{3}{x^3} + C$

Q54:

Steps:

- Find $\int 10 - 6x^2\, dx$. $f(x) = 10x - 2x^3$
- When $x = 1$ the $f(x) = ?$ 8
- When $x = -1$ the $f(x) = ?$ -8

Answer: 16

Q55: c)

Q56:

Steps:

- Solve $y = 18 - \frac{x^2}{8} = 0$ to find A and B.

Answer: A(-12,0) and B(12,0)

Q57:

Steps:

- What is the area of the rectangle? 560 feet^2
- What is $\int 18 - \frac{x^2}{8} \, dx$? $f(x) = 18x - \frac{x^3}{24} + C$
- What is the area under the parabola? 288 feet^2
- What is the area to be repainted? 272 feet^2

Answer: £1360

Q58:

Steps:

- Simplify $x(x - 4)^2$. $x^3 - 8x + 16x$

Answer: $\int_0^4 x^3 - 8x^2 + 16x \, dx$

Q59:

Steps:

- What is $\int x^3 - 8x^2 + 16x \, dx$? $f(x) = \frac{x^4}{4} - \frac{8x^3}{3} + 8x^2 + C$
- When $x = 4$ what is $f(x)$? 21·33
- When $x = 0$ what is $f(x)$? 0

Answer: 21·33 units^2

Q60:

Steps:

- What is $\int_0^4 8 - 2x \, dx$? 16
- what is $\int_4^6 8 - 2x \, dx$? -4
- Remember to ignore the negative sign for areas below the x-axis.

Answer: 20 units^2

Q61:

Steps:

- What is the x-coordinate of points A and B?
- What is $\int x^2 - 6x + 5\,dx$? $f(x) = \frac{x^3}{3} - 3x^2 + 5x + C$
- What is $\int_0^A x^2 - 6x + 5\,dx$? $\frac{7}{3}$
- What is $\int_A^B x^2 - 6x + 5\,dx$? $-\frac{32}{3}$

Answer: 13 units^2

Q62:

Steps:

- What are the two points the curve cuts the x-axis at? $x = -3$ and $x = 5$
- Sketch the curve and shade the area to be calculated.

- What is $\int_0^5 15 + 2x - x^2\,dx$? 58·33
- What is $\int_5^6 15 + 2x - x^2\,dx$? -4·33

Answer: 62·67 units^2

Q63:

Steps:

- The curve $y = 4x - x^2$ cuts the x-axis in two places at $x = 0$ and $x = A$, what is A? 4
- Sketch the curve and shade the area to be calculated.

- What is $\int 4x - x^2\,dx$? $f(x) = 2x^2 - \frac{x^3}{3} + C$

Answer: 10·7 units^2

Q64:

Steps:

- Factorise the polynomial $x^3 - 6x^2 + 9x - 4$. $(x - 1)^2(x - 4)$
- What are the two points the curve cuts the x-axis at? $x = 1$ and $x = 4$
- When $y = x^3 - 6x^2 + 9x - 4$ what is $\frac{dy}{dx}$? $3x^2 - 12x + 9$
- The curve has a maximum turning point at $x = $? 1
- The curve has a minimum turning point at $x = $? 3
- Sketch the curve and shade the area to be calculated.

- What is $\int x^3 - 6x^2 + 9x - 4$? $f(x) = \frac{x^4}{4} - 2x^3 + \frac{9x^2}{2} - 4x + C$

Answer: 6·75 units^2

Q65:

Steps:

- What is the definite integral needed to find the shaded area? $\int_0^2 (2x - 7)^{-2}\, dx$
- What is $\int (2x - 7)^{-2}\, dx$? $f(x) = -\frac{1}{2(2x - 7)} + C$
- What is $f(x)$ when $x = 2$? $\frac{1}{6}$
- What is $f(x)$ when $x = 0$? $\frac{1}{14}$

Answer: $\frac{2}{21}$ $units^2$

Q66:

Steps:

- What is $\int \sin\left(3x + \frac{\pi}{3}\right) dx$? $f(x) = -\frac{1}{3}\cos\left(3x + \frac{\pi}{3}\right) + C$
- What is $f(x)$ when $x = \frac{\pi}{6}$? $\frac{\sqrt{3}}{6}$
- What is $f(x)$ when $x = 0$? $-\frac{1}{6}$

Answer: $\frac{\sqrt{3} + 1}{6}$ $units^2$

Q67:

Steps:

- What is $\int \cos 2x\, dx$? $f(x) = \frac{1}{2}\sin 2x + C$
- What is $\int_{\frac{\pi}{6}}^{\frac{\pi}{4}} \cos 2x\, dx$?

$$\frac{2 - \sqrt{3}}{4}$$

- What is $\int_{\frac{\pi}{4}}^{\frac{\pi}{2}} \cos 2x\, dx$? $-\frac{1}{2}$
- What is the shaded area between $x = \frac{\pi}{4}$ and $x = \frac{\pi}{6}$? $\frac{1}{2}$

Answer: $1 - \frac{\sqrt{3}}{4}$ $units^2$

Finding the area between two curves exercise (page 260)

Q68:

Steps:

- What is the definite integral needed to find the shaded area? $\int_{-2}^{3} 6 + x - x^2 \, dx$
- What is $\int 6 + x - x^2 \, dx$? $f(x) = 6x + \frac{x^2}{2} - \frac{x^3}{3} + C$

Answer: 20·83 units^2

Q69:

Steps:

- To find the points of intersection solve $x^2 - 3x - 4 = 4 + 3x - x^2$. $A = -1$ and $B = 4$
- What is the definite integral needed to find the shaded area? $\int_{A}^{B} 8 + 6x - 2x^2 \, dx$
- What is $\int 8 + 6x - 2x^2 \, dx$? $f(x) = 8x + 3x^2 - \frac{2x^3}{3} + C$

Answer: 41·67 units^2

Q70:

Steps:

- Sketch the curve and shade the area to be calculated.

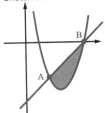

- Solve $x - 4 = x^2 - 5x + 4$ to find the points of intersection. $A = 2$ and $B = 4$
- What is the definite integral needed to find the shaded area? $\int_{A}^{B} (-x)^2 + 6x - 8 \, dx$
- What is $\int (-x)^2 + 6x - 8 \, dx$? $f(x) = -\frac{x^3}{3} + 3x^2 - 8x + C$

Answer: 1·33 units^2

Q71:

Steps:

- The graphs intersect at two points where $x = a$ and where $x = b$ with $a < b$. To find the points of intersection solve $x^2 - 20x + 17 = -1 - x^2$. $a = 1$ and $b = 9$
- What is the definite integral needed to find the shaded area? $\int_{a}^{b} -18 + 20x - 2x^2 \, dx$
- What is $\int -18 + 20x - 2x^2 \, dx$? $f(x) = -18x + 10x^2 - \frac{2x^3}{3} + C$

Answer: 170·67

Q72:

Steps:

- To find the points of intersection solve $x^3 - 3x - 2 = x - 2$. At A, $x = -2$; At B $x = 0$; At C $x = 2$
- What is the definite integral needed to find the shaded area between A and B? $\int_{-2}^{0} x^3 - 4x \, dx$
- What is the area between A and B? 4 units^2
- What is the definite integral needed to find the shaded area between B and C? $\int_{0}^{2} 4x - x^3 \, dx$
- What is the area between B and C? 4 units^2

Answer: 8 units^2

Q73:

Steps:

- The line and the curve intersect when $2x^2 - 7x + 7 = x + 7$ when $x = 0$ and when $x = ?$ 4

Answer: $\int_{0}^{4} 8x - 2x^2 \, dx$

Q74:

Steps:

- Solve $y = 16 - \frac{x^2}{4} = 0$ to find A and B.

Answer: A(-8,0) and B(8,0)

Q75:

Steps:

- What is the area of the rectangle? 560 feet^2
- What is $\int 16 - \frac{x^2}{4} \, dx$? $f(x) = 16x - \frac{x^3}{12} + C$
- What is the area under the parabola? 170·67 feet^2
- What is the area to be repainted? 389·33 feet^2

Answer: £1557

Q76:

Steps:

- Given that $y = x^3 - x^2 - 6x - 2$ then what is $\frac{dy}{dx}$? $3x^2 - 2x - 6$
- When $x = 1$ what is $\frac{dy}{dx}$? -5
- What is the gradient of the road? -5
- The equation of the straight line that represents the road can be written as? $y + 8 = m(x - 1)$

Answer: $y = -5x - 3$

Q77:

Steps:

- To find the x-coordinate of B solve $x^3 - x^2 - 6x - 2 = -5x - 3$ and notice that the x-coordinate of B is less than 0. You should get the solutions $x = -1$ or $x = 1$.
- Since at A, $x = 1$ then at B, $x = -1$ To find the y-coordinate substitute $x = -1$ into the equation you have for the line AB.
- What is the integral which represents the shaded area? $\int_{-1}^{1} x^3 - x^2 - x + 1 \, dx$

Answer: $\frac{4}{3}$ $units^2$

Q78:

Steps:

- The line and the curve intersect when $x^2 - 3x + 4 = x + 4$
- What are the values of x when the line and the curve intersect? $x = 0$ and $x = 4$

Answer: $\int_{0}^{4} 4x - x^2 \, dx$

Q79:

Steps:

- The curve $y = 16 - x^2$ cuts the x-axis in two places at? $x = -4$ and $x = 4$
- Sketch the curve and shade the area to be calculated.

- What is $\int_{-1}^{4} 16 - x^2 \, dx$? 58·33
- What is $\int_{4}^{5} 16 - x^2 \, dx$? -4·33

Answer: 62·67 units^2

End of topic 8 test (page 267)

Q80: $x - 3x^{-\frac{1}{3}} + C$

Q81: $\frac{x^6}{6} + \frac{1}{4x^4} + C$

Q82:

Steps:

- Express $\frac{2}{\sqrt[4]{x^3}}$ in the form ax^n. $2x^{-\frac{3}{4}}$

Answer: $8x^{\frac{1}{4}} + C$

Q83: $\frac{(6x-1)^4}{6 \times 4} + C$

Q84:

Steps:

* Remember that $\int \sin x \, dx = -\cos x + C$

Answer: $f(x) = -\frac{6}{7} \cos x + C$

Q85:

Steps:

* Remember that $\int \cos x \, dx = \sin x + C$

Answer: $f(x) = 4 \sin x + C$

Q86:

Steps:

* Multiply out the bracket before integrating.

Answer: $\frac{1}{2}x - \frac{1}{4} \sin 2x + C$

Q87:

Steps:

* Remember the addition formula for $\cos(A + B)$ is $\cos A \cos B - \sin A \sin B$.

Answer: $\cos 2x \cos x - \sin 2x \sin x$

Q88:

Steps:

* Remember that:
  * $\cos 2x = 2\cos^2 x - 1$
  * $\sin 2x = 2 \sin x \cos x$
  * $\sin^2 x = 1 - \cos^2 x$

Answer: $4 \cos^3 x - 3 \cos x$

Q89: $\frac{1}{4} \cos 3x + \frac{3}{4} \cos x$

Q90: $f(x) = \frac{1}{12} \sin 3x + \frac{3}{4} \sin x + C$

Q91: $\frac{26}{3}$

Q92:

Steps:

* What is $\frac{2}{\sqrt{t}}$ in the form at^n? $2t^{-\frac{1}{2}}$
* Use your answer to integrate then find the definite integral.

Answer: 2·34

Q93:

Steps:

- Simplify $x^2(x + 8)$. $x^3 + 8x^2$
- What is the integral required for this calculation? $\int_{-8}^{0} x^3 + 8x^2\, dx$
- What is $\int x^3 + 8x^2\, dx$? $f(x) = \frac{x^4}{4} + \frac{8x^3}{3} + C$
- If $x = 0$ what is $f(x)$? 0
- If $x = -8$ what is $f(x)$? -341·33

Answer: 341·33 units^2

Q94:

Steps:

- What is $\int \cos 2x\, dx$? $f(x) = \frac{1}{2}\sin 2x + C$
- What is $\int_{\frac{\pi}{6}}^{\frac{\pi}{4}} \cos 2x\, dx$?

$$\frac{2 - \sqrt{3}}{4}$$

- What is $\int_{\frac{\pi}{4}}^{\frac{\pi}{2}} \cos 2x\, dx$? $-\frac{1}{2}$
- What is the shaded area between $x = \frac{\pi}{4}$ and $x = \frac{\pi}{6}$? $\frac{1}{2}$

Answer: $1 - \frac{\sqrt{3}}{4}\ units^2$

Q95:

Steps:

- The line and the curve intersect when $2x^2 - 3x + 4 = x + 4$ when $x = 0$ and when $x = ?$ 2
- What is the integral needed to find the shaded area? $\int_{0}^{2} 4x - 2x^2\, dx$

Answer: $\frac{8}{3}\ units^2$

Q96:

Steps:

- To find the points of intersection solve $x^3 - 3x - 2 = x - 2$.
  At A, $x = -3$; At B $x = 0$; At C $x = 3$
- What is the definite integral needed to find the shaded area between A and B?
  $\int_{-3}^{0} x^3 - 9x\, dx$
- What is the area between A and B? 20·25 units^2
- What is the definite integral needed to find the shaded area between B and C?
  $\int_{0}^{3} 9x - x^3\, dx$
- What is the area between B and C? 20·25 units^2

Answer: 40·5 units^2

Q97:

Steps:

- What is $\int 6x^2 + \frac{10}{x^3}\,dx$? $2x^3 - 5x^{-2} + C$
- What is the value of C? 4

Answer: $y = 2x^3 - \frac{5}{x^2} + 4$

Topic 5: Circles

Properties of a circle exercise (page 277)

Q1:

$\angle ACB = 90°$ (angle in a semi-circle) $\Rightarrow x = 90$
$\angle CBA = 48°$ (third angle in a triangle) $\Rightarrow y = 48$

Q2:

$\angle CAT = 90°$ (radius/tangent) $\Rightarrow y = 90$
$\angle CBT = 90°$ (radius/tangent)
$\angle BTA = 70°$ (fourth angle in a quadrilateral) $\Rightarrow x = 70$

Q3:

$\angle ACT = 60°$ (symmetry) $\Rightarrow x = 60$
$\angle CAT = 90°$ (radius/tangent) $\Rightarrow y = 90$
$\angle CTA = 30°$ (third angle in triangle) $\Rightarrow z = 30$

Answers from page 278.

Q4: The equation of a circle with centre (0,0) and radius r is $x^2 + y^2 = r^2$. Since $r^2 = 9^2 = 81$, the equation is $x^2 + y^2 = 81$.

The equation of a circle with centre the origin exercise (page 281)

Q5: $r = 11$

Q6: $r = \sqrt{85}$

Q7: $r = 2$

Q8: $r = 4$

Q9: $r = \sqrt{34}$

Q10: $r = 10$

Q11: $r = \sqrt{128}$

Q12: $r = 2$

Q13: $r = 6$

Q14: $r = \sqrt{85}$

Q15: outside

Q16: inside

Q17: on

Q18:

- b. $x^2 + y^2 = r^2$
- c. $ax^2 + by^2 = r^2$

Q19: (-8,0)

Q20: $x^2 + y^2 = 89$

The equation of a circle with centre (a,b) exercise (page 285)

Q21:

a) Radius is 7 and the centre is (-2,1).

b) Note that x^2 is the same as $(x - 0)^2$.
Rearrange into the general form.
Radius is 3 and the centre is (0, 2)

c) $(x + 1)^2 + (y + 1)^2 = 1 \Rightarrow$ radius is 1 and the centre is (-1, -1)

d) Radius is $\sqrt{12}$ or $2\sqrt{3}$ and the centre is (-6, 0)

e) Rearrange to give $x^2 + (y - 1)^2 = 3$
Radius is $\sqrt{3}$ and the centre is (0, 1)

f) Rearrange to give $(x - 1)^2 + (y + 4)^2 = 36$
The radius is 6 and the centre is (1, -4)

Q22:

a) $(x + 3)^2 + (y - 4)^2 = 16$

b) The radius r is the distance between the centre and the point.
so $r^2 = (4 - 2)^2 + (-5 - 2)^2 = 53$
The equation is $(x - 2)^2 + (y - 2)^2 = 53$

c) The centre is $(4\sqrt{2}, 0)$
The equation is $(x - 4\sqrt{2})^2 + y^2 = 32$

d) $r^2 = (4 + 3)^2 + (0 + 1)^2 = 50$
The equation is $(x + 3)^2 + (y + 1)^2 = 50$

e) Radius is 3
The midway point is (-2, 3)
The equation is $(x + 2)^2 + (y - 3)^2 = 9$

f) The distance between P and Q is
$\sqrt{(8 - 2)^2 + (-4 + 12)^2} = \sqrt{100} = 10$
The radius is 5
The centre of the circle is the midway point between P and Q which is (5, -8)
The equation is $(x - 5)^2 + (y + 8)^2 = 25$

Q23:

Steps:

- What is the radius of the larger circle? The radius is 8.
- What are the coordinates of the centre of the larger circle? The centre of the larger circle is (2,-4).
- What are the coordinates of the centre of the smaller circle? The centre of the smaller circle is at (14, -4).

Answer: The equation of the smaller wheel is $(x - 14)^2 + (y + 4)^2 =$ 16.

Q24:

Steps:

- What is the radius of the wheels? 37·5 cm
- What is the x-coordinate of the centre of the second wheel (wheel B)? 127·5

Answer:
The first wheel A has centre at (37·5, 37·5) since it rests against the wall and the ground. It has equation $(x - 37 \cdot 5)^2 + (y - 37 \cdot 5)^2 = 1406 \cdot 25$
The second wheel B has centre at (127·5, 37·5). It has equation $(x - 127 \cdot 5)^2 + (y - 37 \cdot 5)^2 = 1406 \cdot 25$

The general equation of a circle exercise (page 290)

Q25:

a) The centre is given by (2,1) and the radius is 3.

b) The centre is given by (-3,2) and the radius is 4.

c) The centre is given by (0,-4) and the radius is 5.

d) The centre is given by (5,0) and the radius is 2.

Q26:

a) The centre is given by (-9,0) and the radius is 14.

b) The centre is given by (0,6) and the radius is 5.

c) The centre is given by (-6,9) and the radius is 8.

d) The centre is given by (-8,3) and the radius is 8.

Q27: y = -5

Q28:

a) 5

b) -3

Q29:

Hints:

- $\sqrt{(g^2 + f^2 - c)} > 0$ so $g^2 + f^2 - c > 0$.
- $g = -3$ and $f = 2$ giving,

$$9 + 4 - c > 0$$
$$13 - c > 0$$
$$-c > -13$$
$$c < 13$$

Steps:

- What range of values should the radius take? $r > 0$
- Use the formula for the radius to find the range of values for c.

Answer: $c < 13$

Relationships between a line and a circle exercise (page 295)

Q30: $-3x + 4y - 10 = 0$
because...

centre of circle C is (3,3)
$m_{radius} = \frac{4}{3}$
$m_{\text{tangent}} = -\frac{3}{4}$

Q31: (4,4)

Q32: (7,3)

Q33: $k = 0$ or $k = 8$

Relationships between circles exercise (page 302)

Q34:

Steps:

- What are the coordinates of the centre of the large circle? (6,4)
- What is the radius of the large circle? 3
- What are the coordinates of the centre of c_2? (7·5,4)
- What are the coordinates of the point of contact of c_2 and c_3? (9,4)

Answer: (10·5,4)

Q35:

Hints:

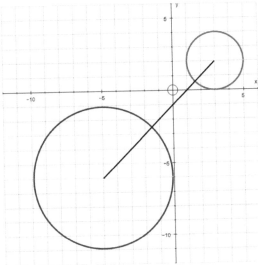

- Since the distance between the centres is greater than the sum of the radii the circles do not touch at all.

Steps:

- What is the distance between the centres of circles A and B? $8\sqrt{2}$

Answer: No

Q36:

Hints:

-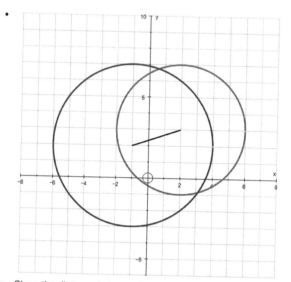

- Since the distance between the centres + radius of the smaller circle is greater than the radius of the larger circle the circles intersect.

Steps:

- What is the distance between the centres of circles A and B? $\sqrt{10}$

Answer: Yes

Q37:

Hints:

- The points of intersection can be found by solving the two equations simultaneously.
- This is only done easily because both equations contain $(x - 3)^2$.
- Subtract equation 2 from equation 1 and solve to find y.
- Substitute the value of y into equation 1 to find the x coordinates.

Answer: (-1,-1) and (7,-1)

End of topic 9 test (page 306)

Q38:

Steps:

- What is the radius of this circle? 3

Answer: (0,0)

Q39: $(x + 8)^2 + (y - 7)^2 = 49$

Q40: (-1,4)

Q41: $\sqrt{30}$

Q42: circle has centre at (-9,0) and radius 14

Q43: circle has centre at (0,6) and radius 4

Q44:

Steps:

- Find the midpoint.

Answer: (1,2)

Q45:

Steps:

- Use the distance formula to find the radius.

Answer: $\sqrt{52}$

Q46:

Steps:

- To find the point(s) where the line and tangent intersect you must substitute for y the equation of the line into the equation of the circle $x^2 + y^2 - 4x - 16 = 0$.
- The line and the tangent intersect when x = ? $x = -2$

Answer: Yes, the line is a tangent to the circle.

Q47:

Steps:

- In order to find the gradient of the tangent, you must first find the gradient of radius CP.
- What is the gradient of radius CP? $-\frac{4}{5}$
- What is the gradient of the tangent at P? $\frac{5}{4}$

Answer: $y = \frac{5}{4}x + 1$

Q48:

Steps:

- The circle has centre (a, b).What are a and b? (-3,3)
- What is the gradient of the radius from the centre to the point (-7,0)? $\frac{3}{4}$
- What is the gradient of tangent T? $-\frac{4}{3}$

Answer: $y = -\frac{4}{3}x - \frac{28}{3}$

Q49: (3,3)

Q50:

Steps:

- What is the distance between the centres of circles A and B? $2\sqrt{13}$
- Compare the distance between the centres with the radii.

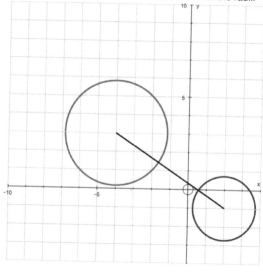

Answer: Circle A does not touch or intersect circle B because the sum of the radii is less than the distance between the centres of the circles.

Q51:

Steps:

- What is the distance between the centres of circles A and B? $\sqrt{2}$
- What is the distance between the centres + radius of the smaller circle? 3·414
- What is the radius of the larger circle? 4
- Consider whether circle Q could lie completely inside circle P.

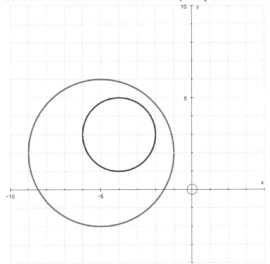

Answer: Circle P and circle Q do not touch or intersect because the distance between the two centres + the radius of the smaller circle is less than the radius of the larger circle.

Topic 6: Logs and exponentials

Growth and decay functions data exercise (page 313)

Q1:   3813

Q2:   8 years

Q3:

Steps:

- What is half the value of the car? £8997·50
- Use trial and error to find how many years will it take to reach this value.

Answer: 4

Q4:   15 years

The exponential function exercise (page 315)

Q5:   148·413

Q6:   42·521

Q7:   0·018

Q8:   1·331

Q9:   0·138

Logarithms and calculator buttons practice exercise (page 318)

Q10: 6·05

Q11: 794·33

Q12: 12·47

Q13: 19·81

Q14: 0·92

Q15: 1·33

Q16: 0·48

Q17: 2·99

Q18: 0·46

Q19: 1·02

Q20: 5·955

Q21: 16·43

Q22: 1·16

Q23: -1·77

Q24: -3·26

Q25: -43·07

Logarithmic functions exercise (page 320)

Q26:

Hints:

- $\log_e 40 = x$

Answer: 2·0588

Q27: $\log_a x = y$

Q28: $\log_a p = 7$

Q29: $\log_3 b = a$

Q30: $\log_2 y = x$

Q31: $a^b = x$

Q32: $4^y = x$

Q33: $r^2 = s$

Q34: 0·70

Q35: 128

Q36: 2

Q37: 100

Q38: 0·24998

Laws of logarithms exercise (page 326)

Q39: $\log_a 6$

Q40: 2

Q41: 3

Q42: 10

Q43: 0

Q44: 1

Q45: -10

Q46: 1

Q47: $\log_{10}8$

Q48: 8

Q49: 1000

Q50:

Steps:

- $2\log_3 12 - \log_3 x$. What is x? 144
- $\log_3 p - \log_3 q = \log_3 r$, what is r in terms of p and q? $\frac{p}{q}$

Answer: 2

Q51: 6

Q52: 6

Problem solving exercise (page 332)

Q53: 5

Q54: $\frac{2}{3}$

Q55: 7

Q56:

Steps:

- What is $\log a + \log b$ as a single log? $\log ab$
- If $\log_x ab = 1$, what does ab equal? x

Answer: 8

Q57: 1

Q58: 6

Q59:

Steps:

- Take the log of each side first.

Answer: 0·861

Q60: 3

Q61: 1

Q62: 2

Q63: -2·32

Q64: 0·85

Q65:

a) *Steps:*
- What is the value of t at the start of the experiment? 0

  Answer: 2000

b) *Steps:*
- What is the value of B when the bacteria double? 4

  Answer: 69

c) 2678862 bacteria are present

Q66:

a) 0·1238

b) 868 minutes

Q67:

a) *Steps:*
- Rearrange the equation and state the value of e^{-kt} correct to four decimal places. 0·3571
- What is the value of $(-9t)$ correct to four decimal places. -1·0296

  Answer: 0·1144

b) The contents will be safe for up to 604·55 minutes.

Q68:

Hints:

-
$$R_t = R_0 e^{-at}$$
$$\frac{R_t}{R_0} = e^{-at}$$
$$\frac{1}{2} = e^{-a \times 11\cdot4}$$
$$\frac{1}{2} = e^{-11\cdot4a}$$

- Turn this exponential equation into a log equation then solve for a.

Steps:

- What is the value of t? 11·4
- What is the value of $\frac{R_t}{R_0}$? 0·5

Answer: 0·061

Formulae from experimental data practice (page 337)

Q69: -1

Q70: 2187

Q71: 2

Q72: 5

Formulae from experimental data exercise (page 341)

Q73: d) $\log x$ against $\log y$

Q74: b) x against $\log y$

Q75:

Steps:

- What is the equation of the straight line? $y = 0 \cdot 5x + 4$
- If $y = kx^n$ then $\log_6 y = n\log_6 x + \log_6 k$.

Answer: $n = 0 \cdot 5$ and $k = 1296$

Q76: Yes

Q77: a) $y = kx^n$

Q78:

Steps:

- What is the equation of the straight line? $y = 7 \cdot 55x - 0 \cdot 07$
- If $y = kx^n$ then $\log_2 y = n\log_2 x + \log_2 k$.

Answer: $y = 0 \cdot 95x^{7 \cdot 55}$

Q79:

Steps:

- What is the equation of the equation of the straight line? $y = -2x + 6$
- If $y = ab^x$ then $\log_3 y = x\log_3 b + \log_3 a$

Answer: $a = 729$ and $b = \frac{1}{9}$

Q80:

The original data may suggest exponential growth of the form $y = kx^n$ or $y = ab^x$. In fitting the data to a straight line we can see from the graph that the y-coordinates have logs applied and the x-coordinates have been left unchanged. This suggests the equation $y = ab^x$.

$$y = ab^x$$
$$\log_e y = \log_e ab^x$$
$$\log_e y = \log_e a + \log_e b^x$$
$$\log_e y = \log_e a + x\log_e b$$
$$\log_e y = x\log_e b + \log_e a$$

The equation shows $\log_e y$ against x.

Q81:

Hints:

- Give the gradient as a fraction.

Steps:

- What is the equation of the equation of the straight line? $y = 2 \cdot 86x - 0 \cdot 498$
- If $y = ab^x$ then $\log_e y = x\log_e b + \log_e a$

Answer: $a = 0 \cdot 609$ and $b = 17 \cdot 41$

End of topic 10 test (page 346)

Q82: $\log 12$

Q83: 8

Q84: 2

Q85: 2·8

Q86: $2^{3 \cdot 4}$

Q87: 29·96

Q88: 4

Q89: $\log_2 48$

Q90: $\log_3 12$

Q91: 3·54

Q92: 7·39

Q93: 15·15

Q94:

Steps:

- If $625 = a^b$, what is a? 5

Answer: 0

Q95:

Steps:

- Use the log law: $\log_x a^b = b\log_x a$

Answer: -7

Q96:

Steps:

- $\log a + \log b = \log ab$: what is ab? $x^2 + 4x - 5$

Answer: -6

Q97:

Steps:

- $\log_x a = y$ if and only if $a = x^y$

Answer: 0·60

Q98:

Steps:

- What is the value of t at the start of the experiment? 0

Answer: 8000

Q99:

Steps:

- What is the value of B when the bacteria double? 16
- Remember t is the time in hours, give your answer in minutes.

Answer: 69

Q100: 10715

Q101: 0·0409

Q102: 2628

Q103:

Steps:

- Rearranging gives $e^{kt} = y$. What is y correct to four decimal places? 18·3333
- If $kt = q$, what is the value of q correct to four decimal places? 2·9087

Answer: 0·5817

Q104: 1·2

Q105:

Steps:

- Regardless of mass, the half life of a substance will give the same value for M_1 / M_0. What is this value? 0·5
- What is the value of $(-kt)$ correct to two decimal places? -0·69

Answer: 12·6

Q106: 25·2

Q107:

Steps:

- What is the equation of the equation of the straight line? $y = 0 \cdot 5x + 4$
- If $y = kx^n$ then $\log y = n \log x + \log k$.

Answer: $n = 0 \cdot 5$ and $k = 1296$

Q108:

Steps:

- What is the equation of the equation of the straight line? $y = -2x + 6$
- If $y = ab^x$ then $\log y = x \log b + \log a$

Answer: $a = 729$ and $b = \frac{1}{9}$

Q109:

Steps:

- Do we apply logs to both coordinates or just the y-coordinates?
- What is the gradient of the line joining the two points modelled using $\log_{10}$ (i.e. log to the base 10)? 0·095
- If $y = ax^n$ then $\log y = n \log x + \log_a$. What is the equation of the line? y = 0·095x + 0·905
-

Answer: $a = 8 \cdot 035$ and $n = 0 \cdot 095$

Q110:

Steps:

- At intersection the value of y is the same for both graphs. Equate the two expressions given for y and solve for x.

Answer: 2·8

Q111:

Steps:

- The graph crosses the x-axis when $y = 0$.

Answer: -1·0

Q112:

Steps:

- Do we apply logs to both coordinates or just the y-coordinates? just y
- What is the gradient of the line joining the two points modelled using $\log_{10}$ (i.e. log to the base 10)? 0·095
- If $y = ab^x$ then $\log y = b \log x + \log_a$. What is the equation of the line? $y = 0 \cdot 014x + 0 \cdot 252$

Answer: $a = 1 \cdot 786$ and $b = 1 \cdot 033$

Q113:

Steps:

- Rearrange the equation and state the value of e^{-kt} correct to four decimal places. 0·75
- What is the value of $(-kt)$ correct to four decimal places. -0·2877

Answer: 0·0575

Q114: 1184